Cooperative Extension

MW00608451

Sustainable Vegetable Production from Start-Up to Market

Written by

Vernon P. Grubinger
Extension Associate Professor
and
Director
Center for Sustainable Agriculture
University of Vermont

Natural Resource, Agriculture, and Engineering Service (NRAES)
Cooperative Extension
PO Box 4557
Ithaca, New York 14852-4557

NRAES–104
August 1999

ISBN-13: 978-0-935817-45-4

ISBN-10: 0-935817-45-X

Library of Congress Cataloging-in-Publication Data

Grubinger, Vernon P., 1957–
    Sustainable vegetable production from start-up to market / written
by Vernon P. Grubinger.
       p. cm. -- (NRAES ; 104)
    Includes bibliographical references.
    ISBN 0-935817-45-X (pbk.)
    1. Truck farming. 2. Organic farming. 3. Vegetables--Marketing.
I. Natural Resource, Agriculture, and Engineering Service.
Cooperative Extension. II. Title. III. Series: NRAES (Series) ; 104.
SB320.9.G78 1999
635' .0484' 0973--DC21
                                             99-13249
                                                  CIP
                                                      r99

Natural Resource, Agriculture, and Engineering Service (NRAES)
Cooperative Extension
PO Box 4557
Ithaca, New York 14852-4557

Phone: (607) 255-7654
Fax: (607) 254-8770
E-Mail: NRAES@CORNELL.EDU
Web site: WWW.NRAES.ORG

Table of Contents

List of Sidebars

List of Figures

List of Tables

Introduction

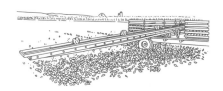

In 1996 the author taught a vegetable production course at the University of Maine, where he was on sabbatical leave from the University of Vermont. The first draft of this book was written for that course, on the premise that vegetable farmers do much more than produce vegetables; they also manage money, people, and natural resources. In fact, growing the crops is often the easy part. It's also the well-supported part. Rather than add to the existing wealth of recommendations on the production of specific vegetable crops, this book attempts to address the systems that comprise a vegetable farm.

This book is intended primarily for aspiring and beginning commercial vegetable growers, but experienced growers, extension personnel, classroom educators, and serious gardeners may also find it useful.

This work was motivated by the fact that existing books on vegetable production have tended to focus on either small-scale, organic production or large-scale, chemical-intensive farming. The most promising model for many growers is between those extremes: moderate-scale production using ecological practices that minimize the need for synthetic inputs and maximize stewardship of resources, with sales directly to "niche" markets.

The first section of the book covers the fundamentals of vegetable farming: sustainability, farm management, marketing, field operations, soil fertility, cover crops, composting, season extension, and pest management. Chapter 19 (beginning on page 180) profiles the actual experience of representative growers and includes enterprise budgets for a number of vegetable production systems. The grower profiles offer real-life examples of how farmers think about and deal with specific conditions. The grower profiles represent the views of the individual farmers and are not intended to convey ideal farm practices, but rather to help readers gain insight into how to best manage their own unique situations. These growers have generously offered the benefit of their experience to help educate others; readers are asked not to contact growers for additional information.

The enterprise budgets were generated by the farmers. To keep things simple, estimates were made of expenses such as average hourly machinery cost and labor cost. The fact that the farm budgets vary in such areas as machinery and labor rates, fixed costs per acre, time needed to perform tasks, and marketing and management costs reflects the variation in practices and perceptions among the farmers interviewed. The approach to budgeting presented here is not as precise as conventional economic analysis, but the aim was to demonstrate a budgeting approach that can make it easy for growers to compare the relative profitability of their crops.

Chapter 1

Sustainable, Integrated, and Organic Production Systems

Sustainable agriculture, integrated crop management, and organic farming are all part of an "alternative" agriculture movement that promotes the use of biological interactions and cultural practices in place of agricultural chemicals. The goal of this movement is a productive and profitable agriculture that protects natural resources and builds strong communities.

Defining Sustainability

The term "sustainable" became widely used to describe healthy farming systems after a U.S. Department of Agriculture (USDA) research and education grants program called Low Input Sustainable Agriculture (LISA) was started in 1988. Several years later, LISA was renamed SARE (Sustainable Agriculture Research and Education), since improving management practices, rather than simply reducing inputs, was increasingly recognized as the core of ecologically sound farming.

Adherents of sustainable agriculture judge farm practices not only by their effect on short-term yield and profit, but also by their impact on water quality, soil productivity, human health, and the local community. Specific farm practices promoted by LISA/SARE are defined by the USDA as those that "lessen the farmer's dependence on purchased inputs, especially synthetic chemical pesticides and fertilizers . . . by greater use of crop rotations, crop and livestock diversification, soil and water conservation practices, greater use of animal and green manures, biological pest controls, and mechanical cultivation where appropriate."

A 1989 report on alternative agriculture by the National Research Council concluded that sustainable farming practices are not a well-defined set of management techniques, but a range of technologies and management options.

Understanding Sustainability

There has been considerable debate about the definition of sustainable agriculture, and the phrase sometimes arouses suspicion or skepticism in mainstream farming circles. Since nobody claims to be a proponent of *un*sustainable agriculture, what's the problem? The difficulty is that new ideas make some people feel that they've been "wrong." Sustainable agriculture is not about being right, however, and it is not an exclusive club for the self-righteous. There is flexibility in defining what constitutes sustainable agriculture. It is a continuum with the unattainable goal of total sustainability at one end. After all, even under the most sustainable management, our farming systems will not last *forever* (see figure 1.1). However, if a manager can move from thinking about getting through the year to thinking in terms of passing the reins to future generations, he or she is more likely to make decisions that preserve long-term resources. As a practical goal for farmers, sustainability—in terms of production and marketing practices, conservation of natural resources, and positive community relations— would preserve a viable farm for their grandchildren or great-grandchildren. If many generations attain that goal, sustainability over thousands of years may indeed be possible.

More Sustainable Thinking	←		Less Sustainable Thinking
Stewardship for many generations	Pass farm to the kids	Next few years make or break	Get through this year

Figure 1.1 Continuum of the sustainable agriculture mind-set

This book emphasizes production practices (see figure 1.2) and marketing practices (figure 1.3. page 4) that the author considers on the high side of the relative sustainability continuum. Obviously, farmers have to balance the long-term goal of sustainability against their short-term financial constraints.

There are no specific rules or required practices that make a farm "sustainable." In contrast, two subsets of sustainable agriculture, Integrated Crop Management and Certified Organic Farming, have specific production standards that must be met in order to qualify. Farmers participate in ICM or certified organic programs for the following reasons: to obtain a label that leads to a market premium, to qualify for government cost-sharing for certain farm practices, or to receive formal guidance or recognition for stewardship efforts.

More Sustainable Practice	←		Less Sustainable Practice
Crop Rotation			
Four years between the same crop planted in the same field	Three years between the same crop planted in the same field	Two years between the same crop planted in the same field	Monoculture (same crop in same field each year)
Organic Matter Maintenance			
Add compost, cover crops, plus crop residues to soil	Add cover crops, animal manures, plus crop residues	Add animal manures plus crop residues	Add crop residues only
Nitrogen Fertilization			
Rely on N from organic residues, in addition to timely fertilization	Band and sidedress fertilizer to match timing of crop uptake	Broadcast bagged fertilizer in spring	Broadcast bagged fertilizer in fall
Insect Management			
Use cultural practices and beneficial insects to control pests	Scout for insect pests, then spray selective, least-toxic pesticide	Scout for insect pests, then spray non-selective insecticide	Calendar spray insecticides (on a predetermined schedule)
Weed Management			
Use allelopathy, smother crops, and mulches to suppress weeds	Cultivate to remove weeds	Apply reduced rates of herbicide and cultivate	Apply herbicides as primary weed control tool
Disease Management			
Plant disease-resistant cultivars	Employ cultural practices that prevent disease	Use disease modeling to time fungicide applications as needed	Apply fungicide on a predetermined schedule (e.g., weekly)

Figure 1.2 Relative sustainability of various vegetable production practices

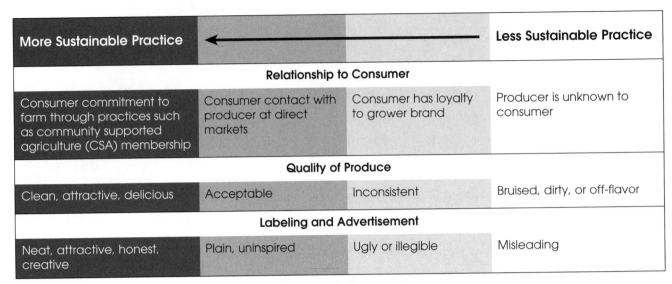

More Sustainable Practice	←		Less Sustainable Practice
Relationship to Consumer			
Consumer commitment to farm through practices such as community supported agriculture (CSA) membership	Consumer contact with producer at direct markets	Consumer has loyalty to grower brand	Producer is unknown to consumer
Quality of Produce			
Clean, attractive, delicious	Acceptable	Inconsistent	Bruised, dirty, or off-flavor
Labeling and Advertisement			
Neat, attractive, honest, creative	Plain, uninspired	Ugly or illegible	Misleading

Figure 1.3 Relative sustainability of various vegetable marketing practices

Integrated Crop Management

Integrated Crop Management (ICM) programs developed by government agencies, university faculty or extension specialists, or commercial enterprises, often working in cooperation, define very specific farming practices that must be followed in order to qualify for financial assistance or marketplace recognition. In a way, ICM programs are an attempt at a practical definition of sustainable agriculture for farmers. The ICM philosophy is still "conventional" in the sense that, unlike organic farming, it allows regular use of synthetic materials. ICM requires farmers to employ "best management" practices, which optimize use of inputs to enhance yields without threatening to deplete or pollute resources. Some states have ICM certification programs that use a point system to weight various practices according to their environmental impact and the effort required to implement them. A minimum number of points are required for certification.

Examples of ICM practices for vegetable farms are given in sidebar 1.1. These were adapted from University of Massachusetts ICM standards for several individual crops and modified in consultation with growers to make the practices appropriate for diversified vegetable farms in Vermont. This list offers guidance to growers but is not part of any formal program.

Integrated pest management (IPM) in its most pure form is a pest-focused subset of ICM (see the chapter on integrated pest management, beginning on page 139). Many IPM programs, however, actually take a more general ICM approach, since they include crop production practices beyond those that specifically affect pests.

Organic Farming

A landmark USDA report of 1980 defined organic farming as "production systems which avoid or largely exclude the use of synthetically compounded fertilizers, pesticides, growth regulators and . . . rely upon crop rotations, crop residues, animal manures, green manures, off-farm organic wastes, mechanical cultivation, mineral-bearing rocks, and aspects of biological pest control to maintain soil productivity and tilth, to supply plant nutrients, and to control insects, weeds, and other pests."

Specific standards and procedures for organic farm certification have been developed in many states by a variety of certifying organizations. Certification programs provide guidelines about how organic food may be produced and processed and how compliance with the standards will be assured through documentation of inputs and farm inspections. Certification is based on food production and processing practices, rather than tests of food quality or pesticide residue levels. The

Sidebar 1.1 Examples of ICM Practices for Diversified Vegetable Farms

Record Keeping

- Maintain annual records that include a map showing all fields (or subfields if they are the management units); location of various crops and green manures; and rates and dates of application of all fertilizers, manures, and pesticides.

Soil Fertility

- Evaluate each field with a soil test for macronutrients and pH at least every three years.
- Based on soil tests, lime all fields to maintain pH above 6.0, except where potatoes will be grown.
- Calculate N (nitrogen) fertilizer needs for each field based on requirements of the crop(s) to be grown, minus credits for residues added, legumes incorporated, and release from organic matter.
- On sloping terrain, maintain permanent sod strips between cultivated areas to reduce erosion.
- Do not apply soluble N fertilizer as a preplant broadcast, but instead apply by banding at planting, side-dressing, or topdressing.
- Calibrate fertilizer spreader(s) yearly, or use and document an accurate method for determining application rates.
- Sow a cover crop, or leave enough organic residues on soil surface to protect against erosion during winter.
- If animal manure supply is limited, use legume green manures to help meet crop N needs.
- Sow grass cover crops to recover late-season available N on all manured or composted fields.
- Plant at least 10% of cropland each season to warm-season, soil-improving cover crop(s).
- Compost all animal manure for at least six months before adding to the soil.

Pest Management

- Rotate annual crops so that the same botanical family (such as crucifers, cucurbits, or alliums) is not grown for more than two consecutive years in the same field and so that at least three years elapse before crops in the same family are planted in a field again.
- Scout for pests regularly, following extension sampling procedures for a particular crop, if possible, or otherwise examining at least fifty plants of each crop in each field every week during the growing season.
- Use pheromone traps, sticky cards, sweep nets, or other tools to assist with insect monitoring.
- When scouting, record crop condition and pressure from insects, diseases, and weeds in each field.
- After harvest, incorporate crop residues promptly, except where under-sowings have been made.
- Calibrate pesticide sprayer(s) before the growing season.
- Where possible, limit the spray area by banding materials "over the row" or by spraying "hot spots" only.
- Do not repeat applications of the same class of pesticides when rotation of pesticides is called for by the label or by the extension management guide.
- Use water-sensitive cards to determine spray coverage at least once a year per crop, and whenever the sprayer configuration is changed.

Insect Management

- Use physical barriers, such as floating row covers, where appropriate.
- Plant trap crops to keep pests off main crop or to concentrate them before spraying.
- Include bio-insecticides such as Bacillus thuringiensis (Bt) as part of management strategies, when possible.

Disease Management

- Buy certified disease-free seed or planting stock, use hot-water treated seed, and select varieties with resistance or tolerance to diseases, if available and appropriate to market demands.
- Maintain wide row spacings to encourage drying of foliage.
- Time overhead irrigation, or use drip irrigation to avoid extending the leaf-wetting period.
- Use raised beds or tile drainage on poorly drained soils.
- Attain good coverage with sprays, and follow a spray schedule that protects new growth.

Weed Management

- Accurately identify primary weeds in each field and make an annual weed map of the farm.
- Select herbicides and cultivation tools based on their ability to control predominant weed species.
- Use non-herbicide control strategies such as cultivation, mulches, smother crops, and flaming.
- Use banded applications, lowest labeled herbicide rates, and stale seedbeds, where appropriate.
- Prevent weeds in fields, alleys, and roadways from going to seed, by using cultivation, mowing, or hand-pulling as necessary through the growing season.

process of developing national organic standards was initiated in 1990 with the passage by Congress of the Organic Foods Production Act. However, the Act has not been implemented as of this writing.

The Federal definition of "organic," designed to eventually supersede all others, specifies that food labeled as organic "shall have been produced without the use of synthetic chemicals . . . not . . . on land to which prohibited substances, including synthetic chemicals, have been applied during the three years immediately preceding the harvest . . . in compliance with the organic plan." Exceptions to the ban on synthetic inputs may include copper and sulfur compounds, pheromones, soaps, oils, treated seed, vitamins and minerals, netting, wraps and seals, insect traps, row covers, mulches, and equipment cleansers. A national organic standards board will assist the USDA in developing and maintaining a national list of approved organic inputs.

Currently, organic farming standards tend to have three categories of practices and inputs. The *allowable* or *acceptable* category includes those that are clearly ideal and naturally-derived, such as crop rotation, cover cropping, and composted manure. The *prohibited* or *unacceptable* category includes relatively toxic or undesirable activities and materials, such as most synthetic pesticides and fertilizers or excessive application rates of manure. The intermediate category, called *regulated* or *permitted*, covers the "gray area" of practices and substances. These have agronomic benefit but also have an ecological downside. Examples include plastic mulch, botanical insecticides, treated seeds, or peat-based potting soils. This intermediate category is where debate as to what constitutes "organic" often occurs within and among certifying organizations.

Because there are strict limitations on synthetic inputs under organic standards, there is a strong incentive for organic vegetable growers to make extensive use of the nonchemical practices that are fundamental to sustainable agriculture. Indeed, to maintain a successful organic system requires the adoption and integration of a majority of the individual sustainable agriculture or ICM tech-

niques listed in sidebar 1.1 (page 5). When comparing organic to nonorganic farming, however, it is important to take into account that management skills vary within any group of farmers, and that organic techniques, if managed badly, will not necessarily result in sustainable farming. Just as there are conventional growers that do an excellent job of resource protection and soil husbandry, so, too, are there organic farmers that contribute to environmental degradation.

Well-run organic farms effectively use biological strategies to minimize many of the problems that have become all too common on conventional, chemical-intensive farms. Core strategies of organic farming include the following, which are covered in later chapters: crop rotation (pages 69–77), mechanical weed control (pages 161–172), least-toxic insect control (pages 149–156), disease management (pages 157–160), and organic matter maintenance (pages 46–62) and recycling of plant nutrients (pages 63–68).

Sustainable Agriculture and Society

Although this book will not dwell on socioeconomic aspects of sustainability, which include public policy (see figure 1.4), their importance cannot be ignored. Some disciples of sustainable agriculture argue that the concept deals only with agro-ecosystem management and does not imply any particular position on socioeconomic issues involving marketing, labor, or taxes. The irony of such an argument is that while progress is being made in the United States toward more ecologically sound farming practices, farms are going out of business because of social and economic policies that are not supportive of those who choose an agricultural way of life. The way to gain ground toward stable, productive, and healthy farms is to incorporate socioeconomic issues into our agricultural agenda, alongside production issues. Just as farmers must integrate market, labor, regulatory, business, and family issues with production issues, those who work with agricultural issues in universities and public agencies must try to affect, not just the practice, but the societal context of farming.

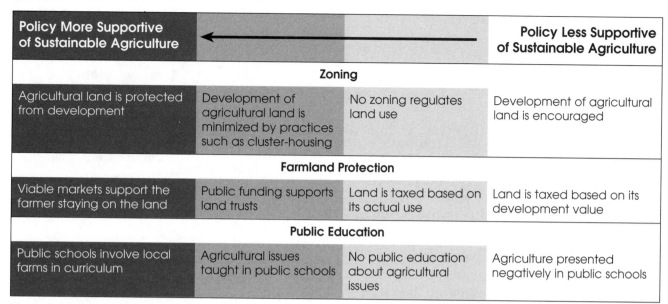

Policy More Supportive of Sustainable Agriculture			Policy Less Supportive of Sustainable Agriculture
Zoning			
Agricultural land is protected from development	Development of agricultural land is minimized by practices such as cluster-housing	No zoning regulates land use	Development of agricultural land is encouraged
Farmland Protection			
Viable markets support the farmer staying on the land	Public funding supports land trusts	Land is taxed based on its actual use	Land is taxed based on its development value
Public Education			
Public schools involve local farms in curriculum	Agricultural issues taught in public schools	No public education about agricultural issues	Agriculture presented negatively in public schools

Figure 1.4 Relative supportiveness of public policies for sustainable agriculture

The problems facing agriculture are not isolated; they are connected to the structure of our entire civilization, much of which is not sustainable over the long haul. Our production and consumption systems are energy-intensive, chemical-dependent, appearance-oriented, and too often driven by short-term rewards. Progress toward a healthier society or food system will not be made by blaming and complaining; rather, everyone must take the steps he or she is capable of toward behavior that is more ecologically sound.

Sustainable agriculture simply recognizes that we can and must find better methods of producing food by seeking out and applying new ideas that promote the long-term well-being of farms and society. The "industrial" paradigm for food production has evolved and achieved wide acceptance over many decades. This model has farmers trying to grow as much acceptable product, as cheaply as they can, for wholesale markets. The industrial model keeps farmers anonymous to the consumer, pitted against other farmers economically, and, all too often, at odds with the environment. In comparison, the "sustainable" agriculture paradigm is one based on community and ecological relationships, whereby farmers produce opti-

mal quantities of the highest-quality products for local or regional markets, using on-farm resources as much as possible. According to this model, sustainable agriculture rewards farmers with fair prices, brand recognition, and consumer loyalty.

Every farm operation can be made more ecologically and socially durable, but the challenge is to do so within the economic constraints of the marketplace. Making agriculture more sustainable is analogous to improving human health: there is widespread agreement that the general goal is important, but a wide range of opinion about how best to pursue the goal. The important part is the pursuit itself, not perfect agreement among those involved.

Understanding ecological connections on the farm is a central focus of sustainable agriculture. For example, connections among pest, crop, habitat, and predator are the basis of biological pest control; and connections among soil biology, tilth, nutrient cycles, and organic matter underlie soil stewardship. However, a healthy agro-ecosystem *must* be accompanied by markets that allow for profitability and by public policies that are supportive of farms and farmers.

Profitability and Sustainability— A Grower Profile

Scout and Matt Proft
Someday Farm, East Dorset, Vermont

A highly diversified 90-acre farm in the hills of southwestern Vermont, Someday Farm produces vegetables, premium poultry, maple syrup, wood products, and compost, all on a small scale. Scout and Matt Proft market these products through a farm stand, a community supported agriculture (CSA) organization, and restaurant sales. The Profts also home-school their children, host three or four interns each year, and educate the public about agriculture through school visits to the farm and through other presentations. All of this makes for a very busy family farm.

"To us, a business that is sustainable is one that is cyclical and balancing while being perpetual, productive, and nonpolluting," says Scout. To help them fulfill this definition, the Profts have developed a sustainability checklist that reminds them of their goals and helps with the evaluation of potential new activities:

- Set personal goals: family time, something to pass on, commitment to educating others.
- Set economic goals: what we can live on, what we can do without, how much we want to save.
- Develop a variety of products and a plan to generate income throughout the year.
- Identify "What ifs?" and plan how to shift gears with little economic loss.
- Develop many markets: sell to as many different kinds of people as close to home as possible.
- Develop unique products: "our own," easily grown, dear to our hearts, not part of a fad.
- Pace the projects: balance tedious and interesting work, schedule off-hours and vacations.
- Have realistic outside commitments: to boards, fairs, trade shows, tours, presentations, etc.
- Allow quality time: set limits to work so we can be available to our partner and children.

"To us, a business that is sustainable is one that is cyclical and balancing while being perpetual, productive, and nonpolluting."

Chapter 2

Getting Started in Vegetable Farming

This chapter addresses important steps in preparing to farm: setting goals, getting practical experience, and obtaining the land and equipment necessary for production. Financial planning, management skills, good marketing strategies, and use of information resources (see appendix A, beginning on page 234) are also essential to running a successful farm business, and these topics will be addressed in subsequent chapters.

Setting Personal Goals

Being clear about what you want to do and why you want to do it is especially important in farming. Given the stress that markets, weather, and pests can cause, farming had better be something you really like, or you probably won't last long. While there's money to be made growing vegetables, farmers tend to be in it for more than just money. If being rich is your priority, there are more promising fields to pursue than agriculture.

It's important to identify your nonfinancial goals, in addition to traditional business goals, prior to starting an agricultural enterprise. For some farmers, independence, working outdoors, rural surroundings, and a sense of community are lifestyle objectives equal to economic considerations. However, the so-called quality of life benefits associated with farming can only be enjoyed with some degree of economic security.

Developing a statement of your personal goals and values is a critical first step in starting an agricultural enterprise. What are your long-term aspirations in terms of family, profession, and surroundings? What kind of lifestyle do you desire and what are the related financial needs? How much risk are you willing to take? How hard do you want to work?

Evaluating Your Enterprise Ideas

However you go about it, giving these matters some thought in a formal manner is a good idea. That means evaluating your enterprise ideas and how well they fit not only your goals and values but also your skills and available resources. First, assess your skills and goals, starting with business management capabilities. Next, identify whether you have qualities that correlate with successful independent businesses: drive, clarity of thought, imagination, leadership, and ability. Then, assess your hopes and concerns for the future, enterprise preferences, and willingness to take risks. Finally, identify your goals and objectives in terms of commodities to work with, annual income desired, and special features you want the new enterprise to possess.

There are publications that can help with this evaluation process (see the references for this chapter, pages 257–258). In particular, _The Small Farm Handbook_ by Humphrey et al. includes a work sheet that can help clarify your goals, skills, and enterprise interests. _Farming Alternatives: A Guide to Evaluating the Feasibility of New Farm-Based Enterprises, NRAES–32,_ by Grudens Schuck et al. provides several sets of work sheets for assessing skills, values, and resources and for evaluating different enterprise decisions.

Holistic Resource Management

Holistic Resource Management (HRM) is a unique tool designed to assist land managers with goal setting and subsequent decision-making. HRM is designed to promote more "sustainable" decision-making based on clear personal goals and ecological awareness. HRM is based on the work of Alan Savory, who concluded that conventional land practices often lead either to marginal financial returns and slow deterioration of the land, or to high financial returns at the expense of rapid depletion of natural resources. (For additional discussion of HRM, see page 26).

The HRM process starts with writing a three-part goal that expresses

1. The quality of life you wish to create from a particular land site
2. What you will produce from the land
3. A description of the landscape as it must be far into the future in order to sustain this production.

Writing a clear, thorough goal statement may not be easy; it takes a lot of thought! But going through the process helps a family, individual, or organization define what it is they really aspire to and how they want to get there. Whether you use HRM or another approach, your written goals should be reviewed on a regular basis, perhaps once a year, and revised if necessary.

Obtaining Practical Experience

Getting hands-on experience allows you to test your goals: do you really want to be a vegetable farmer? On-the-job training can bring book learning to life and is a way to identify what practical training or information you need before starting out on your own. Getting experiential knowledge that matches your interests and learning ability can be a challenge. The options are internships, apprenticeships, and employment. All of them require hard work, initiative, and reliability on your part in order for a host farmer to feel comfortable giving you substantial instruction and responsibility.

In addition to the discussion that follows, consult the references for this chapter (pages 257–258) for more information on getting farm experience.

Internships

Internships are short-term positions, often for the growing season only, and usually low-paid or unpaid but including room and board. They can be great learning experiences, especially for students who spend a limited time as interns, or they can be tedious. How much you learn during an internship has a lot to do with the skill of the host farmer, his or her willingness to teach, and your willingness to learn. Having a plan of what you want to learn will greatly enhance your internship. Before signing up for an internship, learn as much as you can about the farm and the host farmers and their expectations for interns. If possible, talk to previous interns from that farm.

Some states have internship programs run by farming associations, technical colleges, or universities. The function of these programs ranges from simply providing a list of names of potential interns and hosts to match-making that puts interns on farms that seem to best meet their interests and abilities. Interning at the same farm for several summers can build your relationship with the host and gain you more responsibility and management experience, while interning on several different farms will give you a wider perspective of management and production techniques. See sidebar 2.1 for tips on interning.

Apprenticeships

Apprenticeships differ from internships in that they are a longer-term exchange of farm labor for extensive training from the farmer. Because the farmer must have sufficient free time and interest to provide training above and beyond the call of duty, and the apprentice must be in a position to subsist with little or no pay for the period of apprenticeship, this arrangement is less common than internships.

Employment

Employment on a farm that resembles the operation you have in mind for yourself is highly desirable. Besides the chance to earn money

An internship on a working vegetable farm can be extremely satisfying, bringing a bounty of experience and knowledge. On the other hand, choosing the wrong farm can lead to a frustrating season. Farm work can be tedious and exhausting. In order to maintain a good attitude through the season, it is important that you receive a measure of worthy experience along with your lumps. While working at the wrong farm can be helpful in defining what it is you don't want to do, a few years spent doing things the way you would rather not do them can lead to bad attitude. Finding a position at a farm that is suited to your interests is crucial to gaining the experience that you need.

One of the best ways to find yourself the right farm internship is to travel and visit several farms before making a decision. Farm visits are a great learning opportunity in and of themselves. Visits also allow you to make an impression on the farmers before they make hiring decisions. Late winter and early spring are good times to visit because most vegetable farmers have some free time at those points in the season. Visiting during the growing season can provide a more accurate sense of the operation and the mood of the place, but that's not the best time for the farmer to meet with you.

The first step is to define for yourself what kind of farming you want to learn about. Vegetable farms vary in size, market outlets, farming philosophy, and many other aspects. A large farm will often contain big fields of single crops that you will spend days or weeks weeding and harvesting. The larger the farm, the less time the grower will likely be able to invest in the training of individual employees. You might find yourself feeling like a cog in a huge machine. On the other hand, a successful large farm should also show some innovative methods of moving all of that produce out of the field in a timely fashion. Some of those innovations may also be effective, with adjustments, at smaller scales, whereas some will not. A larger farm will most likely provide a good view of how to grow a few crops efficiently. Smaller farms are often more diversified, since they cannot capture economies of scale for any one crop. A season spent working at a smaller farm may provide a broad view of many different crops without specialization in any of them.

The market outlet of a farm has a strong effect on the way the farm operation runs. A farm that wholesales the larger part of its produce through a distributor may not provide as much opportunity to learn about marketing. If you are more interested in learning how to grow than in how to market, such a farm may be an ideal place to intern. Farmers

markets and farm stands both require good interpersonal and display skills. If you enjoy talking with people and making displays and think that you would like to market your own vegetables this way, look for these types of marketing. To get some idea of how skilled the growers are at presenting their produce, you may find it helpful to visit the farm at a time when the farmers are going to markets or when the farm stand is open.

Community Supported Agriculture (CSA) farms offer both opportunities for learning and potential pitfalls for an intern. Some CSAs are effective at generating a group of supportive customers who will stick with the farm through thick and thin. Other CSAs are an afterthought method of getting rid of second-quality produce. Look for a stable or rising number of CSA members as a sign of a successful CSA. Many farms market their produce through more than one outlet, and such a diversified marketing strategy can be very instructive. However, using too many outlets can be indicative of a scattered marketing approach. A farmer who seems to keep good records and who has a good sense of which markets are important and for what reasons is probably a good choice for a host.

There are also internships available on farms run by nonprofit organizations. Usually these farms have missions other than merely producing food for market. Before working for a nonprofit farm, consider carefully where food production fits into the farm's mission. A nonprofit organization does not rely solely on produce sales to generate income and may not need to be an efficient operation. Some nonprofit farms do have a strong mission to produce food and satisfy customers, and may be comparable to commercial operations. These farms can be exciting places to work because they also fulfill some educational, research, or community mission. Be sure, however, that their mission is in line with your own interests.

Many commercial farms also have a sense of mission. It's probable that farmers you meet can list several non-economic reasons for wanting to farm. It is important that you find a farm that shares a similar sense of purpose to your own. Use of chemicals and plastic, relationship to the local community, marketing practices, and waste disposal are just a few examples of conflicts that may arise. When asking about specific practices, keep in mind that your opinion may change after working on the farm; pay as much attention to the way a farmer justifies his or her practices as to the substance of the answer.

(continued on following page)

(continued from previous page)

Finding a farm that matches your interests does not assure a positive experience. You need to be sure you will be given a position with the right mix of learning and responsibility. Apprenticeships and internships should be explicitly designed for learning, and not for providing a source of cheap labor. Make sure that that understanding is clear.

You should have a clear agreement with the farmer, possibly in writing, covering such things as how many hours of work are expected, duration of employment, housing arrangements, and pay. Some farmers regularly hire college students or other young people and enjoy training new employees. These are often the best places for a neophyte to work, regardless of whether it's billed as a job or an internship. In either case, the best way to learn is to be helpful and dedicated. It takes the farmer

valuable time and energy to provide instruction, and he or she will be more likely to do so if you are enthusiastic and quick-learning. You may face frustration if the farmer is unwilling to assign independent tasks, if experienced workers get first choice on learning new jobs, or if tasks are assigned without adequate explanation. Talking to previous employees is an excellent way to find out about the management style and teaching ability of a farmer.

Taking the time to consider your goals and looking for a farm that matches them can help to make your farm experience more fruitful and satisfying.

— by Jeremy Plotkin, Graduate Student, University of Maine Sustainable Agriculture Program

toward your own farm, you have the opportunity to gain more responsibility than is typical of internships and to learn from experience over several growing seasons. There are many examples of hired hands who work for four or five years on farm, rising to a high level of management responsibility, and then start out on their own. Often, if the employee is forthright about his or her intentions, the farmer will be supportive, as long as the new operation will be located sufficiently far away to avoid direct competition.

Finding a Place to Farm

With sufficient experience and capital under your belt, the next challenge is to locate some land that is suitable to vegetable production and marketing. Some lucky people have a family farm to work with, but even this situation calls for a critical assessment of the characteristics that contribute to a successful vegetable operation (see "Assessing Land You Already Own," page 17). In some cases, it may be advisable to sell the farm and seek out land better suited for vegetables, although this can be a difficult decision because of sentimental attachment to the land.

Key factors to consider in finding a farm, in approximate order of importance, are market potential/demographics, soil quality and topography, availability of irrigation water, climate (growing season), existing structures, traffic

pattern, local competition, local labor, prior stewardship of the land, zoning, and property taxes. In addition, if you have young children, the quality of local schools may be high on your list.

Given that most people will have limited resources toward the purchase of a farm, compromises will have to be made since it is unrealistic to expect to find an affordable farm with all the desirable attributes. A situation analysis in checklist form is provided in sidebar 2.2, to assist with identifying your own strengths and weaknesses as well as the relative potential of a particular farming site for vegetable farming and marketing.

Price, of course, is also a consideration and may be of prime importance, depending on your financial situation. Since high-quality farmland near high-value markets is often expensive, alternatives to buying should be considered. Renting or leasing land, housing, farm structures, or machinery can reduce the amount of up-front capital required to start farming. Renting can limit debt, preserving limited funds for essential operating expenses. In addition, rental expenses may offer a tax advantage compared to ownership expenses.

A long-term rental agreement or a rental with an option to buy is advisable if significant investment will be required to improve the land or structures for vegetable farming. For many farmers, renting with an option to buy is often a stepping-stone toward purchase, so that eventually their labor and investment will contribute to building equity in a property.

Soil Quality

Soil quality is of primary importance to vegetable production. Deep, well-drained soils are the most productive, forgiving, and responsive in terms of weather and management. In the Northeast, river bottom or valley soils of moderate texture (sandy loams, loams, silt loams) and free of rocks are desirable. Soils of lesser quality can be improved, but this may be an arduous, long-term task. Sandy soils that are very light-textured and excessively well-drained are often useful for early season production and can be successfully cropped with regular inputs of organic matter and frequent irrigation. Heavy-textured soils that contain a lot of clay and drain poorly may also be improved with organic matter additions, subsoil tillage and/or tile drainage. In general, however, it is probably better to err on the side of soils that are too light, rather than too heavy.

Soil survey books are extremely helpful in determining the quality of soil on a particular piece of land. These books are available for nearly every county and contain detailed maps showing the location of different soil types. Soil survey maps identify the location of different soil types and their suitability for various uses. Also provided are extensive descriptions of the characteristics of all the soil types in the county, their relative suitability for different uses, their management requirements, and even local data on annual precipitation and temperature.

Use the soil survey maps to identify the potential productivity or "capability class" of the soils on the land that you are considering, as well as the physical and chemical characteristics of that land. To determine the land's suitability for vegetables, pay particular attention to the table entitled "Land Capability Classes and Yields per Acre of Crops and Pasture" (figure 2.1). This table shows the potential productivity of soils, usually in terms of corn silage, alfalfa, or hay yield. In the Northeast, vegetable yields are not often listed, so use other crop yields, especially corn and alfalfa, to compare soil productivity.

"Capability class" numbers are used to rank soils by potential agricultural productivity. Class I soils have little or no production limitations, making them the most prime farmland. Classes VI through VIII have severe limitations that make them unsuitable for cultivation. In between, Classes II through V have increasing limitations, indicated by the "capability subclass," which is indicated by a small letter that follows the class Roman numeral. For example, "e" indicates risk of erosion; "w" shows excessive water in or on soils; and "s" indicates shallow, droughty, or stony soils. Ideally, vegetable production should be attempted only on Class I or II soils, although this is not always possible since many other uses such as housing, roads, and industry compete for good soils.

Spend time with the soil survey when considering a parcel of land. The surveys are available at offices of the USDA Natural Resource Conservation Service (formerly Soil Conservation Service), Cooperative Extension, and some local libraries. The first two are likely to have staff that can help you interpret the surveys. As you compare potential farm sites, it's a good idea to make photocopies of the soil maps and descriptions of the soil types on each.

Water

Availability of water is critical to vegetable production for irrigation, mixing sprays, postharvest cooling, and washing. High-quality soils may be able to produce good vegetable yields in most years without irrigation, but in a dry year even they will suffer yield reductions. Access to a river, large stream, well, or pond or the potential to build a pond should be weighed heavily when considering land for vegetables. If you will rely on a well, it should be deep, with a high flow and recharge rate sufficient for irrigation as well as vegetable washing and in some cases domestic use. Be sure to check out regulations regarding use of the body of water in question.

Climate

Climate is a two-sided coin: on the one hand, warm climates obviously have longer growing seasons, but colder climates generally have the advantage of leading to less grower competition and much lower pest pressure. For example, insect and disease pressure in the mid-Atlantic states almost always exceeds that in New England. If you will be farming in a relatively cold area of the country, the relative importance of *microclimates* within a local area increases, since warmer locations will both help you capture early market premiums and delay the onset of killing frosts.

There are big differences, a month or more, in the length of the frost-free season between some locations just a few miles apart, due to differences in elevation and exposure. The frost-free season is

LAND CAPABILITY CLASSES AND YIELDS PER ACRE OF CROPS AND PASTURE

Soil name and map symbol	Land capability	Corn silage	Alfalfa hay	Grass-legume hay	Grass hay	Grass-clover	Pasture	Potatoes, Irish
		Tons	Tons	Tons	Tons	AUM*	AUM*	Cwt
22D, 22E-------- Marlow	VIs	---	---	---	---	---	---	---
23------------- Ondawa	I	26	4.5	4.0	3.5	6.6	5.3	330
24------------- Podunk	IIw	24	4.0	4.5	4.0	7.5	6.0	300
25B------------ Westbury	IIIw	16	---	3.0	3.0	5.0	4.0	---
25C------------ Westbury	IVe	14	---	3.0	3.0	5.0	4.0	---
26B, 26C-------- Westbury	VIs	---	---	---	---	---	3.5	---
26D------------ Westbury	VIs	---	---	---	---	---	---	---
29------------- Walpole	IIIw	18	---	3.0	3.0	5.0	4.0	---
31B------------ Wilmington	VIs	---	---	---	---	---	3.4	---
33------------- Rumney	IIIw	20	---	3.5	4.0	5.8	4.6	---
34C**---------- Lyman-Rock outcrop	VIs	---	---	---	---	---	1.5	---
34D**---------- Lyman-Rock outcrop	VIs	---	---	---	---	---	1.5	---
34E**---------- Lyman-Rock outcrop	VIIs	---	---	---	---	---	---	---
37------------- Hadley	I	28	5.0	4.5	4.0	7.5	6.0	340
39------------- Winooski	IIw	26	4.5	4.0	4.0	6.6	5.3	330
40------------- Limerick	IIIw	20	---	3.5	4.0	5.8	4.6	---
41D, 41E-------- Londonderry-Stratton	VIIs	---	---	---	---	---	---	---
43B------------ Mundal	IIe	---	---	3.5	3.5	5.5	4.2	---

*AUM = Animal Unit Months, or thirty days' worth of feed for one cow.

Figure 2.1 Sample table of land capability classes and yields per acre
Source: USDA Soil Survey of Windham County, Vermont

the number of days between the date of 50% probability of the last spring frost and the date of 50% probability of the first autumn frost. In north-central New England, the frost-free season averages about one hundred days. In southeast coastal New England, the average is two hundred frost-free days. In both areas, a wide variety of vegetables can be grown, especially with season-extending techniques. Colder areas have not only shorter growing seasons, but also lower minimum temperatures. The average coldest temperatures of the year are shown on USDA maps of hardiness zones, which, for example, in Vermont range from zone 3b (minus 35° F) up to zone 5a (minus 20° F). However, average minimum temperatures do not have much impact on vegetables except for perennial crops, and hardiness zones do not necessarily correlate well with lengths of the frost-free season. In colder areas, vegetable growers tend to cope with untimely frosts by relying heavily on season extenders, cold-tolerant field crops, and overhead irrigation (see chapter 13, "Season Extension," beginning on page 130).

Existing Structures and Equipment

Existing structures such as houses, barns, sheds, greenhouses, and farm stands can sometimes be helpful to starting a new farm, but they should not necessarily be a deciding factor in evaluating the farm site. Obviously, the farm family needs a place to live, and on-farm housing for workers is desirable. However, if housing is lacking on an otherwise suitable farm site, it may be quicker and cheaper to build structures than it would be to improve poor soil. It's better to seek out good land without habitable buildings, or to live elsewhere or construct temporary housing, than to get stuck with a nice house on poor soils.

Barns in the Northeast were generally designed for livestock farming and often require substantial work to convert them for vegetable production. If the layout is amenable to housing equipment and setting up washing and packing lines, cold storage, and loading docks, consider getting a professional assessment of the structural condition of the building. An assessment should include the

likely cost of needed improvements to electric service, water, ventilation, heating, and sanitary facilities.

It may cost more to repair or remove greenhouses in poor condition than to construct new greenhouses, and a farm stand is only of value if it fits your marketing plans.

Equipment, such as irrigation equipment, tractors, and implements, that may be included as part of a purchase or rental agreement should be evaluated carefully for its condition and appropriateness to your farming plans (see "Equipment," page 18).

Traffic Pattern

Traffic pattern is an issue that must be weighed in terms of personal preferences as well as potential impact on markets. While farming offers the possibility of living in a very rural setting complete with peace, quiet, and pastoral surroundings, a busy road offers a steady supply of customers for roadside marketing. Sometimes there is a compromise, such as a farm just a short drive off the main road or a layout that minimizes exposure of the fields and housing to the road. In other cases, a lot of customers can be lured many miles from main roads in pursuit of high-quality products and experiences, but this requires some time to establish a reputation.

If the site is not well-suited to a roadside stand, how far a drive is it to farmers markets, upscale restaurants, food co-ops, producer marketing cooperatives, or other marketing opportunities? If the farm of your choice is really in the middle of nowhere, your options still include mail-order sales, some type of wholesale niche, or setting up a stand elsewhere and doing a lot of driving back and forth (see chapter 4, "Marketing Your Crops," beginning on page 38).

Local Demographics

Local demographics refers to the characteristics of the nearby population that you could expect to draw customers from. Is the area relatively wealthy or middle-class, or is it a blue-collar town that will turn a blind eye to pricey mesclun mix and expensive greenhouse tomatoes? Is there a regional lifestyle conducive to community supported agriculture, if that's your intent? Are there many tourists, who will likely prefer value-added products that travel well, rather than fresh produce? Or maybe there are lots of restaurants that would purchase highly perishable produce. The objective is to match your plans and products to the community, so that your potential customers will respond positively to the products you intend to produce and the prices you must charge to make a profit.

A simple but effective demographic assessment method is thorough observation of retail businesses, people on the street, newspapers, and events in the locality. Have discussions with restaurateurs, chamber of commerce personnel, and other retailers in town to see what they think of your proposed operation. Supplement this information with data on population, income, education, and other indicators that may be obtained from libraries or the local public agency that handles commerce or economic development.

Local Competition

Local competition can pose a problem if you plan to go head-to-head with another enterprise offering a similar selection of goods and services. However, this may not be a cause for concern if there are both a relatively high population of potential customers and a short supply of the product. There is also the possibility of complementing the competition by offering a different line of related products. For example, an established farm specializing in pick-your-own berries is unlikely to be threatened by a nearby farm that primarily offers vegetables, since its proximity may draw more customers to the area. Talk to local growers to find out if they collaborate in marketing, purchasing, or equipment use. If not, are they open to doing so? Visit nearby supermarkets, food co-ops, or farm stands to see which products are not sold locally, which are already abundant, and what prices are charged.

Zoning Regulations

Zoning regulations need to be considered for their short- and long-term implications. If a site is agriculturally zoned, permits or variances for farming and marketing may be unnecessary or easy to obtain, and objections to farm activities are likely to be fewer than if the site is zoned for mixed use that includes residential housing. Industrial zoning may be advantageous if you plan a large-scale composting or food-processing operation, but such zoning may also lead to undesirable neighbors in terms of aesthetics and retail marketing. Inquire about long-range town or county plans for highway and residential development, and consider the potential impact of future development on your farm and market plans.

Property Taxes

When choosing a site for farming, look into property tax rates and agricultural tax abatement programs. In locations near population centers where there are many affluent consumers, taxes on farm land may be very high because property is assessed at its development value. However, some states have "use-value" programs that reduce the property tax assessment as long as the land is in agricultural production. Consult with nearby farmers and state tax agencies for information on such programs.

Assessing Land You Already Own

If you already own land, farm inventory work sheets such as those provided in *Farming Alternatives: A Guide to Evaluating the Feasibility of New Farm-Based Enterprises,* NRAES–32, by Grudens Schuck et al. can be used to identify four types of available resources, their limitations, and the opportunities they provide. First, physical resources such as buildings, land, and machinery are inventoried. Second, marketing resources such as road frontage, farmers markets, and nearby population are listed. Third, a management and labor resources inventory looks at skills of on-farm people and also identifies potential off-farm labor, such as local college students or migrant workers. Fourth, a waste product resources inventory helps identify free or cheap materials that could be turned into a salable product.

Equipment

In addition to a suitable place to farm, farmers need equipment to enhance production efficiency. It's important to anticipate the type and cost of equipment that will be needed. Table 2.1 lists equipment typically found on farms with one to three dozen acres of diversified vegetables (also see chapter 9, "Tillage Equipment and Field Preparation," beginning on page 87). Since equipment costs are significant, most growers build up their inventory gradually, and many seek out used equipment (see "Cautions on Buying Used Equipment" below). The selection and cost of equipment will vary from farm to farm, depending on such factors as crops, markets, growing conditions, production practices, or location.

The cost of equipment is justifiable only when a tool fits your production system and will save on labor, increase marketable yield, or improve quality. In other words, it must generate profit after the expense of purchase, maintenance, storage, and repair. In some cases, convenience, health, safety, or reduced physical stress can justify an equipment purchase, regardless of its impact on profits. For example, automated greenhouse ventilation is one less thing to worry about; floor padding in packinghouses prevents slipping; high-quality protective gear for applying pesticides or dusty fertilizers reduces health risks; and an extra cultivating tractor can save time and reduce banged knuckles and sore backs from frequent implement changes.

Vegetable farming generally requires equipment for soil preparation, planting, pest control, irrigation, harvesting, postharvest handling, storage, and distribution. Small farms often rely on direct human labor, sparse and simple equipment, and less-specialized tools that would not be practical on larger farms. For example, produce may be washed in a sink and graded on a table, rather than being run through a mechanized washing, sorting, and packing line. In farms of all sizes there is reliance on human labor, but on larger farms, mechanization allows the labor to be more productive when performing repetitive tasks.

It is critical to match equipment to the scale of production. Small farms with just a couple of acres cannot justify lots of large equipment, and relatively large farms with many acres of crops must find ways to minimize the need for hand labor. At either end of this scale, equipment decisions are more obvious than in the mid-range. With farms of 5 to 20 acres, it may be difficult to afford certain equipment, but difficult to do without it.

Equipment purchases should be made with an eye toward systematic efficiency. Consider whether implements are interchangeable on the tractors, if they fit your crop spacing system, and if they can be used on multiple crops or field activities. Specialized tools have their place but are usually not purchased before equipment with wider application.

Cautions on Buying Used Equipment

New equipment is expensive, but used equipment, especially tools with lots of moving parts, can be troublesome and sometimes dangerous. Safety is an especially important consideration if young or inexperienced workers will be operating the equipment. Consult a guide to used equipment, such as *Used Farm Equipment: Assessing Quality, Safety, and Economics,* NRAES–25, by Garthe et al. (listed in the references section, page 257). Carefully examine used equipment and buy it only from reputable sources.

The availability of new and used equipment for vegetable production is limited outside of intensive vegetable growing regions. Be cautious when buying vegetable equipment from dealers that know nothing about it. Dealers that do specialize in vegetable production equipment are usually quite knowledgeable and are a good source of advice. In some cases, long-distance travel to a vegetable growing region is worthwhile to obtain needed equipment in good condition. Also see "Used Tractors," page 88.

Table 2.1 Equipment common on diversified vegetable farms of one to three dozen acres

Item	Useful Life* (years)	Cost Used*	Cost New*
15–20 horsepower high-clearance cultivating tractor	20–30	$7,500	$20,000
30–50 horsepower tillage tractor with bucket loader	20–30	$7,500	$25,000
Pickup truck	10–15	$5,000	$20,000
Delivery truck/step van	10–15	$5,000	$25,000
Flatbed harvest wagon	10–15	$500	$2,000
Manure spreader	15–20	$1,500	$5,000
Three-bottom plow	30–40	$500	$3,000
Heavy disks	30–40	$500	$2,500
8-foot field cultivator	30–40	$1,000	$2,500
5-foot rotavator	10–15	$2,000	$3,000
Bed-former or mulch layer	10–20	$300	$1,000
One-row push seeder (small seeds)	15–20	$200	$400
Two-row tractor-mounted precision seeder	15–20	$2,000	$5,000
Two-row tractor-mounted plate-planter	15-20	$500	$2,000
Two-row mechanical transplanter	10–15	$500	$2,500
Shanks, sweeps, shovels, duckfeet	20–30	$300	$1,200
Two-row rolling cultivator	10–20	$500	$1,800
Three-row basket weeder	10–20	$300	$1,000
Spring-tine or flex harrow	20–30	$500	$2,000
Brush hog or flail mower	15–20	$500	$2,000
Fifty hand tools (hoes, rakes, shovels)	3–5	$250	$750
Two wheelbarrows, two garden carts	5–10	$200	$500
8-horsepower rototiller	5–10	$500	$1,600
Overhead irrigation for two to three acres (pipe, pump, etc.)	parts vary	$5,000	$10,000
Two wash tanks, hoses, barrel washer	5–20	$500	$1,500
Washing line, sorting table	10–15	$1,500	$2,500
Two-row gravity fertilizer sidedressers	20–30	$200	$600
Spinner spreader, tractor-mount	20–30	$200	$500
Drop spreader	20–30	$300	$1,300
Grain drill or Brillion seeder	20–30	$500	$1,500
Boom sprayer and spray tank	15–20	$750	$2,000
Backpack tools: sprayer, seeder, flamer	20–30	$200	$500
Shop tools (drills, grinders, compressors, etc.)	varies	$1,000	$3,000

*Rough estimates

Affordable Equipment Acquisition— A Grower Profile

Paul and Sandy Arnold
Pleasant Valley Farm, Argyle, New York

Paul and Sandy Arnold grow a variety of vegetables on 4 acres of land, in addition to an acre and a half of cover crops, an acre of tree fruit, a half-acre of small fruit, and 24 acres of hay. Nearly all of their produce is direct marketed through farmers markets. The vegetables and small fruits are produced in accordance with organic standards, but the farm is not certified. The tree fruits are sprayed just a few times each year with synthetic pesticide. The soils at Pleasant Valley Farm are rocky, silt loams.

The Arnolds bought the 40-acre farm ten years ago. One 5-acre field had been in continuous corn for over twenty years, and the remaining tillable land had been in hay. In their first year, their priority was to put up barns to store equipment and provide a base of operations. This was accomplished by dismantling two old barns in a nearby town, transporting them, and rebuilding them on new foundations. Under one barn a root cellar was built. A small greenhouse was attached to the other barn for growing all the farm's transplants.

"We started with an old pickup truck, some hand tools, and one piece of new equipment, the only major piece of equipment we bought new for eight years—a BCS 10-horsepower walk-behind tractor with a 26-inch rototiller and a 44-inch cutter bar. The price at the time was about $2,100. We were looking for appropriate equipment for farming just a couple of acres. Even though the new BCS was more expensive than a used small tractor, we felt that the operating and maintenance cost over the long run would be a lot less. So far, we have only had to replace the tiller unit, for about $400.

"Over the next couple of years we did come across and buy two older tractors, a 23-horsepower International 200 for $200, and a 53-horsepower International 400 for $1,500. The tractors were found through word of mouth and purchased because there was an International dealership nearby that could readily supply parts and service for these older machines. A few years later we came across a 23-horsepower International Farmall Super C that was rusty but mechanically sound. We bought it for $750 and restored it to working condition for another $400. This tractor is important to us because it has a wide front end that can straddle crops, whereas our other tractors have narrow front ends.

> *"Profitability is when you can maintain what you have, reinvest, put money away for retirement, and still make a decent living. We are able to do all this and raise two kids."*

"Three-point-hitch conversion systems were installed on two of the Farmalls for less than $100 each. Then we sought out used equipment from neighbors, equipment dealers, and auctions. We had a two-bottom moldboard plow that came with the Farmall 200, which has been adequate to turn under cover crops and prepare fields. Next we bought a set of 8-foot-wide double disks for $100, then cut them down to a single set, which made it easier for a small tractor to pull and maneuver. We found an inexpensive brush hog and built low-cost wagons and trailers for hauling hay and produce on the farm.

"In the early years the Farmall 200 was used for all vegetable field preparation, but recently it has been used only for cultivating and pulling wagons since we got the Super C. We saw a used mid-mount two-row cultivator for the Farmall 200 sitting out on someone's front lawn, and bought it for $75. We use this unit in our acre of potatoes to mark rows and cultivate weeds. By attaching two sets of disks in place of the cultivating teeth, it also covers the seed pieces and hills the plants.

"We use the Super C for plowing, disking, harrowing, and digging carrots and potatoes. In our sixth year we realized that the soil needed some deep tillage, so for $500 we fabricated a homemade tool bar for the Super C that we fitted with two new 24-inch chisel shafts. We also use the tool bar with a single chisel to loosen the soil between carrot rows, which makes it easy to pull them by hand. In potatoes, we take off the chisel point and bolt on a 'tater-point' that undercuts and lifts the tubers out of the hills. This tool is designed for digging sweet potatoes, and cost only $22, a lot less than buying a one-row potato digger!

"The only tractor implement we've purchased new was a 5-foot-wide Perfecta II rolling harrow, made by Unverferth, for $1,500. We decided to buy this tool after four years on the farm because it's useful for secondary tillage prior to transplanting a variety of crops, and it's light enough that both our small tractors could pull it. We also use it for leveling potato ground after harvesting, for incorporating cover crop seed, and for working stale seedbeds.

"Our large tractor, the Farmall 400, is primarily used on our hay land. It operates the 6-foot Gehl flail-chopper we purchased in our second year on the farm for $400. Ever since then we chop our hay, blow it into a wagon, and then fork a 4- to 6-inch layer onto the vegetable fields after the annual crops are harvested. We've found that the hay is easier to incorporate with disks or a rototiller if we leave it lying on the surface until the following spring. The annual addition of chopped hay to our fields has been crucial to the success of our farm because we've been able to raise our soil organic matter level from 2.4% to 4.6%; and that's allowed us to do more double-cropping, and it's improved crop quality and returns per acre. The chopped hay has also been ideal for weed suppression in widely-spaced, full-season crops. We apply a heavy layer of chopped hay to peppers, tomatoes, and zucchini, as well as to perennials like asparagus, strawberries, and blueberries. In addition to adding organic matter and suppressing weeds, this system conserves moisture."

The Arnolds use a lot of hand tools because many of their crops are grown in rows that are 12 inches apart, requiring close cultivation, and because they make small weekly seedings of many crops to meet their retail market needs. They started with an old high-wheel cultivator that was given to them. Then they purchased an Earthway precision seeder for $60, a hand-held broadcast spreader for $40, a push-type broadcast spreader for $100, and a Real wheel-hoe with two blades for $260.

"For our first eight years on the farm, we never borrowed any money to get equipment, but last year we decided to take a two-year loan to buy a 27-horsepower Ford 1630 [tractor] with a loader for $18,800, and a 5-foot Kuhn rotavator for $2,250. With two young children, we are looking for ways to come up with more free time, and using the walk-behind rototiller to prepare fields for planting had become too time-consuming. It had taken four hours each week to prepare the fields for planting. With the new tractor, it takes just twenty minutes. The new tractor will also help us do a better job mowing around field edges to keep weeds down and reduce rodent pressure."

"Keeping records is essential in order to know where an investment in equipment will result in the most improvement. There has to be an obvious payback on anything we buy, and we always consider whether it can be maintained at a low cost. Each year we make equipment purchases based on the perceived weak link in the farm's operation. Last year, we finally got to the point where a new tractor made sense. The year before that, we tiled some fields to improve drainage. Before that, the most needed equipment was an 8-foot barrel washer to clean potatoes, carrots, rutabagas, turnips, beets, and even apples. We bought one for $1,000, and it paid for itself in two weeks in saved labor. That year we also got a used 8 x 10 walk-in cooler for $2,500 to control the quality of crops after harvest. And before that, we improved our irrigation over a couple of years by putting in a large pond and then buying a solid-set overhead irrigation system powered by a 5-horsepower electric pump. That was in response to suffering much loss in a dry year with a drip irrigation system that had an insufficient water supply.

"For the first three years all the farm income was reinvested to make the farm more profitable. Both of us worked off the farm during the winter months, and during the summer Sandy worked fifty hours a week on the farm and also fifty hours a week off the farm. In the fourth year, the farm became our sole source of income. Now, our return is $10,000 minimum gross sales per acre cultivated."

Profitability, says Paul, is "when you can maintain what you have, reinvest, put money away for retirement, and still make a decent living. We are able to do all this and raise two kids. I've heard farmers say off-the-cuff that they wanted to get a certain piece of equipment, and I think to myself: do they really know how much it will save them, or how much more they will make if they had it? I feel it's important for farmers to make knowledge-able decisions about equipment purchases."

With careful records of how much is picked and sold, how much space each crop takes up, and how much time it takes to harvest each crop, the Arnolds have a very good idea of the value that each crop generates per unit of land. Then they can look at how much time various activities take for that crop, and decide if it's worth investing in equipment to increase efficiency. They haven't kept track of how much time is spent for each crop on each individual field operation, such as weeding or plowing, in part because many operations are done at one time for all crops and they do most of the work themselves. However, Paul says they are going to move toward keeping track of field work to keep their growing labor expenses under control.

"We normally put about $10,000 per year back into the farm for capital improvement. We are able to do this because we are both savers, not spenders, and we can afford things because we wait until they make sense to buy. We try to spend smart, and we use good management to get the maximum income off small acreage."

Chapter 3

Farm Business Management

To successfully manage a farm business, being a good grower and marketer just isn't enough. In addition to production and sales ability, skills in business management, including budgeting, strategic planning and whole-farm planning, labor management, and record keeping are necessary. Successful farm management relies on organized and timely record keeping, the ability to make sound decisions based on good data and observation, and the interpersonal skills to motivate and focus the work of others on the farm. On many successful farms, production and management tasks are divided among two or more people, based on their individual strengths.

Financial Planning
Writing a Business Plan

As you prepare to start up your farm business, writing a formal *business plan* is a useful endeavor for three reasons. First, it will force you to thoroughly think through the financial details of your proposed project so that nothing is missed. Second, it can be used as an operational guide when making decisions. Third, it is essential to obtaining financing from banks, other lenders, or potential investors. A good plan should be thorough, enthusiastic, and honest.

Your business plan reflects how well you can plan, organize, and market. It can make or break your ability to obtain funding. Most business plans provide a neat and professional presentation of information about the legal identity, management, location, purpose, assets held and needed, finances, and marketing of the business, as well as specific supporting documents. Sidebar 3.1 (page 24) presents an outline of a basic five-part busi-

ness plan. Although business plans vary, they must meet the standards of the financial community; if you have difficulty crafting a high-quality plan, consider getting professional assistance.

Budgeting and Financial Management

Managing money effectively is critical to survival in farming. Budgets should be developed before starting an agricultural endeavor in order to predict its economic feasibility. With established endeavors, budgets are the basis of *financial management,* i.e., monitoring economic health and taking corrective action when needed.

Three types of budgets commonly used for farm financial planning are enterprise budgets, partial budgets, and whole-farm budgets. *Enterprise budgets* are often the most useful since they thoroughly explore the income and expenses associated with one specific crop or enterprise. *Partial budgets* are used to examine the effect of modifications to an existing enterprise, such as switching from wholesale to retail sales. *Whole-farm budgets* consider costs and income from all enterprises on the farm and are used to manage significant changes in the farm operation. An example of a whole-farm budget is shown in sidebar 3.2 (page 25).

Enterprise budgets vary based on local production practices, expected yields, and markets. The weakness of pre-prepared enterprise budgets is that no two farms are alike, and a customized budget is required to accurately reflect the profitability of an enterprise on a particular farm. Good data on purchases, labor, and other expenses, as well as volume of sales and prices received, is essential to developing accurate budgets and making good financial decisions. However, published pre-prepared enterprise budgets can be very helpful to developing your own budgets. Sample enterprise budgets for many crops are available from cooperative extension. Chapter 19 of this book (beginning on page 180) includes a number of farmer-generated enterprise budgets for different crops and different farms.

When first starting to develop enterprise budgets for crops on your farm, you can simplify the task by using educated guesses for certain costs, such as tractor ownership and operating expenses and average labor costs. If the goal is to compare the relative profitability of different crops, such estimates are adequate as long as they are consistent from budget to budget. Over time, more accurate record keeping will allow for a closer estimate of various costs, and budgets will then be more useful for accurately determining overall profitability. Appendix D (pages 248–249) is an enterprise budget work sheet that you can customize as needed.

Most budgets account for two types of costs, fixed and variable. *Fixed costs*, including the cost of land rent or mortgage payments, taxes, equipment

Sidebar 3.1 Outline of a Basic Five-Part Business Plan

I. Introduction
1. Cover sheet: name, address, and phone of the business and the principal(s)
2. Statement of purpose that captures the essence of the proposed business
3. Table of contents

II. The Business
1. Description of business: legal identity (such as sole proprietorship, partnership, corporation), products and services, markets, customers
2. Location: where is it, why it is there, important attributes of location (such as acreage, soil and water resources, rent or buy and why, terms of lease, parking, neighbors)
3. Management: who does what, your management training and experience
4. Personnel: current and future number of employees, their qualifications, rates of pay, training and benefits, supervision
5. Assets needed: facilities, equipment, or improvements to property
6. Insurance: how much you have; future needs

III. Marketing
1. Marketing method, such as wholesale or retail, roadside stand, farmers market, value-added
2. Who your primary customers will be
3. Customer demographics, such as their age, sex, income, education, lifestyle, and where they live
4. Major competitors and their location, strengths, and weaknesses in comparison with yours
5. Trends in the market based on data available about your product(s)
6. Expected sales of your product(s) in quantity and dollars over the next few years

7. Services needed for marketing, including storage, packing, processing for value-added, advertising, or transportation

IV. Finances
1. Sources of funds and how and when they will be used
2. Profit and loss statements for last three years, or projected for next two years if business is a start-up
3. Balance sheet: current assets and liabilities (for past three years if business existed) and projected (sometimes called "pro forma") for next two years
4. Cash flow statement: income and expenses on a monthly or quarterly basis for past three years
5. List of collateral, debts, and financial agreements made with others
6. Capital equipment on hand and improvements: date purchased or performed, dollar amount
7. Capital equipment needed: estimated cost and time line
8. Historical data: last three years of business tax returns

V. Supporting Documentation
1. Personal resumes of principals
2. Personal financial statements of principals
3. Letters of reference for principals
4. Credit reports for principals
5. Literature that describes or advertises your product
6. Leases, contracts, letters of intent, or other relevant documents
7. Photographs of real estate, equipment, or products

ownership, and insurance, comprise the overhead you pay regardless of production decisions. *Variable costs* are determined by the volume of production and to what extent equipment is used. Variable costs tend to increase proportionally with production levels. Variable costs include seeds, fertilizers, mulches, sprays, and machinery operation costs (fuel, oil, and repairs on a per hour or per acre basis). Labor is also a variable cost and can be divided into skilled and unskilled categories or into production categories such as machine operation, hand-weeding, and harvesting. Interest on operating expenses, as when money is borrowed to buy seed and fertilizer, is a variable expense.

Strategic Planning

Once the enterprise is underway, whole-farm thinking is critical to long-term success. Strategic planning is a process of setting objectives for the future and evaluating and selecting strategies based on whole-farm thinking. This means analyzing all aspects of management: natural and human resource use, production efficiency, marketing mix, and finances. Unlike short-term planning for control of pests, management of nutrients, or pricing of products, strategic planning looks ahead at least several years and takes a broad focus on all factors that affect the farm, including trends in agriculture and society in general. The result of this analysis might be new enterprises, market modifications, business expansion or contraction, capital investment, or even going out of business. Strategic planning is important to set a clear direction and define specific outcomes that you can use to measure your success. It is important to include others besides farm owners, such as family members, managers, and top employees, in the planning process and to set aside uninterrupted time for strategic planning. There are seven steps to strategic planning:

Step 1 Define the Mission

Define the farm's mission: identify the products, enterprises, and services supported by the farm's production. Then, state the goals that define the farm's purpose, such as desired level of profits, family security and enjoyment, independence,

Sidebar 3.2 Sample Whole-Farm Budget

Dan Kaplan
Brookfield Farm CSA,
Amherst, Massachusetts

Expenses

Full-time labor (salary, FICA, workers compensation, health insurance)	$48,238
Apprentices (stipends, recruiting, housing, training, meals, FICA, workers compensation, health insurance)	$25,412
Part-time labor (hand-weeding, bookkeeping)	$5,000
General expenses (maintenance, repair, supplies, veterinarian)	$9,750
Vegetable production (seeds, plants, cover crops, greenhouse, land, fertilizer)	$10,550
Livestock production (piglets, chicks, lambs, pasture and barn rental, feed, hay, slaughter, processing)	$4,290
Utilities (electric, phone, water, propane, trash)	$3,550
Administration (taxes, legal, accounting, insurance, office supplies, postage, copies, dues and subscriptions, vehicle registration and insurance)	$7,500
Marketing (promotional items, advertising, printing)	$1,000
Capital (debt repayment)	$3,400
Total Expenses =	**$118,690**

Income

Member shares (fifty full shares, three hundred half-shares)	$115,000
Extra sales (bulk produce, shop sales, livestock)	$1,200
Meat (beef, pork, chicken, lamb)	$4,700
Promotional items (tee-shirts, mugs)	$300
Total Income =	**$121,200**
Profit/(Loss) =	**$2,510**

stewardship of resources, and connection to the community.

Step 2 Establish Objectives

Establish straightforward and quantifiable goals that are expressed in specific terms, such as increasing sales by 20%, doubling production of a particular crop on the same acreage, providing health insurance for all full-time employees, taking a two-week vacation with the family every year, or starting a farmer discussion group.

Step 3 Assess the On-Farm Environment

What are the farm's present strengths and weaknesses in such areas as abilities of the owner or manager, skill level of employees, condition and extent of equipment and facilities, soil quality, availability of water, and financial resources?

Step 4 Assess the Off-Farm Environment

What forces or trends affect the farm's chances of long-term success? These factors include consumer demand for your products, extent of competition, availability of reliable hired labor, government regulations, changes in consumer lifestyle, local population trends, and new techniques for pest control.

Step 5 Identify Opportunities and Threats

Identify opportunities and threats based on the strengths and weaknesses identified in steps 3 and 4.

Step 6 Develop Alternative Strategies

Develop alternative strategies for meeting objectives. These can include adopting new production practices, producing alternative products, improving product quality in order to obtain higher prices, expanding operations in order to lower the per-unit cost of production, expanding into marketing and distribution in order to capture more of the consumer's dollar, diversifying to reduce risks and explore new markets, differentiating products through higher quality, improving service, and improving brand labeling.

Step 7 Evaluate and Select Strategies

Evaluate and select strategies likely to achieve your objectives. The most promising strategies can be identified by using commonsense reasoning and financial comparisons such as enterprise budgets and break-even analysis, or other methods such, as the Strength, Weakness, Opportunity, Threat (SWOT) technique or the Holistic Resource Management (HRM) method, both described in the following section.

Assessing Management Choices

There are several ways to evaluate the relative merit of specific management options, keeping in mind your goals and plans. The Strength, Weakness, Opportunity, Threat (SWOT) technique (sidebar 3.3) is a method of identifying, assessing, and comparing strategies by writing down their strengths and weaknesses as well as the potential opportunities they may create and the threats they may pose.

Holistic Resource Management (HRM), introduced in the previous chapter as a goal-setting tool (page 10), also provides an approach to comparing land management decisions prior to implementation by considering seven types of possible consequences of any option (sidebar 3.4). Although it is impossible to avoid undesirable consequences in all of the areas, the testing process is intended to compare the relative impact of different management decisions on the farmer's ability to fulfill economic, ecological, and social goals.

Labor Management

Vegetable crop production is a labor-intensive endeavor. The USDA reports that labor accounts for an average of 18% of production expenses on horticultural farms—higher than any other type of agricultural operation. On smaller, less mechanized farms, labor may account for an even higher proportion of expenses. It's important to get the most out of your labor, in terms of creativity and initiative as well as efficiency. However, hiring, training, and retaining quality employees is a two-way street. Without positive management practices, employees are unlikely to fully express their abilities. Good management practices and a good working environment are often as important to employees as rate of pay.

Human resources, the labor workforce on the farm, may include family members, partners, hired hands, migrant workers, and interns. Whatever the mix, matching labor needs to the right human resources is key to good management. First, assess and define labor needs by making an inventory of tasks and identifying job positions. What are the major categories of jobs and skills required on the farm? How much time do they take during the course of a year, and on a monthly basis? Write clear, specific job descriptions that describe the skills and time commitment needed for optimal effectiveness. Then decide how many additional people, full-time, part-time, or seasonal, should be hired to supplement family labor. Try to match people and their skills to the job. If family members or partners don't have the right skills, acknowledge this and arrange for appropriate training, or plan to hire a skilled person.

Organizational Structure

Organizational structure can be represented by a chart that shows the relationship of various jobs on the farm, the level of responsibility for each job, and the chain of management. An organizational chart should show that each employee has only one supervisor, as in figure 3.1.

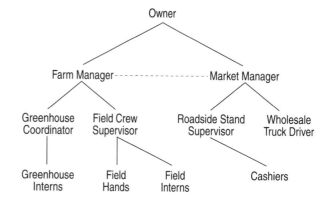

Figure 3.1 Sample organizational chart of labor management on a vegetable farm

Supervision

Supervision is fundamentally a process of ongoing communication about the jobs that need to be done, who will do them, and how. People appreciate and respond best to supervision when expectations are clear and the authority that the supervisor exercises matches the responsibility that he or she takes. Supervisory skills include effectively taking initiative, providing leadership and organization, and motivating employees to do their best work. Employees expect supervisors to be competent, fair, patient, considerate, tactful, and firm but supportive.

The following are widely accepted as principles of effective supervision:
- People must always understand what's expected of them.
- Good work should always be recognized, while poor work should be constructively criticized.
- People should be provided with opportunities to accept greater responsibility.
- People deserve a safe and healthy working environment.

Motivation

Motivation among employees is created by a climate of good working conditions, material incentives, personal appreciation, and respect. Good employees will know what they are doing and why, and feel valued for their contribution. Supervisors contribute to a motivational climate by regularly giving honest recognition and feedback about performance, making people's jobs as meaningful as possible, getting to know them as individuals, being available to employees, asking for information, and encouraging participation.

A positive attitude at the top is important. As head of your business, express your own enjoyment of farming, talk about good experiences you have with other people, and frequently catch employees doing something right!

Give employees a break so they can recharge their batteries. Adequate rest is essential to productivity. During the work day, break time should be regularly provided. At least one full day off each week is necessary for most people to do their best work.

Participatory Management

Participatory management is a set of key management practices including listening, questioning, negotiating, and clarifying mutual expectations between supervisor and employees. Participatory management allows employees to influence decisions without challenging the supervisory structure. Participation by employees in management encourages early recognition of problems, creative solutions, personal development, job satisfaction, and productivity.

Hiring Employees

Hiring employees begins with a clear description of job responsibilities and skills required, rate of pay, and potential for training and advancement. An effective advertising strategy must then get the word out to a wide enough pool of applicants to assure that some high-quality candidates apply. Employment application forms should be used to help with the screening process and to learn more about special skills of applicants. The form should include specific questions about previous employment, experience, and skills related to the job. An open-ended question that asks why the person feels qualified for the job can be helpful. The form should also ask for references.

Once applications are reviewed and ranked, interviews can be arranged. Structure these to get similar information from all the candidates, so that you are able to effectively compare them. Make a list of core questions that will be asked of all applicants, and write down noteworthy responses. References of top candidates should be contacted and asked about the length of their relationship with the candidate, the quality and nature of work the candidate performed, and the candidate's level of responsibility and ability to cooperate. Try to find out why the candidate left the previous job.

Training

Training can boost productivity and profits, avoid costly errors, and enhance job satisfaction if done right. Training objectives must be clear: What are the organizational needs that warrant the development of new skills on the part of employees? Exactly which tasks will be taught? Once the goal of training is clear, the best opportunities for training can be identified, and a combination of methods may be used. Training may be done on-farm by supervisors or off the farm through courses or conferences with experts.

Orientation for new employees is a minimum level of training. Some farms have employee handbooks that can minimize misunderstandings by providing written reinforcement of expectations. Special training may be appropriate if specific skills are needed to perform a job, a new piece of machinery or crop needs to be managed, or an employee demonstrates specific interests or aptitudes.

Record Keeping

Intuitive decisions will inevitably be made on the farm; most farms couldn't be run without them! But data-based planning is much more reliable, and can actually enhance the effectiveness of "gut-level" calls when they are needed.

A host of records should be kept on the farm to monitor performance in key areas that affect profitability and sustainability. Records should document all sources of income and expenses, sales, equipment purchase and maintenance, labor costs and appropriation to various tasks, pesticide and nutrient applications, crop yields and rotations, all test results, pest scouting, and marketing activities (sidebar 3.5). Few growers do a good job keeping such extensive records, but most have a system that at least meets the minimum requirements for tax and payroll purposes and for legal obligations related to labor and pesticide use. Adequate and accurate data is key to improving the efficiency of your operation. In addition, having organized your record-keeping system into categories that match those on the Federal tax form for farms, Schedule F, can be helpful when it's time to file your income tax returns (figure 3.2, page 30).

Getting organized is essential to good record keeping, so that data can be retrieved when needed. Pen and notebooks can do the job, although many computer programs are also available. However, no software can do the record-keeping job for you; accurate data must be collected first. Remember the software-use rule: garbage in, garbage out.

Whole-Farm Planning

Whole-farm planning is the comprehensive effort to consider all aspects of the farm and farm community that affect the realization of economic, environmental, and social goals (sidebar 3.6, page 31). This is a complex process, and one that farmers engage in all the time, although not always in a structured fashion. Analyzing one aspect of the farm system at a time is a way to identify priority or problem areas that warrant detailed planning and action. The process of whole-farm planning consists of identifying problem areas, comparing alternative solutions to the problem, developing an action plan, measuring and assessing progress, and reevaluating the action plan.

Sample only. Do not use to file taxes. Obtain current tax forms from the United States Department of the Treasury Internal Revenue Service.

Schedule F (Form 1040) 1998

Part III Farm Income — Accrual Method (see page F-7)
Do not include sales of livestock held for draft, breeding, sport, or dairy purposes; report these sales on Form 4797 and do not include this livestock on line 46 below.

38	Sales of livestock, produce, grains, and other products during the year	38
39a	Total cooperative distributions (Form(s) 1099-PATR)	39a ... 39b Taxable amount ... 39b
40a	Agricultural program payments	40a ... 40b Taxable amount ... 40b
41	Commodity Credit Corporation (CCC) loans:	
a	CCC loans reported under election	41a
b	CCC loans forfeited	41b ... 41c Taxable amount ... 41c
42	Crop insurance proceeds	42
43	Custom hire (machine work) income	43
44	Other income, including Federal and state gasoline or fuel tax credit or refund	44
45	Add amounts in the right column for lines 38 through 44	45
46	Inventory of livestock, produce, grains, and other products at beginning of the year	46
47	Cost of livestock, produce, grains, and other products purchased during the year	47
48	Add lines 46 and 47	48
49	Inventory of livestock, produce, grains, and other products at end of year	49
50	Cost of livestock, produce, grains, and other products sold. Subtract line 49 from line 48*	50
51	**Gross income.** Subtract line 50 from line 45. Enter the result here and on page 1, line 11	51

* If you use the unit-livestock-price method or the farm-price method of valuing inventory and the amount on line 49 is larger than the amount on line 48, subtract line 48 from line 49. Enter the result on line 50. Add lines 45 and 50. Enter the total on line 51.

Part IV Principal Agricultural Activity Codes

Caution: File **Schedule C** (Form 1040), Profit or Loss From Business, or **Schedule C-EZ** (Form 1040), Net Profit From Business, instead of Schedule F if:

- Your principal source of income is from providing agricultural services such as soil preparation, veterinary, farm labor, horticultural, or management for a fee or on a contract basis, or
- You are engaged in the business of breeding, raising, and caring for dogs, cats, or other pet animals.

These **new** codes for the Principal Agricultural Activity classify farms by the type of activity they are engaged in to facilitate the administration of the Internal Revenue Code. These six-digit codes are based on the new North American Industry Classification System (NAICS) and do not resemble prior year codes.

Select one of the following new codes and enter the six-digit number on page 1, line B:

Crop Production
111100 Oilseed and grain farming
111210 Vegetable and melon farming
111300 Fruit and tree nut farming
111400 Greenhouse, nursery, and floriculture production
111900 Other crop farming

Animal Production
112111 Beef cattle ranching and farming
112112 Cattle feedlots
112120 Dairy cattle and milk production
112210 Hog and pig farming
112300 Poultry and egg production
112400 Sheep and goat farming
112510 Animal aquaculture
112900 Other animal production

Forestry and Logging
113000 Forestry and logging (including forest nurseries and timber tracts)

CAA   8   F12   NTF 16953   GLD 2855

SCHEDULE F (Form 1040)
Department of the Treasury
Internal Revenue Service (99)

Profit or Loss From Farming

▶ Attach to Form 1040, Form 1041, Form 1065, or Form 1065-B.
▶ See Instructions for Schedule F (Form 1040).

OMB No. 1545-C
1998
Attachment Sequence No.

Name of proprietor — Social security number (SS#

A Principal product. Describe in one or two words your principal crop or activity for the current tax year.

B Enter NEW code from Pai ▶

D Employer ID no. (EIN), if i

C Accounting method: (1) ☐ Cash   (2) ☐ Accrual

E Did you "materially participate" in the operation of this business during 1998? If "No," see page F-2 for limit on passive losses. ☐ Yes

Sample only. Do not use to file taxes. Obtain current tax forms from the United States Department of the Treasury Internal Revenue Service.

Part I Farm Income — Cash Method. Complete Parts I & II (Accrual method taxpayers complete Parts II & III, and line of Part I.) Do not include sales of livestock held for draft, breeding, sport, or dairy purposes; report these sales on Form 4:

1	Sales of livestock and other items you bought for resale	1
2	Cost or other basis of livestock and other items reported on line 1	2
3	Subtract line 2 from line 1	3
4	Sales of livestock, produce, grains, and other products you raised	4
5a	Total cooperative distributions (Form(s) 1099-PATR)	5a ... 5b Taxable amount ... 5b
6a	Agricultural program payments (see page F-3)	6a ... 6b Taxable amount ... 6b
7	Commodity Credit Corporation (CCC) loans (see page F-3):	
a	CCC loans reported under election	7a
b	CCC loans forfeited	7b ... 7c Taxable amount ... 7c
8	Crop insurance proceeds and certain disaster payments (see page F-3):	
a	Amount received in 1998	8a ... 8b Taxable amount ... 8b
c	If election to defer to 1999 is attached, check here ▶	8d Amount deferred from 1997 ... 8d
9	Custom hire (machine work) income	9
10	Other income, including Federal and state gasoline or fuel tax credit or refund (see page F-3)	10
11	**Gross income.** Add amounts in the right column for lines 3 through 10. If accrual method taxpayer, enter the amount from page 2, line 51	11

Part II Farm Expenses — Cash and Accrual Method. Do not include personal or living expenses such as taxes, insuranc repairs, etc., on your home.

12	Car and truck expenses (see page F-4 — also attach **Form 4562**)	12	25	Pension and profit-sharing plans	25
13	Chemicals	13	26	Rent or lease (see page F-6):	
14	Conservation expenses (see page F-4)	14	a	Vehicles, machinery, and equipment	26a
15	Custom hire (machine work)	15	b	Other (land, animals, etc.)	26b
16	Depreciation and section 179 expense deduction not claimed elsewhere (see page F-5)	16	27	Repairs and maintenance	27
			28	Seeds and plants purchased	28
17	Employee benefit programs other than on line 25	17	29	Storage and warehousing	29
			30	Supplies purchased	30
18	Feed purchased	18	31	Taxes	31
19	Fertilizers and lime	19	32	Utilities	32
20	Freight and trucking	20	33	Veterinary, breeding, & medicine	33
21	Gasoline, fuel, and oil	21	34	Other expenses (specify):	
22	Insurance (other than health)	22	a		34a
23	Interest:		b		34b
a	Mortgage (paid to banks, etc.)	23a	c		34c
b	Other	23b	d		34d
24	Labor hired (less employment credits)	24	e		34e
			f		34f

35	**Total expenses.** Add lines 12 through 34f	35
36	**Net farm profit or (loss).** Subtract line 35 from line 11. If a profit, enter on **Form 1040, line 18,** and ALSO on **Schedule SE, line 1.** If a loss, you MUST go on to line 37 (estates, trusts, and partnerships, see page F-6)	36
37	If you have a loss, you MUST check the box that describes your investment in this activity (see page F-6).	37a ☐ All investment is at risk.
	• If you checked 37a, enter the loss on **Form 1040, line 18,** and ALSO on **Schedule SE, line 1.**	37b ☐ Some investment i at risk.
	• If you checked 37b, you MUST attach **Form 6198.**	

For Paperwork Reduction Act Notice, see Form 1040 instructions.   Schedule F (Form 1040)
CAA   8   F12   NTF 16952   GLD 2855

Sustainable Vegetable Production from Start-Up to Market

Figure 3.2 Sample Federal tax Schedule F, "Profit or Loss From Farming"

Sidebar 3.6 Whole Vegetable Farm Planning

Process
1. Identify problem areas
2. Compare alternatives
3. Develop action plan
4. Measure, assess progress
5. Reevaluate action plan

Sources of Technical Information and Advice
Bankers
Consultants
Dealers
Regulators
Extension
NRCS
Peers

Sphere of Personal Influence and Advice
Farmer
Family
Friends
Customers
Neighbors

Family Goals
For business, lifestyle, landscape, next generation

Profitability
Yields, income, fixed and variable costs

Marketing
Options, value-added, trends, promotion efforts

Labor
Source, tasks, timing, training, housing, incentives

Physical Plant
Machinery and buildings maintenance, improvement

Record Keeping
Data collection, collation, analysis

Crop Mix and Rotation
What, where, when for next three to five years

Soil Stewardship
Cover crops, compost, manure, erosion control

Nutrient Management
Soil tests, liming, fertilization

Pest Management
Key pest monitoring, prevention, control options

Water Management
Irrigation needs, water supply and delivery system

Harvest and Handling
Picking, washing, packing, and storing methods

Health and Safety
Emergency plans, employee training, signage

Community Relations
On-farm education, off-farm activities

Record Keeping for Profitability— A Grower Profile

Richard Wiswall
Cate Farm, Plainfield, Vermont

"I used to say that I grew 20 acres of vegetables, had five greenhouses, and all that stuff. Now I say I'm in the collection business—as a solar collector and recycler. I've had an attitudinal shift: I see an acre of carrots as collecting sunlight and taking up nutrients and water, whereas I used to think of plowing, fertilization, and pest control as the way the farm worked. As a manager, I try to imagine there's a mile-high fence around my farm and try to think of what comes in and what goes out. A sustainable farmer's job is to use what we have for free and turn that into dollars, rather than import petroleum-based products and turn them into something else. The fact that farming can make something from sun and soil makes it a noble profession.

"Although I do my share of grunt work, the thing I have realized is that real farming happens from the neck up. For years I scraped by based on sweat and perseverance primarily, grossing about five grand an acre but not really knowing what any crop was making. Now I have made it a priority to sharpen my pencil. A basic rule of business is stop doing things that loose money. I now farm with profit, not production, as my goal. To do that, I've developed some tools to monitor and manage my farming system. The first are planning tools, and the second are analysis tools (sidebar 3.7).

"Every year I make a marketing chart with a list of all the crops I plan to grow on one side, and a list of all the accounts I anticipate will buy each crop on the other (figure 3.3). A grower may have to do some market research and try to make educated guesses about the demand for various crops from various markets at first, but once a track record is established with accounts, it is pretty easy to get a good idea of what you'll need to produce in subsequent years. This method starts with where the money will be coming from, before you even plant, rather than planting crops and trying to sell them. The latter approach leads to selling crops too cheap, throwing product away, or never even harvesting some crops."

After Richard has made estimates of what he needs to grow in order to meet his market demands, he estimates average yield per acre of each crop, how much area needs to be planted, and the dates plantings should be made (figure 3.4). For crops that are transplanted, he calculates how many plants will be needed and when the flats should be started (figure 3.5, page 34). Then, for all the fields in his available land base, he constructs a plan of where the crops will go (figure 3.6, page 34). This is done taking into consideration for each area such conditions as high deer pressure and needs for crop rotation, cover cropping, and access to water. The result is a very detailed set of field plans describing his entire farm plan for the year. The chart and plan have to be prepared far ahead of production, since there is no time for planning once the season begins. The plan hangs in the farm office and is followed all year, as is the seedling chart which guides transplant production so that crops will be ready when the plan says it's time to put them in. Every Monday the charts and plan are checked, and a weekly schedule of activities planned accordingly.

> *"A basic rule of business is stop doing things that loose money. I now farm with profit, not production, as my goal. To do that, I've developed some tools to monitor and manage my farming system. The first are planning tools, and the second are analysis tools."*

Sidebar 3.7 Farm Management Planning and Analysis Tools

Planning Tools
- Marketing Chart
- Production Plan
- Detailed Field Plans
- Seedling Chart

Analysis Tools
- Crop Journal
- Sales Spreadsheet
- Crop Enterprise Sheets
- Index of Profitability

Year: 1997	Projected Sales by Account					
Crop	Hunger Mountain Co-op	State Street Market	Maple Valley Cafe	Onion River Co-op	Farmers Market	Totals
Beets (25 pounds)	30 bags	30 bags	10 bags	20 bags	10 bags	100 bags
Carrots (25 pounds)	120 bags	75 bags	5 bags	100 bags	50 bags	350 bags
Lettuce (24 heads)	40 cases	80 cases	80 cases	40 cases	60 cases	300 cases
Peppers (1 1/9 bushels)	40 cases	15 cases	0	30 cases	30 cases	115 cases
Potatoes (50 pounds)	60 bags	30 bags	10 bags	60 bags	40 bags	200 bags

Figure 3.3 Sample marketing chart of projected sales per season

Year: 1997	Crop Production Plan				
Crop	Projected Unit Sales	Marketable Yield/Acre	Area to Plant	Projected Gross Income	Field Planting Date
Beets	100 bags	400 bags	$1/4$ acre = 3 beds	100 @ $15 = $1,500	5/1 (1 bed), 5/22 (1 bed), 6/11 (1 bed)
Carrots	350 bags	700 bags	$1/2$ acre = 6 beds	350 @ $16 = $5,600	6/1
Lettuce	300 cases (set out 35 plants per 24-head case)	450 cases	$2/3$ acre = 8 beds	300 @ $16 = $4,800	4/22 (2 beds); 5/8, 5/22, 6/8, 6/22, 8/15, 9/1 (1 bed each)
Peppers	115 cases	1,380 cases	$1/12$ acre = 1 bed	85 @ $18 + 30 @ $34 = $2,550	5/15
Potatoes	200 bags (50 pounds)	200 bags	1 acre = 12 rows on 6-foot center	200 @ $20 = $4,000	5/1

Figure 3.4 Sample crop production plan

A crop journal is at the core of Richard's analysis of the farm. A loose-leaf notebook is maintained each growing season with a separate journal page for each crop. The pages for various crops are arranged in alphabetical order, and every time a function is performed on a crop, either Richard or the crew chief writes it down. By organizing specific activities into large blocks of time (an entire morning or afternoon versus an hour or two for weeding or working in the greenhouse) it is easier at lunch and at the end of the day to write down what was done. The journal tracks everything, from disking to fertilizers and sprays applied, and it includes estimates of field yields and records of time spent harvesting (sidebar 3.8, page 35). Based on crop journal records, standards are developed that describe how long it should take to do things. "Then I can say to a crew, 'If you can't pick a bushel of spinach in twenty minutes, stop doing it and do something else.' "

"One of the things about record keeping is that a lot of it is hindsight; the numbers from this year will tell you a lot about what you can shoot for next year. The record for a crop is comprehensive but simple: it may take up just a single-spaced page with short entries such as 'June 18: hand-weed 4 hrs, harvest 30 bu.' "

Richard tracks crop yields in three ways, with all records kept in a loose-leaf binder, so that he can account for everything that is sold from the farm through various markets. For wholesale markets, he fills out a triplicate sales invoice for all transactions. One copy goes to the account, one is used for billing (to make sure he gets paid), and the other goes in the binder, arranged by account and in order by date of sale. For the farmers market,

Year: 1997	Transplant Seeding Chart										
	Planting Date										
Crop	March 1	March 15	April 1	April 15	May 1	May 15	June 1	June 15	July 1	July 15	August 1
	Number of Plants Needed										
Broccoli		400	400	400				400			
Cabbage			200		600						
Cauliflower			100		100						
Cucumbers				60							
Kale		600		600							
Leeks	1,000										
Lettuce, red		1,400	700	700	700	700				700	700
Lettuce, green		1,200	600	600	600	600				600	600
Onions, red	4,000										
Onions, yellow	4,000										
Peppers, bell		1,200									
Tomatoes		400									
Zucchini				200		200					

Figure 3.5 Sample transplant seeding chart

Year: 1997		Map of Brick Field (four acres)			
.083 acre Pepper	.67 acre Lettuce	.50 acre Carrots	.25 acre Beets	1 acre Potatoes	1.4 acre Cover Crop
5/15: 1 bed "Ace" black plastic row cover	4/22: 2 beds 5/8: 1 bed 5/22: 1 bed 6/8: 1 bed 6/22: 1 bed 8/15: 1 bed 9/1: 1 bed	Plant 6/1: "Artist": 1 bed "Nelson": 1 bed "Bolero": 4 beds	"Red Ace" 5/1: 1 bed 5/22: 1 bed 6/11: 2 beds	Plant 5/1: Red: 4 rows White: 4 rows Gold: 4 rows	6/1: Buckwheat 9/1: Winter rye

Figure 3.6 Detailed plan of "Brick Field"

Sustainable Vegetable Production from Start-Up to Market

the day's sales are written down for each crop by pounds and by dollar sales, and the sheets go into the binder in chronological order. For the farm's CSA, the mix of crops supplied each week, by pounds, is recorded. The goal is to provide a constant dollar-value of produce to the members each week.

From these records, Richard compiles a sales spreadsheet (figure 3.7, page 36) that should reflect closely the original market chart. The spreadsheet will have year-end total of sales of each crop to each market, with subtotals both by crop and by market. He uses a grid, with totals for all crops on one axis, and totals for the markets on the other. The figures on both axes should add up to the same grand total.

All this information provides an accurate record of sales and expenses per crop. Next Richard

Sidebar 3.8 Sample Enterprise Budget from a Crop Journal

Enterprise Budget for Carrots — ½ Acre in Brick Field, 1997

Date	Task	Labor Hours	Tractor Hours
4/23	spread 250 pounds 3-4-3 fertilizer, 200 pounds sul-po-mag	1	0.75
	disk one time	0.5	0.5
4/24	chisel one time, bedform two times	1.75	1.75
4/25	seed 100,000 Artist, Planter Hole #10	0.5	-
	seed 200,000 Bolero, Planter Hole #9	1	-
6/6	cultivate with Buddinghs	0.5	0.5
6/9	hand-weed	6.5	-
6/10	irrigate	5	3
6/20	cultivate with Buddinghs	0.5	0.5
6/29–30	hand-weed	60	-
7/3	irrigate	5	3
8/3	bed-lift 1 bed	0.5	0.5
8/4	dig one bed, forty-five bushels	12	-
	wash thirty bags #1, eight bags #2, to cooler	6.5	0.5
8/5–9/15	lift, dig, wash, and bag five other beds	107	2.5
9/20	spread manure, twenty tons per acre	1.5	1.5
9/20	disk one time	0.5	0.5
9/20	seed rye and vetch, then chain harrow	1	0.5
Total Hours		211.25	16
		@ $8	@ $10
		$1,690	$160
Cost of labor and tractor hours		**$1,850**	
Materials: carrot seed—$120, fertilizer—$65, bags and labels—$84, cover crop—$25. Total Materials	=	**$294**	
Total In-Field Production Costs	=	**$2,144**	

Year: 1997			Sales per Account			
Crop	Hunger Mountain Co-op	State Street Market	Maple Valley Cafe	Onion River Co-op	Farmers Market	Crop Totals
Beets	$600	$450	$80	$300	$200	$1,630
Carrots	$1,920	$1,000	$100	$1,600	$1,500	$6,120
Lettuce	$600	$700	$950	$320	$1,200	$3,770
Peppers	$750	$250	0	$580	$970	$2,550
Potatoes	$1,500	$700	$250	$900	$400	$3,750
Market Totals	$5,370	$3,100	$1,380	$3,700	$4,270	$17,820

Figure 3.7 Sample sales spreadsheet

constructs a crop enterprise sheet for each crop (figure 3.8). He lists the production expenses for the crop, then the total yield from the area planted. To keep things relatively simple, he does not include fixed costs such as land, insurance, or utilities; or variable costs, such as plowing, spreading manure, or cover cropping; that are similar for all the crops. After calculating expenses and income on the crop, he extrapolates profits to a per-acre basis. To compare all crops side by side, he constructs an index of profitability showing relative income after expenses from each crop (figure 3.9). "That is probably the most important piece of paper on my farm, as it shows the relative profitability of the crops I grow. Gross sales have nothing at all to do with it, and I don't worry about having all the crops that other people grow; I just grow those that are profitable.

"Since I started doing this, we stopped growing crops like sweet corn that were not profitable for us. Which crops are profitable will change from farm to farm. We have kept the same acreage in production but have switched to all profitable crops since there is sufficient market demand for them. When people ask for sweet corn, I tell them that I stopped growing it because I wasn't making money on it. They seem to understand, and buy the crops I do have.

"If the market for these crops were to shrink, I would grow less acreage rather than go back to growing less profitable crops. I would still net more income than I did with my former crop mix. Before, I used to *gross* about $5,000 per acre; now

Crop Enterprise Sheet for Peppers* (one bed in Brick Field, 1997)	
Expense per Bed	Approximate Cost per Bed
Plow cover crop	Constant—all fields
Manure and disking	Constant—all fields
$1/4$ hour chisel and bedform	$5
$1/2$ hour lay plastic mulch	$9
Buy plastic mulch, 700 feet	$20
Seed, soil, trays for 1,200 plants	$73
4 hours seeding, pricking	$40
Greenhouse heat, water, overhead	$80
3 hours hand-transplanting	$24
4 hours place and remove row cover	$32
3 hours hand-weeding	$24
Buy hay mulch for aisles	$8
1 hour apply mulch	$8
1 hour remove plastic	$8
Harvest, 115 cases to washroom	$280
Buy boxes and labels as needed	$54
Total in-field cost per bed	$665
Gross sales per bed	$2,550
Net return per bed	$1,885
*Labor @$8 per hour; tractor time @$10 per hour	

Figure 3.8 Sample crop enterprise sheet

Sustainable Vegetable Production from Start-Up to Market

Year: 1997	Index of Profitability			
Crop	Production Cost per Bed	Gross Return per Bed	Net Return per Bed	Net Return per Acre
Beets	$217	$408	$191	$2,292
Carrots	$357	$1,020	$663	$7,956
Lettuce	$219	$471	$252	$3,024
Peppers	$665	$2,550	$1,885	$22,620
Potato	$143	$313	$170	$2,040

Figure 3.9 Sample index of profitability

I can *net* $5,000 or more per acre on many crops, before accounting for fixed costs. I don't bother to consider fixed costs in my calculations since they don't affect the relative profitability of different crops. I use the numbers as a profitability index rather than a statement of true profitability.

"Although the enterprise list is extrapolated out to an acre basis, it doesn't matter how small a crop is in terms of profitability. Some crops have a limited market, so I only have a tenth or a twentieth of an acre, but if you can put together two acres of these crops, you're doing just fine. When I have a high-profit crop, even though it's on a limited scale, I make sure to saturate the high-value market—I don't want to run out."

"A good system of record keeping resulted in some surprises. Often, my seat-of-the-pants reasoning about what crops were making money was way off. For example, like a lot of market gardeners I looked at lettuce as money-maker. When I did the figures it turned out that very little profit was made, and sometimes money was lost due to deer damage and lack of mechanization, even though sales were substantial. On the flip side, some crops that I thought were not making money, like parsley, turned out to be highly profitable. Another surprise was seeing how little some things cost in terms of their contribution to the total cost of production, and how much other things cost. That showed me where it was worth sharpening my pencil to reduce costs."

"Most of us are market-driven, not profit-driven. For example, like a lot of farmers, I could sell as much sweet corn as I could grow, but I wouldn't make any money. I do grow speculation crops all the time, on an experimental basis and on a small scale. I try to estimate a hypothetical enterprise sheet, then gather the data on the small scale; and if it looks good, I may expand. A lot of farms have certain 'profit centers' and they just need to plug some of the 'profit holes' in the sinking ship and they'll be fine."

"Once you have the data to work with, it makes the business part fun because it's incredibly creative. However, I had a huge mental resistance to actually doing what it takes to get the data. Perhaps it's because I didn't want to spend five days with a calculator and record sheets each year, or maybe I didn't even really want to know if I was farming profitably or not. If I wasn't, it would invalidate my whole existence, and what else was I going to do? But now that I'm over the hump, sharpening my pencil is getting me closer to my goals of economic security and peace of mind. The process needs to continue because year by year there will be changes to make in response to markets and growing conditions."

Chapter 4
Marketing Your Crops

It's a brutal market out there—competitive, volatile, fickle, and demanding. With the right products, customers, and skills, it can also be rewarding. You had better have your marketing plans together before production takes off, or you'll not be long for the farming world. In fact, some enterprises stay in business just by being good at marketing and not producing a thing. Supermarkets do it, some roadside stands do it, and most mail-order houses do it. But as a farmer you won't stay in business just by being good at production if you ignore marketing!

Two fundamental rules for long-term survival are sell quality, and find your niche. Smaller-scale vegetable farms don't have the economy of scale or the resources to weather competition with large, low-cost producers of wholesale produce. But superior product freshness, flavor, and variety, combined with superior customer service, are factors that can create viable economic niches for the small-scale grower.

Marketing Options

Marketing options for the individual grower fall under two broad headings: *wholesale or retail.* Wholesale marketing means selling in quantity to a middleman for eventual resale to consumers. Selling retail directly to the consumer is the obvious choice for most small-scale growers, but only if it fits the grower's personality and situation in terms of crop mix and available time. Also known as *direct marketing,* selling retail allows the grower to keep much more of the final sale price, the consumer's dollar, when all the intermediate marketing channels (middlemen) are avoided. Of course, the grower takes on the extra time, expense, management responsibilities, and

risks associated with direct marketing (see "Retail Marketing Skills," pages 44–45). Direct marketing options include roadside stands, "pick-your-own" sales, farmers markets, community supported (subscription) agriculture (CSA), mobile marketing, and mail-order (catalogue) sales, all of which are discussed on pages 40–44.

Wholesale Marketing

Larger vegetable farms, as well as many productive smaller farms, will no doubt need to do some wholesaling, especially when they are located far from population centers. Selling quality produce to supermarkets, brokers, or distributors may be convenient, but smaller farms may not be able to make a profit if they rely solely on wholesale markets because the profit margin per unit of production is often small. There are many wholesale vegetable farms of several thousand acres in western New York, Florida, and California, and these have a huge economy-of-scale advantage over the smaller farm. In addition, produce from farms outside the United States, which may have been produced at much lower cost, often competes for wholesale markets. If you do sell wholesale, distinguishing your product as "local," "fresh," "organic," or "IPM" may increase demand and price over mass-marketed produce.

Programs such as the Jersey Fresh™ advertising and promotional program, administered by the New Jersey Department of Agriculture, can help growers in a number of ways. In addition to informing consumers of the availability of seasonal products, such programs can provide producers and retailers with marketing strategies and promotional materials (figure 4.1).

Cooperative Wholesaling

Small and medium-scale growers may improve their ability to compete in wholesale markets by joining forces as a cooperative. Cooperatives are formal affiliations of growers who team up to address common market challenges or overcome economy-of-scale problems. The process of starting and maintaining a cooperative is time-consuming and requires strong organizational skills. The potential benefits of cooperatives are numerous, however, and include improved buying or selling power; reduced cost of technology, information, and services; improved efficiency of product transportation and distribution; and enhanced camaraderie and reduced isolation among growers.

The process of developing a cooperative should involve more than just the grower members. Outside advisors, consultants, lenders, support staff, and, in some cases, customers and community members, must also be involved. The six steps to developing a cooperative are as follows:
1. Identify the opportunity.
2. Build consensus on the potential that the cooperative may have.
3. Develop trust among potential members.
4. Secure commitment from members.
5. Secure commitment from lenders and other stakeholders.
6. Start the cooperative enterprise.

Direct Wholesale

If you do your own distribution to local markets, food co-ops, or restaurants, you are a hybrid between retail and wholesale—a *direct wholesaler*. This means selling at the prices that a distributor would get, which allows you to pocket the markup that the distributor would have added to the price paid to the grower. If you have enough volume, enough customers within a reasonable distance, or sufficient "upscale" accounts such as fancy restaurants and hotels, direct wholesaling can be a viable strategy. As with all direct marketing, service, along with quality and a unique product identity, is key. Direct wholesaling can also be an opportunity to develop a brand name for your products.

Figure 4.1 Jersey Fresh™ logo
Source: Used with permission of the New Jersey State Department of Agriculture

Direct wholesale markets usually require a consistent supply of produce year-round, or, for local produce, as long as the growing season allows. Establishing a regular delivery schedule and a pre-ordering protocol with direct wholesale customers is essential. In the case of a poor quality crop or crop loss, don't hesitate to buy the product from another grower and resell it in order to keep your customers supplied with what they expect, especially when it comes to key items such as sweet corn on a summer weekend! Be careful to keep quality high and prices fair.

Restaurant Sales

Success with restaurant sales will usually depend on establishing a personal relationship with the owner or executive chef and reliably providing produce at its peak quality in terms of flavor and appearance, along with specialty crops that facilitate culinary creativity. Be prepared to supply hard-to-find items, such as certain herbs or ethnic greens, in small quantities. However, it may be your tasty, totally ripe tomatoes or delicate, just-picked leaf lettuce that gets their attention, since these products do not transport well and are not available through conventional wholesale sources.

For restaurant sales, you will need to arrange reliable transportation, maintain a dependable delivery schedule, and set policies for minimum orders, pricing, and payment. Are verbal agreements acceptable, or will you want written contracts? Are you going to sell enough volume of a product at a price that will pay for the cost of making up and delivering custom orders? A list of crops, prices, units (by the box, dozen, bunch, or pound) and anticipated dates of availability will help restaurants plan their orders. Promotion provided by you or the restaurant can enhance this market. Prepare an attractive, brief brochure or card to give to the chefs you are courting. In some cases, local farms can be described on table cards that call attention to the local, fresh produce on the diners' plates. This is especially appropriate where farms and restaurants maintain formal relationships, such as the Chefs' 2000 Collaborative, or the Vermont Fresh Network (figure 4.2).

Retail Marketing

Roadside Stands or Markets

Roadside stands offer direct retail sales, usually with little or no off-farm transportation costs. The marketing expenses depend on the number of products and types of services offered by the retail outlet. These range from self-serve tables at the

Figure 4.2 Table card for Vermont Fresh Network
Source: Used with permission of Vermont Fresh Network

end of driveways to quasi-supermarkets with a large selection of off-farm products in addition to the farm's produce. Large farm stands usually have evolved from smaller operations. Starting small is advisable, as it takes time to build a customer base and get a sense of how much of a product can be sold at a certain location, as well as the costs of operation. As volume, traffic, quality, and selection increase, so too will stand size, operating costs, and management time.

Farm-fresh produce displayed attractively in a pleasing environment will attract many customers. Exceptional service and a variety of products will add to that number. Many vegetable farm stands also sell bedding plants—greenhouse-grown cell packs of vegetables and flowers—to extend the selling season and bring in early-season cash. Adapting to the era of convenience shopping, some stands offer local beverages, baked goods, cheeses, jams, salsas, eggs, sandwiches, ice cream, and other food, allowing an entire meal to be purchased at one location. On the horticultural side, some stands sell nursery stock and seeds, fertilizers, tools, books, and other gardening supplies.

In addition to offering fresher produce, a real advantage that roadside stands have over their primary competitors, supermarkets, is that they can offer a more enjoyable shopping experience. An attractive rural theme, which might incorporate a barn-like decor, colorful plantings, live animals, antique agricultural implements, site-specific information, and homemade signage, can make the roadside stand highly distinct from the supermarket. A well-managed roadside market can create an ambience of rural charm, supported by attractive displays indoors and out, along with community interactions more akin to those of the local corner store than of the department store. Good-quality produce is essential, but the experience of a rural setting will make the produce even more salable.

Even if your roadside market is small, be sure to design it carefully, with future expansion in mind. Sufficient easy, safe parking is essential, as is highly visible and attractive road signage that gives travelers plenty of time to stop. The stand should be well-lighted and incorporate an aisle and cashier arrangement that can accommodate easy flow of the maximum number of customers you can expect at any one time. Cleanliness inside and out is essential. Trash facilities, loading docks, storage, and washrooms should be concealed.

Artful arrangement of products should still allow easy access and removal by the customer. All products should be clearly priced and accompanied, when appropriate, by helpful, honest information about the product (such as its on-farm, local, or organic origins; or recommendations for freezing). Extras such as volume discounts, baker's dozens, free recipes and taste samples, or complimentary beverages such as coffee or cider will enhance the shopping experience and earn you repeat customers. And earning repeat customers is a key to success.

Before you invest in a roadside stand, be sure to find out about the legal regulations that apply to the structure and enterprise you have in mind. Local zoning, health, and tax administrators should be consulted. State agencies probably regulate sales licenses, signage, weights and measures, sales tax, food handling safety, and sanitary facilities.

Determine in advance whether it is in your best interest to run the stand as part of your farm business or as a separate retail enterprise. This decision has management as well as tax implications. For example, will the stand have a manager, or will those duties be added to the farmer's responsibilities? How will income and expenses related to the stand be reported for income taxes—on tax schedule F (figure 3.2, page 30) along with farming activities, or as a separate sole proprietorship, corporation, or partnership? In addition, be aware that the quantity of off-farm products you sell and the time that employees work in the field compared to their hours at the stand may affect how the government views your retail operation in terms of labor regulations and income taxes. Consult with a knowledgeable accountant to come up with the financial design that's best for you.

Pick-Your-Own (PYO) Sales

Pick-your-own (PYO) sales, where customers come to the fields and harvest the product directly, are more common to fruit farms than vegetable farms. This is most likely due to the short peak season in which various fruits are available in abundance; to consumer interest in capturing this abundance in jams, pies, or frozen goods; and to the appeal of eating ripe fruit right off the plant. With proper promotion and management, people can be enticed to pick their own vegetables, flowers, and herbs, too. Additional produce and related goods, such as canning supplies and recipe books, can also be sold at PYO businesses.

Because fewer families preserve large quantities of food anymore, experiencing the farm environment has become a more important reason that people go to pick fruits or vegetables at a farm. It's critical that the grower do everything possible to make the PYO experience an enjoyable one for individuals and families. With PYO, you are selling recreation as well as produce.

While PYO may reduce the need for hired labor to harvest crops and can enhance the marketing of related goods, there are also serious disadvantages to be considered. Crop plants may be injured due to improper picking techniques. Extra labor will be needed to manage facilities where customers park, pick, pay, and go to the bathroom. Advertising or mailing lists will be needed to get customers out to the farm when the crop is in, and very hot or rainy weather will keep many away. Matching the timing of customer flow to product availability is crucial to PYO; customers who find poor pickings won't be back, and crops that go unpicked won't be profitable.

Despite the challenges, many fruit farms and some vegetable farms located within an easy drive of population centers do offer PYO in addition to other direct or wholesale marketing. Some PYO businesses are extremely popular, having cultivated an enthusiastic customer base over the years. Successful management practices concerning cleanliness, signage, and parking similar to those that apply to roadside stands are also important for PYO operations. Designing a controlled one-way flow of auto traffic can help customers avoid having accidents or getting stuck in fields.

Managers must also provide adequate liability insurance; groom fields and walkways; post signs, flags, or fences to direct pickers; offer transportation from parking to picking with golf carts or hay wagons; provide shade and drinking water in the field for overheated customers; and ensure speedy checkout procedures. The last concern can be addressed by positioning the cashier at the picking area in a shed or open vehicle, although this arrangement may reduce the opportunity to sell additional items. Charging by volume, rather than weight, may also speed checkout and make it possible to pre-charge for containers and then let people fill them. However, sales by weight, which are mandatory in some states, have the advantage of avoiding conflict over what constitutes a "full" pint.

Although PYO prices are lower than retail, usually by about half, be sure to set a fair price that covers your costs. Emphasize freshness and quality, and offer volume discounts. PYO customers will often purchase larger volumes of produce than retail customers, because they plan to store some of their purchase, because they enjoy the picking experience, or because prices are attractive.

Farmers Markets

Farmers markets are regularly scheduled events at which farmers and other venders sell their products retail, usually at individual displays or booths. Farmers markets may offer a desirable option for direct marketing with low overhead and no long-term marketing investment or obligation. When farmers gather together to direct market on a regular basis at a location near a population center, many advantages accrue. Costs may be shared for advertising and promotion, liability insurance, sanitary facilities, entertainment, site rental, and hired management. A much larger customer base may be developed than an individual small grower could attract. Farmers markets offer a unique start-up opportunity for growers as they learn the ropes of production and marketing. After building skills and increasing

sales at a farmers market, many growers move on to, or add on, other retail or wholesale endeavors.

Successful farmers markets usually have good management and leadership. Initially a few committed growers provide leadership, but later a manager may be hired. Also important for a profitable farmers market is a location near populations with plenty of disposable income and an interest in local, high-quality produce. Farmers markets that are starting up may struggle until they achieve a critical mass of at least twelve to fifteen vendors that offer the right mix of produce, prepared foods, crafts, and entertainment to draw a crowd. On the other hand, thriving farmers markets can be difficult to join.

Selling at farmers markets, which are most often held on weekends, requires timing weekly production and harvest so that the truck can be loaded with the best you have to offer each week. In addition to fresh produce, you'll need to load display containers; sales containers; a cash box with change; a scale if selling by weight (check your state requirements); drinking and wash water; promotional materials such as a farm sign, product labels, price cards, and recipes; and foul-weather gear if needed. A tarp or canopy to provide shelter from sun and rain is a good idea, too. You will be competing with other vendors at the same market, and the appeal of your display, the quality of your produce, and the service, selection, convenience, and price you offer will affect how well you do.

The farmers market organization may limit your flexibility in terms of marketing hours, products, prices, space, size of signage, and other conditions. Poor weather, competing events, traffic problems, travel time, and vehicle breakdowns can all lead to a poor return on the expense involved in loading the truck and spending the day at a market. However, farmers markets can be reliably lucrative for growers that have developed a loyal following.

Community Supported Agriculture (CSA)

Community supported agriculture (CSA) is the umbrella name for many variations of subscription or membership sales where people buy "shares" in a farm in exchange for a season's worth of products. The vast majority of CSAs are vegetable operations, although some also offer fruits, flowers, or animal products. CSAs range in size from a handful of members from the neighborhood to several hundred shareholders from miles around the farm. Because CSAs foster a commitment and connection to the farm, they not only provide fresh food but also, perhaps more than any other type of market, educate consumers about farming.

Most CSAs have brochures that explain the cost of membership and project the seasonal availability of products. Brochures should also spell out that the member is accepting the risk of crop failure, but that it's unlikely that more than a few crops will fail in a given year. Most CSAs require payment in full prior to the growing season, although some allow split or installment payments. Share prices generally range from $250 to $500, although farms that offer many animal products along with produce may charge up to twice as much. Because shares are typically designed for a family of four, half-shares are offered by some farms.

Many CSAs have member newsletters that explain the farm budget and production practices, offer tips on how to use unusual crops, and provide updates on membership and distribution. Some CSA members get involved in production and harvest activities; for example, there may be a scheduled weed-pulling day or a "pick-your-own peas" event. More extensive involvement in the farming operation is usually undertaken on a volunteer basis or in exchange for savings in membership cost. Often, membership fees are reduced for individuals who coordinate the CSA newsletter, manage share pickup activities, or provide some other service.

CSAs are gaining in popularity because the farmer gets a good price—somewhere between wholesale and retail—and the consumer gets a good deal: the freshest possible produce at below retail cost. CSAs also reduce marketing costs such as packaging, storage, and delivery. However, CSAs are definitely not for beginning vegetable farmers. If crops are poor, members who paid for the harvest

in advance will lose confidence in the grower, and recruiting members in subsequent years may be difficult.

Some management concerns associated with successful CSAs are member recruitment, communication, and retention; arrangement and supervision of produce distribution; coordination of traffic during pickups; and careful planning to assure sufficient quantity and variety of products for all members.

Mobile Marketing

Mobile marketing means taking the product to where the customers are. Farmers markets cooperatively organize a mobile marketing site, but individual growers can also load up a truck and travel to a suitable direct-marketing location. Often, this means going into an upscale or ethnic population center and finding a place where it's legal, easy, and safe for people to stop. A grower could simply send a teenage employee off with a load of sweet corn in the back of the pickup to sell downtown on a corner. Or perhaps an experienced salesperson takes a full array of crops in a large van into the city and sets up an attractive display, complete with signage, awnings, display tables, and cash register.

Check with local officials to make sure you are aware of any regulations concerning vendor permits, signs, or traffic. A city or town clerk is a good place to start. You may have to get permission from a landowner to use a particular site. If you do not have a regular spot, keep a close record of sales at various times and locations so that you can return to only the most promising sites. If you have a planned route, use leaflets or other advertising to let people know where and when you'll arrive.

Mail-Order Sales

Mail-order, also known as direct mail, sales are best suited to enterprises with the following characteristics: there are not enough consumers nearby to purchase all that's produced; the business provides a specialized, value-added, high-quality product line that can be shipped; and management has the creative and organizational skills needed to successfully market products through a catalog, fulfill orders in a timely fashion, and maintain mailing lists.

Although higher prices than retail can sometimes be obtained through direct-mail sales, small volumes per customer are likely. Printing, shipping, and handling costs can be considerable. However, it's easier to set your own hours and pace with mail-order marketing, since customers don't have to come to your door. There are many mail-order firms, so your products must have unique features to distinguish themselves and pique consumer interest. Repeat buyers are key to profits in direct mail, so you must earn them with superior quality, careful packaging, prompt service, plenty of product information and consumer education, and no-nonsense guarantees. Although it takes ingenuity to come up with an agricultural product line for mail order, such an enterprise can be quite successful.

Retail Marketing Skills

Skills essential to successful direct marketing are discussed below. These include developing and maintaining attractive product displays, setting fair prices, providing good customer service, and conducting reliable initial and ongoing market analysis.

Displaying Produce

Display your produce as attractively as possible. People buy with their eyes, as the saying goes, so give them a visual feast. Use themes in your display, and pay attention to placement, color, light, and height. Poor lighting is all too common at roadside stands; single height bins or shelves are boring; and dirty containers, scrawled signs, and carelessly placed goods may discourage sales. Take advantage of seasonal, regional, nutritional, agricultural, ethnic, or other themes to add excitement to displays. Arrange diverse products and container sizes to create visual contrast, and take the time to make appealing, artful signs with a personal touch that tell not only the price, but the variety of a product, where it was grown, and some ways to prepare it. If you are not willing to put some creativity into these aspects of display, hire someone who is.

Setting Prices

Pricing must be fair to both you and the consumer. You need to make a decent profit to stay in business, and the consumer needs to have a desire fulfilled at a cost they are willing to bear—more than just once. It's crucial to set the right price early, because you will have a hard time adjusting upwards with regular customers. Remember, you can always lower prices, but raising them without prompting a reduction in sales is almost impossible.

There are some cases in which you won't make a profit. For example, if a production problem keeps yields very low, you cannot compensate with astronomical prices. And there will usually be consumers who do not desire a product enough to pay the price. However, if nobody at all finds the price too high, perhaps you are not charging enough. How much is "enough"? You have to know your costs of production in order to know what range of prices will keep you in business.

Some growers set, or at least modify, their prices based on what they see charged at local supermarkets, farmers market, or neighboring stands. Others look at price reports published by state departments of agriculture or by wholesale distribution centers. Simply matching prices with a competitor is unwise, though; they may have lower costs or higher sales volume; or they may be on their way out of business.

Customer Service

Customer service is all about attitude. Think and act like a winner, not a whiner. Salespeople must know the products, like the products, and like working with the public, or they should not be in sales. There's plenty of work to be done in the back room or the fields for employees who do not understand that they are there to serve the customer. In fact, their primary goal is to make the customer feel good! Once that happens, loyalty is created and the importance of price diminishes. Customers are more likely to feel good when they are greeted cheerfully, their questions are answered completely and honestly, extra services or products are provided without cost, complaints are handled positively, and salespeople remember their names or their product preferences.

Your salespeople represent you and the farm enterprise. It's your job to provide leadership, and to give them an attitude adjustment if they need it. Explain the concepts discussed above and reward staff for high-volume sales, positive feedback from customers, consistent performance, and the habit of going the extra mile. Involve them in marketing research, decision making, and discussion of how to improve sales and profits.

Market Analysis

Initial Market Analysis — This chapter ends where marketing should really begin—with the task of gathering data that indicates who your customers are likely to be and what they will purchase and why. Market analysis is research, which means asking questions, organizing and analyzing the answers, and forming conclusions.

Market analysis questions can be asked in person, by mail, or electronically. Before you have customers, ask questions of people with knowledge related to the industry. You can collect the answers yourself, hire someone to do it, or find out if the information already exists. Planning commissions, chambers of commerce, local business schools, and transportation agencies may have numbers that can be used to get a general sense of the suitability of an area for an enterprise: population trends, average income and education, retail sales expenditures, traffic patterns, and so on.

Assuming you have some initial ideas about crops you'd like to grow, how you'd like to grow them, and who you think would buy them, start with some commonsense concerns that an investor might have if these ideas were put forth in a proposal. For example, you may have a roadside vegetable market in mind. What are the vegetable crops grown in the region? What is their total acreage and dollar value? What is the existing mix of wholesale and retail sales among local producers? How many farm stands, farmers markets, food co-ops and supermarkets offering local produce are there within twenty miles? Is the supply of agricultural labor adequate? What do people think the market potential is for such an operation?

Develop a list and ask the same questions of such people as local retailers, extension agents or specialists, chamber of commerce personnel, and farm bureau members. Ask the same questions of officers of the statewide vegetable grower association or market specialists at the state agriculture department, small business development agency, or local college. In addition to soliciting their observations and advice, ask people if they have additional market data, such as trends in sales of particular crops or food products over the past several years.

Ongoing Market Analysis — Understanding your customers is an ongoing process. Once you have an enterprise underway, you can focus and collect your own market data simply by analyzing your sales records. Additional insight can be gained by surveying customers, by either asking questions or passing out questionnaires. You want to get a profile of your customers, find out what they are buying and why, learn what attracted them to your business, and solicit suggestions for improvements in product line, services, or market features. Collecting names and addresses will help you develop a mailing list for promotion of special events and allow for follow-up surveys after a reasonable delay after new market strategies are implemented. Be sure to offer incentives—such as free samples, discounts, coupons, or eligibility to win prizes—for those who participate in surveys. Finally, an opportunity for ongoing market analysis that should not be overlooked is communicating with customers, noting their inquiries, complaints, requests, and suggestions.

In conclusion, if you set prices that you have reason to feel comfortable with; do a good job with display, service, and market research; and never sell low-quality goods, success will follow.

Chapter 5

Soil Fertility Management

Soil fertility is the capacity of soil to provide nutrients for plant growth. Soil fertility is a function of the biological, physical, and chemical characteristics of soil. In order to optimize and maintain crop production over many years, a sustainable soil fertility program considers the management of all these factors and how they interrelate. The biological and physical aspects of soil fertility are maintained primarily through the regular addition of organic residues via cover crops, manures, compost, and crop residues and through management practices that prevent erosion, compaction, salinization, and accumulation of toxins. Managing the chemical aspects of fertility has to do primarily with assessing crop nutrient needs and applying appropriate fertilizers.

Figure 5.1 illustrates the creation and loss of organic matter in the soil. Soil humus, or stable soil organic matter, is formed when animal manures, crop residues, compost, and cover crops are decomposed by soil microbes. Soil organic matter is lost when erosion takes place and when soil microbes continue the decomposition process.

Organic Matter Management

Organic matter is a key factor, if not the key factor, to sustaining soil productivity over time, since organic matter enhances the biological, physical, and chemical suitability of soil for agricultural uses. Organic matter has a positive effect on the soil's biological processes because it provides carbon that fuels microbial activity, which in turn transforms nutrients into forms that are available to plants. Organic matter improves the soil's physical condition (its structure, or tilth)

and thus improves aeration, drainage, and the ability of plant roots to proliferate in the soil. In addition, organic matter has a positive effect on the soil's chemical condition by increasing levels of nutrient reserves, retention of soluble nutrients, and ability to buffer against rapid change or toxic effects.

Soil tillage, including cultivation of row crops, promotes the oxidation, or "burning up," of soil organic matter by microbes and therefore its loss into the atmosphere as carbon dioxide. Managing organic matter on vegetable farms is basically a two-pronged approach:
1. Conserve organic matter you've already got.
2. Add residues to the soil to maintain or increase organic matter levels (figure 5.1).

Conservation of Soil Organic Matter

Conservation of soil organic matter is achieved by avoiding unnecessary tillage and by minimizing erosion of topsoil by wind and water. The desirability of a fine, fluffy seedbed free of surface residues leads many vegetable farms to rely on rotavators to prepare soil for planting (figure 9.4, page 90). This tool causes aggressive tillage that can be harmful to soil structure, but intensive additions of organic matter seem to mitigate the damage. Seeking alternatives to rotavators, which literally churn up the soil, some growers are switching to field cultivators (figure 9.8, page 92), which less aggressively prepare a seedbed. These units have numerous S-tines mounted on a rigid frame, followed by roller cages and/or leveling teeth to turn in light residues, break up clods, and smooth the soil surface. There is also interest in soil spading machines (figure 9.5, page 91), which

Sustainable Vegetable Production from Start-Up to Market

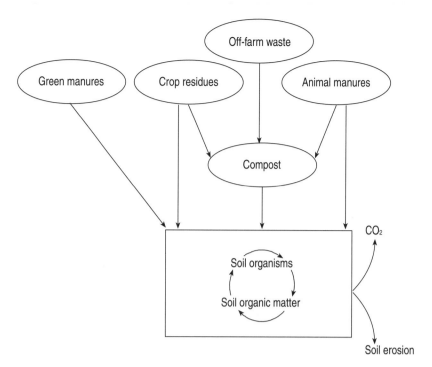

Figure 5.1 Creation and loss of soil organic matter

turn the soil more slowly and gently than rotavators. Finally, no-till vegetable production is gaining in popularity because under some conditions it is an excellent way of reducing both tillage and erosion (see "Conservation Tillage," page 93). For additional information, see chapter 9, "Tillage Equipment and Field Preparation," beginning on page 87.

Soil erosion can be minimized by reducing the flow of water or wind over the soil. One way to slow the flow of water is to leave the soil surface completely or partially covered with plant residues through cover cropping, no-till cropping, or mulching. Planting along the contour of land, leaving strips of sod in between cropped areas on slopes, and putting in diversion ditches are other practices used to manage the flow of water to reduce erosion. Windbreaks, such as fences, trees, or strips of cover crops, can reduce wind erosion. Maintaining good soil organic matter levels reduces erosion by improving water infiltration and by creating a soil structure that resists the forces of erosion.

Addition of Organic Residues

Adding organic residues is necessary to maintain soil organic matter levels in fields where annual crops are cultivated. Incorporating cover crops, manures, composts, and crop residues compen-

sates for the loss of soil organic matter that results from tillage. In many soils, especially those that are sandy and well drained, it may be difficult—and perhaps economically unfeasible—to significantly raise soil organic matter levels, because so much material would be needed. The goal in such fields should be to maintain or perhaps modestly increase levels. In heavy soils or soils with physical limitations such as intense surface crusting or poor drainage, it may be easier to try and raise organic matter levels, although this will still require substantial inputs of organic residues. On most soils, a realistic short-term goal is not necessarily to increase organic matter content, but rather to promote biological activity and improve soil structure over time. Consistently adding affordable quantities of organic residues to a cropping system not only provides nutrients for crop growth, but also enhances soil aggregation and tilth.

The benefits derived from adding organic residues to the soil will depend on the soil type, crops grown, markets, and quantity and quality of residue additions.

Nutrients from Organic Residues

A guiding principle of nutrient management in sustainable cropping systems is to *use organic residues to meet the nutrient needs of crops, supplementing with fertilizers only when necessary.* If organic residues can be generated on-farm or obtained locally, their cost may be low enough to allow them to be added to the soil in quantities sufficient to meet most or all of a vegetable crop's needs, reducing a farm's dependence on purchased nutrients.

Decaying organic residues release nutrients to a crop so long as soil temperature, moisture, and aeration support microbial activity. The better the conditions for microbial activity, the faster nutrients will be released, or *mineralized*. When soil is not well-drained or well-warmed, mineralization tends to be slow. As a result, early-planted crops on cool or wet soils often benefit from fertilization with soluble forms of nutrients even when the soil is fertile.

Nutrients from organic residues alone will not be sufficient to meet crop needs under any of the following conditions:
1. Soils have inherently low levels of a nutrient, as some do of phosphorous (P) or potassium (K), and the reserves need to be built up;
2. The quantity of organic residues applied is not sufficient to meet crop nutrient needs;
3. Nutrient availability from residues and the timing of crop uptake do not coincide; or
4. Crops are grown on soils that are compacted or otherwise physically suboptimal.

Assessing Nutrient Needs

Assessing nutrient needs for optimal crop production is essential to the appropriate use of fertilizers. Soil tests and tissue tests are used to determine the nutrient status of soil and crops, allowing sound estimates to be made of the additional nutrient needs of specific crops. Soil tests are also useful for monitoring soil characteristics, such as organic matter level, soluble salt content, and nutrient ratios, all of which can affect plant uptake of nutrients.

Soil Testing
Soil testing is conducted by a laboratory, usually by treating soil with a weak acid solution to extract and then analyze plant nutrients. This gives an idea of the quantities of available nutrients that crop roots are exposed to in the soil. A soil test should be performed about once every three years in each field that is managed as a unit. Testing laboratories may use different extraction procedures, so do not compare the *analytical results* from different labs. Stick with one lab and monitor changes in your soil over time. Doing otherwise is analogous to weighing something on different scales—the numbers cannot be safely compared. However, it may be informative to compare the *interpretations* of test results from different labs, in terms both of whether the available levels of nutrients are considered high, medium, or low; and of how much fertilizer is recommended.

Remember that the analytical results, or soil test values for different nutrients, are just an index of nutrient availability. Analytical results should not be interpreted as exact measurements of nutrients available to plants.

Tissue Analysis
Tissue analysis or testing is a direct measure of the nutrient content of a crop, usually as measured in recently matured leaves. Tissue analysis is most useful early in the season, while fertilizer can still be applied to correct nutrient deficiencies in annual crops. Tissue testing is more commonplace in perennial crops such as the small fruits, where the response to fertilizer can be seen in subsequent years. Tissue tests require timely sampling of comparable plant parts to obtain meaningful results, since the concentration of nutrients varies over time and within the plant, depending on the maturity of tissues.

With annual crops, even when a consistent protocol is worked out for sampling, it may be difficult to modify fertility in response to tissue testing in time to affect crop performance. However, as tools are developed for on-the-spot tissue analysis, this problem may be overcome. Fertilization through trickle irrigation systems in particular ("fertigation") allows the rapid placement of soluble nutrients in the crop root zone in response to tissue analysis (see "Fertigation," pages 116–117).

Fertilizer Recommendations

Soil and tissue test analytical results are almost always accompanied by fertilizer recommendations, which are estimates of the amounts of nutrients a crop will require for best growth based on the test results. Ideally, these are estimates determined by "field calibration," where different levels of fertilizer are applied to soils with a range of different soil or tissue test results, and crop yields are analyzed to determine optimal fertilizer rates. This process is costly and hence not done for all crops, or on the full range of soils that people grow vegetables on. Thus, recommendations are often specialists' opinions based on observation plus extrapolation from research done elsewhere. Use fertilizer recommendations along with your own observations and experience, yield goals, and field management records to develop an appropriate fertility program for your crops. Also see "Calculating Fertilizer Application Rates," pages 55–57.

Soil Test Results and Recommendations
Soil pH

Perhaps the most important information from a soil test is the *pH*, a measure of soil acidity that indicates whether lime needs to be applied. Most vegetable crops do best on soils with a pH between 6.0 and 7.0. A pH of 7.0 is neutral. A pH of 6.0 is ten times more acid than 7.0. Some crops, such as potatoes or watermelon, will still grow well at a pH below 6, and others, such as hybrid asparagus, require that the pH be near or even slightly above 7 for best performance. Soil pH is fundamental to your fertility program because the availability to plants of nutrients in the soil is strongly influenced by soil pH. Above a pH of 7 and below a pH of 6, overall nutrient availability declines, and trace mineral toxicities or deficiencies may occur.

Soil pH is naturally lowered over time by a variety of chemical reactions that result from microbial activity. These include the transformation of ammonium to nitrate and sulfur to sulfate, the formation of carbonic acid from carbon dioxide and water, and the production of organic acids. All these reactions promote soil acidity by increasing the amount of free hydrogen. The result is that calcium (Ca), magnesium (Mg), potassium (K), and sodium (Na) become less available, or are lost through leaching, while hydrogen (H) and aluminum (Al) become more available on the microscopic surfaces of soil particles and in the soil solution. To raise soil pH, limestone is added to neutralize H and Al with Ca and Mg. Occasionally, soils may have a lot of Ca-containing minerals and a very high pH. These soils can be adjusted to a more neutral pH by acidifying them with the addition of sulfur (S). Soils high in clay and organic matter are more buffered against chemical changes, and will require more lime or sulfur to change their pH.

Liming materials vary in their ability to raise soil pH, depending on their Ca and Mg content, the proportion of Ca and Mg content that is in the form of oxides or carbonates, the fineness of grind, and the amount of impurities. All limestone products are labeled with a "calcium carbonate equivalent," which describes their relative liming value compared to pure calcium carbonate. Limestone with a high magnesium content is called dolomitic lime. The magnesium content of dolomitic lime varies, but averages 11%.

Although the size of lime particles does not affect the ultimate neutralizing value of a liming material, particle size does affect the speed of the neutralizing process. Very fine lime particles react with the soil quickly, raising the pH fairly rapidly if properly mixed into the soil. Larger particles may take a year or more to fully react. The label on lime products describes the size of the particles, stating what proportion is the finest grind, able to pass through a 100-mesh-per-inch sieve.

Prior to planting vegetables, no more than four tons to the acre of lime should be added at one time. More than that can "shock" the soil and result in tie-up of trace elements like boron, and reduced availability of potassium. If more lime is called for, apply it in "split" applications, divided between spring and fall, or over several years. Thoroughly incorporating lime into the rooting zone is important, since it moves downward slowly over time. Deep rotavating or several heavy diskings are effective at mixing lime into the soil. Lime will mix better with dry soil than wet soil, where it tends to cake.

Percent Organic Matter

There is no "ideal" percent organic matter for soil. Percent organic matter (% om) varies with soil type, texture, and cropping history. Intensive cultivation reduces organic matter, and the regular addition of organic residues can help compensate for this loss. Testing for organic matter every few years helps keep tabs on the effectiveness of organic matter management strategies. The "loss on ignition" test for organic matter, which burns off all carbon-containing material in the soil, may be included in a basic soil test or offered as an additional option by some labs.

Cation Exchange Capacity

Cation exchange capacity, or CEC, describes the ability of a soil to hold on to positively charged ions (cations) such as Ca^{++}, Mg^{++}, $^+$, NH_4^+, H^+, and Al^{+++}. The holding power that creates CEC results from the negative charges on the microscopic surfaces of soil particles that attract positive charges. In effect, CEC is a measurement of how effective a "sponge" the soil is for nutrient cations. Increased CEC results in greater nutrient availability to plants. CEC may be expressed in milli-equivalents (meq) per 100 grams (g) of soil, or centimoles per kilogram (cmol/kg) of soil. CEC may range from below 5 meq/100g in sandy soils with little organic matter to over 20 meq/100 g in clayey soils and those high in organic matter. The CEC of pure humus or organic matter-based potting mixes may be over 100 meq/100 g. To improve soil CEC, add organic residues regularly.

Base Saturation Ratio

Base saturation ratio describes the relative proportion of Ca, Mg, and K cations that are held by soil particles. There is a wide range of ratios that are suitable for plant growth, but a Ca: Mg: K ratio in the ballpark of 20: 4: 1 (expressed as the elemental forms of nutrients) is desirable, especially on low-CEC soils and when the target pH is above 6.0. Many labs express base saturation ratio as percent of cation exchange, in which case the ideal ranges are 65-80% Ca, 5-15% Mg, and 2-5% K.

Attempting to achieve the ideal base saturation ratio may lead to uneconomic fertilization. However, paying attention to the balance of nutrients, particularly between Mg and K, can be important to avoid an excess of one nutrient that may suppress uptake of another. Fertilizer materials should be selected to try and adjust the ratio in the desirable direction by adding nutrients that are needed and not those that are already at high levels. For example, on a soil testing high in K but low in Mg, use of a blended fertilizer like 10-10-10, or a mineral like sul-po-mag (0-0-22-11 Mg) adds K when it is not needed. In this case, any N, P or Mg that is needed should be added using materials that supply little or no K. Similarly, if soil Ca is low but Mg is not, use calcite rather than dolomite lime to adjust soil pH.

Conductivity

Conductivity measures the level of soluble salts in soil. Salinization is rarely a problem in field soils of humid regions since rainfall leaches salts from the soil. In greenhouses, an excess of soluble salts can be a problem since fertilization tends to be high and leaching is low. Composts and manures can be high in soluble salts. These materials should be tested for salt content before being applied at substantial rates when growing salt-sensitive crops such as beans, carrots, onions, radish, peppers, and lettuce.

A high level of soluble salts results from a high concentration of water-soluble ions. Some of these ions, such as potassium, calcium, and phosphate, must be abundant for good plant growth; while others, such as chloride and sodium, are needed in minute quantities or are not needed at all. Excessive levels of soluble salts can damage plant roots and reduce their ability to take up water, while very low levels of soluble salts indicate a lack of available nutrients.

Soluble salt levels are measured as the electrical conductivity (EC) of a water extract of the soil (or other growing medium, such as a peat-lite mix) and are usually expressed as millimohs per centimeter (mmho/cm), or the equivalent millisiemans per centimeter (mS/cm). Whether a specific EC level is determined to be high, moderate, or low depends on the growing medium, the laboratory procedure used to obtain the water extract, and the age and species of crop. For most vegetables growing in mineral soils, an EC in the range of 1-2 is desirable for a 1:2 soil: water extract. When vegetables are grown in compost or peat-lite mix, or if a saturated media extract is analyzed, the desirable EC level may be two or three times greater.

Phosphorous

Phosphorus (P) is naturally low in many soils, and a deficiency of P can limit crop growth, especially early in the season. Soils testing low in available P or available phosphate (P_2O_5) usually require substantial applications of phosphorus-containing fertilizer to meet vegetable crop needs. Yet, many agricultural soils have been regularly fertilized with P over the years, and have little or no need for P fertilization since P does not leach from the soil. However, because plants are not efficient at taking up P when soils are cold, placing a small amount of P near the roots by banding or fertigating can be beneficial to early season plant growth, even when a soil tests high in available phosphorus.

There is usually a reserve of P that's not measured by a soil test because it's chemically bound in the soil and only slowly available. Liming the soil to a pH between 6 and 7, stimulating biological activity with frequent incorporation of organic residues, and promoting soil warming through good drainage, raised beds, and/or plastic mulches will encourage reserve P utilization.

The superphosphates, such as 0-46-0 or 0-20-0, are commonly available synthetic P fertilizers, produced by acid treating natural phosphate deposits. The P they contain is highly soluble and available to plants. Mono-ammonium phosphate (MAP) and di-ammonium phosphate (DAP), contain available N as well as P, and are often used as starter fertilizers on crops like sweet corn.

If soils are P-deficient, phosphorus fertilization on organic farms can be costly, since organically-approved materials tend to be low in available P. Although untreated mineral deposits of rock phosphate contain up to 30% phosphate, it is very slowly available, so large quantities of rock

phosphate are usually needed to meet crop demands in low-P soils. Hard rock phosphate contains about 2% available P_2O_5, and soft, or colloidal, rock phosphate contains 3% available P_2O_5. Thus, a ton of these materials provides only 40–60 pounds of available P_2O_5 per acre. Because of the chemical composition of rock phosphate, the P it contains will be more available to plants in acid than in neutral soils. Bone meal contains several times more available P_2O_5 by weight than rock phosphate but is much more expensive.

Although many composts and manures tend to contain smaller quantities of phosphate than of nitrogen or potash, the regular use of compost or manure can help build soil P reserves. Compared to other types of manures or composts, those containing poultry wastes are an excellent source of phosphorus.

Potassium

Potassium (K) fertilization of vegetable crops is affected by the type and amount of clay a soil contains. In general, heavier soils with more clay content tend to have large K reserves, and light textured soils have little reserve K. Since soil test recommendations often average all soil types together, it may be beneficial to reduce the recommended application rates slightly on heavy soils and increase them slightly on light soils. Although K is moderately prone to leaching from most soils, fertilizer K is particularly vulnerable to loss from soils with a low cation exchange capacity (see "Cation Exchange Capacity," page 50).

Potassium chloride (muriate of potash) or KCl (0-0-60) is a common K fertilizer, a natural salt that is included in many blended formulations. Although its potassium is very available to plants, potassium chloride is high in soluble salts that can dehydrate (burn) plant roots when applied in large amounts in the row. Potassium nitrate (KNO_3) is a relatively expensive fertilizer usually reserved for use on greenhouse crops or for side-dressing (spreading along the crop row) or fertigation of high-value field crops when both K and N are needed. Sul-po-mag (potash of sulfate magnesia), 0-0-22-11 Mg, can be used to supply K as well as Mg if both are needed.

Organic farmers can use animal manure (with restrictions on the application of raw manure), compost, or minerals like sul-po-mag, potassium sulfate, greensand or granite dust to supply potash. Currently, organic certification rules vary in their acceptance of naturally-mined Chilean nitrate (nitrate of soda-potash). Although KCl comes from naturally-occurring mineral deposits, its use on organic farms is prohibited due to high salt content.

Manures and composts contain significant amounts of K, and their consistent application over time can boost soil K reserves. However, old compost or manure may have had much available K leached out. Granite dust and greensand are relatively costly, slow-release sources of K that can be applied at several tons to the acre to build up K reserves. Wood ashes contain soluble K, but must be used with caution. Wood ashes will raise the pH rather rapidly and can be high in soluble salts that are caustic and may cause injury to sensitive plants. The liming effect of 1 pound of ashes is roughly equal to ⅔ of a pound of lime-stone.

Calcium

Calcium (Ca) is usually provided in sufficient quantity for crop growth by liming to maintain the proper soil pH (see "Soil pH," pages 49–50), although light-textured soils with high pH may still test low in Ca in terms of optimal levels for vegetable production. These soils may benefit from application of gypsum (calcium sulfate) in order to add Ca without raising the pH. Because supplemental calcium can be beneficial to the quality of "soft-fruited," high-value crops like tomatoes, peppers, melons, and berries, some growers sidedress or fertigate nitrogen as calcium nitrate ($CaNO_3$) to assure a good supply of available calcium during fruit development.

Magnesium

Magnesium (Mg) is most economically applied as dolomite, or high-mag lime, which provides a lot of Ca, but also contains a significant amount of magnesium. Dolomite should be used if liming is recommended and Mg tests low. If Mg tests high, use calcite, or regular lime. If Mg reserves are moderate, the decision should be based on price, and on moving toward a more desirable base saturation ratio (see "Base Saturation Ratio," page 50). When liming is not required, other Mg sources are sul-po-mag or Epsom salts (magnesium sulfate). Sul-po-mag is the better choice if K is also required, as it is less expensive per unit of Mg than Epsom salts. Use Epsom salts to supply Mg if neither lime nor K are needed. Commercial fertilizer blends can also be formulated to contain a small percentage of magnesium. "Emergency" foliar sprays of soluble Mg, such as Epsom salts, are used to alleviate Mg deficiency symptoms on crops such as spinach, tomatoes, or celery.

Trace Elements

Trace elements, or "minor" elements such as boron (B), zinc (Zn), copper (Cu), and manganese (Mn) are needed by plants in very small quantities and are also referred to as micronutrients. Deficiencies of trace elements are not common, because trace elements are generally supplied to plants in sufficient quantities by regular additions to the soil of organic residues such as manure, compost, and cover crops. Because trace elements are needed in such small amounts, the results of soil tests can be difficult to interpret in terms of whether trace element levels are sufficient. However, soil tests can alert you to the potential for problems. Tissue tests are more effective for determining whether plants are getting sufficient quantities of trace elements.

Boron is the trace element that is most often low in northeastern soils. If soil tests indicate low levels of B, an application of several pounds of B per acre is advisable for crops with high B needs, such as beets, cole crops, celery, radishes, and asparagus. Regular, low-level applications (1–2 pounds per acre) of B are often recommended for these crops on light-textured soils. Since small quantities are needed, B is most easily applied to the soil when mixed in with other fertilizers. Several forms of B are organically permitted, including Solubor (20% B) and Borax (11% B). Use care in applying B. Excessive levels of B are toxic to plants, and certain crops, such as beans, peas, and some cucurbits, are especially sensitive to high B levels.

Sustainable Vegetable Production from Start-Up to Market

On soils with high pH or high soil organic matter content, zinc (Zn), or manganese (Mn) fertilization may also be advisable

Nitrogen Management

Nitrogen (N) management is complicated by the fact that N is not usefully measured by routine soil testing because available amounts fluctuate depending on environmental conditions and microbial activity. Some labs do report nitrate and/or ammonium levels, but these vary so much during a growing season that single measurements are not very informative. It's like trying to estimate the temperature of the soil over the growing season with one measurement. The "pre-sidedress N test" for corn *is* a useful predictor of N fertilizer needs because single measurements have been correlated with subsequent N availability. This test requires that soil samples be taken using a specific protocol: corn at a height of 6–12 inches, soil samples taken to a depth of 12 inches and then dried promptly to stop microbial activity, and rapid delivery to the lab so that fertilizer can be side-dressed in time if needed. For growers with a large acreage of corn, the pre-sidedress N test can save a lot of money by avoiding unnecessary fertilization. In the near future, there will likely be enough data to make this test useful for other long-season vegetable crops, too.

Optimizing Nitrogen Fertilization

For most vegetables, a *nitrogen budget* is the best way to determine N fertilization needs. Vegetable crops require 50–200 pounds of N per acre per year in the Northeast, pretty much in relation to the biomass they produce. Specific N requirements and suggested fertilization rates are given for individual crops in extension vegetable management guides (see appendix E, pages 250–251) and in soil test recommendations. Starting with the total crop need, subtract existing sources such as the release of N from soil organic matter, manure and compost applications, and legume plow-downs. Any unmet need should be applied in fertilizer.

Optimizing the use of N fertilizer means accounting for all organic sources of N and then applying only that fertilizer N which is needed, and at the right time. Applying too little N reduces crop yield and quality; applying too much N or applying it at the wrong time threatens water quality and wastes money and can also reduce the quality and yield of certain vegetables by promoting excessive foliage growth or suppressing fruit production. The N requirements for most crops are greatest when the growth rate is greatest. Germinating or seedling crops use very little nitrogen. For annual crops in general, the maximum growth rate is approximately a month after emergence or transplanting. Thus, side-dressing soluble N at this time is most efficient. Usually, 30–40 pounds per acre of soluble N is side-dressed, often as ammonium nitrate (100 pounds per acre), urea (75 pounds per acre), or calcium nitrate (200 pounds per acre).

Because soluble N fertilizers approved for organic farming are expensive, it pays to be careful to optimize the timing of their application, and it is advisable to use slightly lower application rates than recommended for synthetic fertilizers. In general, a side-dressing of 25 pounds per acre of actual N is a reasonable practice for organic vegetable crops growing in a fairly fertile soil. That requires about 200 pounds per acre of dried blood, 150 pounds per acre Chilean nitrate, or 400 pounds per acre soy meal or cottonseed meal, for example.

Animal Manures as a Nitrogen Source

Up to half the N contained in fresh animal manures can become available to plants during the season following incorporation if the manure is mixed with the soil promptly after spreading. The N contribution from dairy manure and other manures is highly variable and depends on the manure's composition (quantities of bedding, urine, and feces), handling (age and amount of exposure to air and rain), and moisture content, as well as soil conditions and timing of mineralization and crop uptake. Having manure tested by a soil test laboratory is the way to be sure of its nutrient content prior to application. Knowing the nutrient content of a manure when it is applied is useful for making better estimates of its nutrient value to subsequent crops.

In general, a ton of typical dairy manure, spread and promptly incorporated a few weeks before planting crops, can provide about 6 pounds of N per acre in the same year. Thus, 20 tons per acre of manure may meet or even exceed the N needs of many vegetable crops. Poultry manure contains several times more N per ton than dairy manure, and 3–5 tons per acre may provide sufficient N for many crops; more than that can also lead to formation of excess ammonia, which may cause crop damage. Release of N from manure continues for many years after the manure has been applied, although the amount of N declines rapidly as the years go by. Soils that have been manured consistently for decades may be able to meet most or all of a vegetable crop's N needs without additional fertilization.

Green Manures as a Nitrogen Source

Green manures are cover crops that are added to the soil to enhance soil fertility. Green manure N is most significant to subsequent crops when the green manures are strong stands of vigorous legumes, such as clovers, alfalfa, or hairy vetch. When plowed down and followed by warm weather and adequate but not excessive rainfall, a green manure can contribute about half the N it contains to a following vegetable crop. This assumes that the timing of N release matches the timing of crop uptake. Hairy vetch or alfalfa can release up to 100 pounds per acre of N after incorporation, while clovers may release about half that. Green manure N content can be estimated by multiplying yield times the percent N in the crop. The *Northeast Cover Crop Handbook* by M. Sarrantonio (see the references for this chapter, page 259) describes simple methods for on-farm estimation of green manure N contribution to subsequent crops.

Compost as a Nitrogen Source

The release of N from compost is a less clear matter. With very mature compost, the release of N may be only slightly greater than that from soil organic matter itself, which each year is only a few percent of the total N it contains. However, composts that are not fully mature probably behave somewhere between soil organic matter and manure. A compost analysis is necessary to get a good estimate of N availability. Composts with a high C: N (carbon-to-nitrogen) ratio may provide very little N to a crop. Since composts tend to contain nutrients in the range of 15–30 pounds N per ton, 5–10 pounds P per ton, and 30 or more pounds K per ton, their nutrient contribution can be significant when applied at several tons per acre. Unfortunately, the variability of compost nutrient levels makes suppliers reluctant to specify nutrient concentrations, which most states require to assure a consistent synthetic fertilizer industry. If a farm uses a substantial quantity of compost, a compost nutrient analysis is highly advisable as part of a nutrient management program. For more information, see chapter 6, "On-Farm Composting," beginning on page 63.

Nitrogen Release from Soil Organic Matter

The release of N from soil organic matter varies among soils and seasons, mostly as a function of organic matter content and the physical and environmental conditions that affect mineralization. The rate of N release is greatest in warm and moist, but not wet, soils, and may not be well timed to crop uptake. Only a few percent of the N contained in soil organic matter is mineralized each year, but this can be a significant source for crops. A reasonable estimate is that for each 1% of soil organic matter, up to 20 pounds per acre of N can become available to crops in a single growing season. This assumes there are 2 million pounds of soil in an acre furrow-slice (the top 6 inches of soil), and each 1% (or 20,000 pounds) that is organic matter contains about 5% N (or 1,000 pounds of N). Of this N per acre, 2% (or 20 pounds) will be mineralized and made available during the period of crop growth. In general, early and/or short-season crops will not be able to utilize N released from soil organic matter as well as late and/or full-season crops. To be conservative when calculating fertilizer credits, assume that for each 1% soil organic matter, 10 pounds of N per acre will be available to a vegetable crop, up to 4% soil organic matter. At higher soil organic matter levels, some of the N-containing material is protected from decomposition within soil micro-sites.

Applying Fertilizer

Choosing among Fertilizers

The fertilizer recommendations that accompany soil test results often suggest specific quantities of nutrients to apply, rather than particular fertilizer materials. There is a wide array of fertilizers and amendments that can be used to provide nutrients to vegetable crops. Table 5.1 indicates the major nutrient content of some common fertilizer materials. Choosing which fertilizers to apply requires balancing crop needs, the cost of materials, application constraints, and for organic farmers, permissibility.

Calculating Fertilizer Application Rates

The difference between crop nutrient needs and the ability of the soil and organic residues to supply nutrients should be the basis for fertilizer application rates. See appendix E (pages 250–251) for nutrient recommendations for various vegetable crops. Soil tests and a good record of management history are key to optimizing fertilizer applications. Use a work sheet such as that shown in figure 5.2 (page 56) to determine the need for nutrients from fertilizer; then calculate the amounts of fertilizer materials that will pro-

Table 5.1 Major nutrient content of fertilizer materials commonly used on vegetable farms

Fertilizer	N (Nitrogen)	P_2O_5 (Phosphate)	K_2O (Potash)	Mg (Magnesium)
Synthetic	(% available by weight)			
Ammonium nitrate	34	0	0	0
Urea	45	0	0	0
Calcium nitrate	15	0	0	0
Potassium nitrate	13	0	44	0
Diammonium phosphate (DAP)	18	46	0	0
Normal superphosphate	0	20	0	0
Triple superphosphate	0	45	0	0
Minerals	(% available by weight —varies with source)			
Chilean (sodium) nitrate	16	0	14	0
Epsom salts	0	0	0	10
Potassium chloride	0	0	60	0
Potassium sulfate	0	0	50	0
Rock phosphate	0	3	0	0
Sul-po-mag	0	0	22	11
Animal Manures	(pounds available per ton —varies with origin and handling)			
Cattle	5–10	3	3	0
Pig	5–10	2	2	0
Poultry	25–50	20	10	0
Green Manures	(pounds available per acre —varies with stand vigor)			
Alfalfa	75	0	0	0
Hairy Vetch	75	0	0	0
Clovers	50	0	0	0
Soybeans (whole plant)	40	0	0	0
Organic Residues	(% available by weight —varies with product origin)			
Compost (mature, dry)	1	0.5	1	0
Dried blood	13	2	0.5	0
Bone meal (raw)	4	21	0	0
Wood ash	0	2	5	0

Source: Adapted from Orzolek et al., 1999; and Ferro, ed., 1998

Soil Fertility Work Sheet

1. Management History

Field Name_____ Acreage_____

Year	Crop(s)	Cover crop	Manure (tons/acre)	Compost (tons/acre)	Lime (tons/acre)
____	_____	_____	____	____	____
____	_____	_____	____	____	____
____	_____	_____	____	____	____

2. Soil Test Results

Year_____ Lab_____

pH: _____

(Circle one: in parts per million [ppm] or pounds per acre [lb/ac]):

P: _____   K: _____   Ca: _____   Mg:_____   Al: _____   B:_____

% om: _____ CEC: _____   Base Saturation Ratio   (Ca:_____   Mg:_____   K:_____)

3. Soil Test Fertilizer Recommendations for _____ (Crop)

(in pounds per acre):

	Nitrogen	Phosphate	Potash
Pre-plant broadcast	_____	_____	_____
Band at planting	_____	_____	_____
Sidedress	_____		_____
Lime (in tons per acre)_____			
Total Recommended _____	_____	_____	_____

4. Estimated Nutrient Credits

From animal manure	_____	_____	_____
(type:_____, tons/acre:_____)			
From compost	_____	_____	_____
(age:_____, tons/acre _____)			
From green manure	_____		
(type:_____, % stand _____)			
From soil organic matter	_____		
(_____%)			
Total Nutrient Credits	_____	_____	_____

5. Fertilizer Needed

Fertilizer needed = total recommended – nutrient credits

Broadcast and incorporate	_____	_____	_____
Band at planting	_____	_____	_____
Sidedress	_____		_____

Figure 5.2 Soil fertility work sheet
Source: Adapted from Howell, 1996

Sustainable Vegetable Production from Start-Up to Market

vide those nutrients, as shown in sidebar 5.1.

Application Methods

Fertilizer effectiveness is influenced by how, when, and where materials are applied. *Preplant* fertilization is normally accomplished by *broadcast and incorporation* over the entire field, or over crop beds. This technique is best suited to large volumes of material not prone to leaching and on soils that have a significant shortage of nutrients. *Banding* is the application of fertilizer *at-planting*, several inches below and to the side of the seed or transplant row. Putting seeds or roots directly in contact with fertilizer will result in crop injury. *Side-dressing* is the post-emergence application of fertilizer alongside the crop row, often at *lay-by* (last cultivation for weed control), and is used mainly to apply nitrogen. *Topdressing*

Sidebar 5.1 Calculating Amount of Fertilizer Materials to Meet Crop Nutrient Needs

Fertilizer Needed for a Sweet Corn Crop

| | (pounds per acre) | | |
	N	P_2O_5	K_2O
Sweet corn nutrient needs*	125	160	160
– Nutrient credits**	70	40	0
= Fertilizer needed	55	120	160

Method and Timing of Application

	N	P_2O_5	K_2O
A. *Broadcast and incorporate* pre-plant	0	100	120
B. *Band* at planting	20	20	40
C. *Sidedress* when 8–10 inches tall	35	0	0

Possible Choices of Fertilizer Materials

A. To *broadcast* 100 pounds per acre P_2O_5 and 120 pounds per acre K_2O:
- 500 pounds normal superphosphate (0-20-0)
  or
- 217 pounds triple superphosphate (0-46-0)
  or
- 1 ⅔ tons rock phosphate (0-0-3) *plus*
  - 200 pounds potassium chloride (0-0-60)
    or
  - 240 pounds potassium sulfate (0-0-50)
    or
  - 545 pounds sul-po-mag (0-0-22)

B. To *band* 20 pounds N, 20 pounds P_2O_5 and 40 pounds K_2O per acre:
- 200 pounds 10-10-10 *plus* 33 pounds potassium chloride (0-0-60)
  or
- 43 pounds diammonium phosphate (18-46-0) *plus* 34 pounds ammonium nitrate (34-0-0) *plus* 67 pounds potassium chloride (0-0-60)
  or
- 107 pounds Chilean nitrate (15-0-14) *plus* 133 pounds bone meal (3-15-0) *plus* 117 pounds sul-po-mag (0-0-22)

C. To *sidedress* 35 pounds N per acre:
- 103 pounds ammonium nitrate (34-0-0)
  or
- 230 pounds calcium nitrate (15-0-0)
  or
- 78 pounds urea (45-0-0)
  or
- 292 pounds dried blood (12-0-0)

* From appendix E, pages 250–251
** From a work sheet such as figure 5.2

---

describes broadcasting, or spinning-on fertilizer over the entire crop canopy using a spinner spreader (figure 5.3). *Fertigation* is the application of soluble fertilizer through an irrigation system. *Foliar feeding* is spraying a dilute solution of nutrient(s) onto the crop canopy, a practice usually reserved for applications of nitrogen, magnesium, or micronutrients to meet emergency crop needs or to enhance appearance, as with the greening of sweet corn husks.

Application Equipment

Since the form of fertilizer materials varies widely—from organic residues such as manures or mineral deposits such as lime or rock phosphate, which are usually applied in bulk, to concentrated chemical salts that must be applied with precision—fertilization equipment must match the type of material to be applied.

Animal manures or compost are usually applied with *manure spreaders* (figure 5.4). For longevity, manure spreaders and fertilization equipment need to be cleaned and washed and metal parts oiled regularly to prevent rust. Smaller *drop spreaders* are box hoppers mounted on wheels, which are pulled behind the tractor, dropping fertilizer directly out of the bottom of the box (figure 5.5). They range from 4 to 12 feet wide. They are suited to applying lime and other minerals, as well as some granular fertilizers. The rate of application depends on fertilizer particle size and on adjustment of the opening size at the bottom of the hopper. The agitation mechanism is usually driven by the ground wheels.

Spinner spreaders are large conical hoppers with electric or PTO-powered spinners at the bottom of the cone (figure 5.3). Spinner spreaders mount behind the trucks or tractors and disperse granular fertilizers or lime in a band up to several times wider than the vehicle. The application rate and width of dispersal depend on granule size and weight, ground speed, spinner rotation speed, and the size of the opening at the bottom of the hopper.

Banding or side-dressing of granular fertilizers is accomplished with *tractor-mounted fertilizer hoppers with drop tubes* that dribble out the

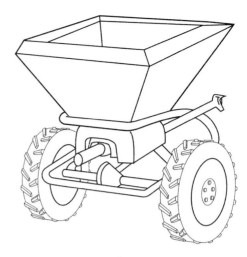

a. Trailer-mounted spinner spreader

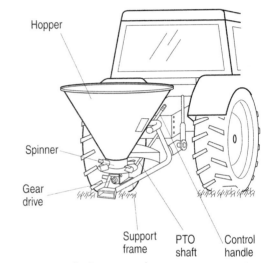

b. Tractor-mounted spinner spreader

Figure 5.3 Spinner spreaders
Source: *Fertilizer and Manure Application Equipment,* NRAES–57

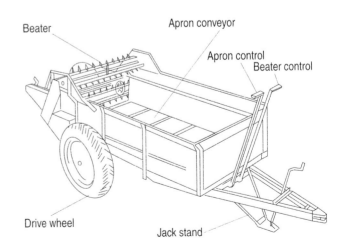

Figure 5.4 Manure spreader
Source: *Fertilizer and Manure Application Equipment,* NRAES–57

Sustainable Vegetable Production from Start-Up to Market

fertilizer next to the seed furrow or the plant roots, followed by a sweep, disk, or other cultivation implement that covers the fertilizer up or incorporates it (figure 5.6). Some push-type seeders also have small fertilizer hoppers for banding at planting.

Fertigation requires the manual or mechanical mixing of dry soluble fertilizer into water to create a concentrated "stock solution" that is injected into irrigation water. The injector or proportioner is powered by the flow of water, or by electricity. This technique is more commonly used with drip than sprinkler irrigation systems. Required by law in some states, backflow prevention devices are needed to prevent fertilizer from entering the clean water source, whether a private or a public water supply (also see "Fertigation," pages 116–117).

Planning a Sustainable Fertilization Program

An effective fertility program is based on knowing the difference between crop nutrient needs and the ability of the soil and organic residues to supply nutrients. The "shotgun" approach, in which a standard amount of fertilizer is applied every year without regard to soil testing, may lead to over- or under-fertilization and reduce profits and possibly cause pollution. Field by field records of soil tests and organic residue applications are key to planning a fertilization program. The following are major steps to implementing an effective, sustainable fertilization program:

1. Know the nutrient needs of the crop and the nutrient status of the soil. The amount of nutrients removed from soil by vegetable crops varies, as does the fertility of soil. Test your soil regularly and follow the fertilizer recommendations for the specific crops you plan to grow. If your soil test reports do not provide this information, consult an extension vegetable management guide. Give each crop all that it can utilize, but not much more.

2. Estimate non-fertilizer nutrient contributions. Rarely should all of the nutrient needs of a crop be supplied by fertilizers. Use informa-

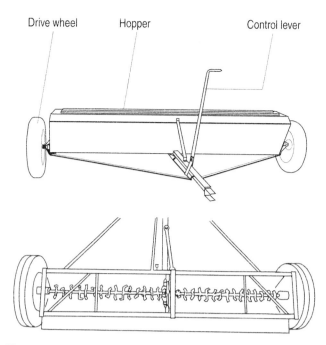

Figure 5.5 Drop spreaders
Source: *Fertilizer and Manure Application Equipment*, NRAES–57

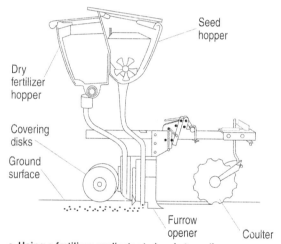

a. Using a fertilizer applicator to band at seeding

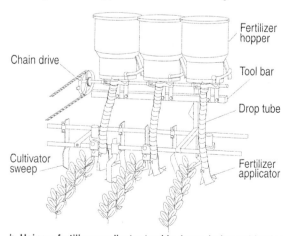

b. Using a fertilizer applicator to side-dress during cultivation

Figure 5.6 Fertilizer applicators for banding and side-dressing
Source: *Fertilizer and Manure Application Equipment*, NRAES–57

tion in extension guides and appropriate books to account for the release of available nutrients from animal and green manures, compost, and soil organic matter. A conservative estimate is better than ignoring these nutrient sources.

3. Consider the timing of crop nutrient uptake. Crops don't use a lot of nutrients early or late in their growth, so applications of soluble fertilizers should be timed accordingly. In particular, "spoon-feeding" N as much as is practical while crops are actively growing can increase the efficiency of fertilizer use (see "Nitrogen Management," pages 53–54).

4. Place fertilizer where it is needed. Although organic residues and minerals of low solubility are usually spread over the entire field due to their large volume, soluble fertilizers should be placed near plant roots to facilitate efficient nutrient uptake. Use a starter fertilizer with transplants, or band fertilizer near seed, or incorporate it into beds. Sidedress N near the plant roots during the period of peak crop demand for N.

5. Use cover crops. Leguminous green manures can provide N, and winter cover crops such as rye or oats can capture nutrients that are available late in the growing season before they are lost to leaching or erosion. Cover crops also add organic matter to soil, improving its physical condition, or structure, thus promoting crop root growth and nutrient uptake.

Minimizing Off-Farm Nutrient Inputs— A Grower Profile

Russell Pocock and Therese Shaheen
Sanders Farm, Compton, Quebec
Russell Pocock and Therese Shaheen farm about 30 miles north of the Vermont border, on sandy loam soil. The couple own 100 acres, of which 60 are tillable, and they rent another 20 acres from a neighbor. Last year they grew 30 acres of vegetables. The rest of the tillable land is in rotation

with legume hay or small grains. Recently, a couple who had worked for Russell and Therese bought 80 acres of land next door. The two couples continue to work together, sharing machinery and markets. Both farms sell most of their produce through the Deep Root Co-op in Vermont.

In addition to field vegetables, there are eight Quonset-type greenhouses on the farm for growing tomatoes and cucumbers. These high-value crops help make the costs associated with long-distance transport of produce worthwhile. Locally, Sanders farm supplies vegetables to a natural food co-op. They also have a CSA with 80 families in Montreal, which is two hours away. They deliver boxes biweekly to the families. The CSA is year-round, so they buy in organic fruit and vegetables to provide families with a full complement of produce.

"When we bought this farm in 1974 it was abandoned, the soil pH was quite low, and only 15 acres were tillable. The cost of $10,000 seemed expensive at the time. We limed the whole farm and did a lot of green manuring with sweet clover and buckwheat for three or four years while working off the farm before starting to grow vegetables. We belonged to a group that bought colloidal rock phosphate in bulk, and a half ton per acre was applied to the whole farm. The only imported soil amendment that we have used since then is the dairy manure we use to make compost, and occasionally we have had pig manure from local farms put on after a first cut of hay. We do soil test, and the pH stays up there; and the other nutrient levels are up there, too. The land originally had 2% organic matter and now averages 4–6% organic matter."

Sanders Farm is certified both organic (by OCIA) and biodynamic (by Demeter). The biodynamic ideal is that each farm should function as an individual ecosystem, minimally dependent on outside inputs. Over the years, Russell and Therese have been heavily influenced by biodynamic farmers who have immigrated to Canada and the United States from Europe. Before farming on his own, Russell apprenticed on a biodynamic farm in France.

"We try to use green manure crops as our primary source of fertility, complemented with compost. With this approach, it should be possible to meet most crop fertility with on-farm resources, once initial mineral deficiencies are corrected. We are working toward that, as well as diversifying our farm. We recently made the addition of a dozen Dexter cows so that we will have adequate compost to supplement our legume rotations and feed our greenhouses. Right now we have to buy in manure to make compost, and that is getting more difficult as time goes by. Also, it is hard to control the quality of the manure, i.e., the amount of bedding and C: N ratio. By building up our own herd, we will have control of that, as well as the ability to feed hay from our rotation to the animals instead of selling hay and shipping nutrients off the farm.

"At present we are keeping the females and butchering the bulls. Our CSA customers love the low-fat, high-quality meat and are willing to pay a good price for it. There is some demand for breeding stock as it is a rare breed, and we have sold a few bulls for that purpose. However, to do that well is another big time commitment."

"In Germany, biodynamic farms are applying all their compost in the early fall onto legume cover crops when they are making their taproot. None of the compost is put on immediately prior to planting vegetables, but instead the goal is to stimulate cover crop growth and nitrogen fixation in the rotation. This requires matching the vegetable acreage to legume acreage and compost supply. Here, we usually put the compost directly on the vegetable ground, and have to work on designing our legume rotation to match what the vegetables require."

"Our vegetable crops are divided into three categories in terms of compost applications: little or no compost goes on the carrots and peas. Other crops, including onions, leeks, and beets, get compost applications of about 10 tons to the acre depending on soil fertility. Heavy applications of up to 20 tons of compost per acre go on cabbage, winter squash, and sometimes broccoli."

"One thing that really impressed me in Europe in terms of compost production was the amount of bedding that was put down for the animals; they were often up to their knees in straw, so that the bedding captured all the nutrients. So the whole farm management situation gets more complicated: besides matching vegetable and legume acreage, how many cows you can have for production of compost depends in part on straw supply; you have to have sufficient land in grain crops. We have grown quite a bit of grain in the past, but we have tried to build up our vegetable market over the past few years so our grain acreage has declined a lot. Now we are getting back into it in big way with about 40 acres.

"In recent years, with an average of three-fifths of the farm in vegetables, we would plant alfalfa or clover with a nurse crop, keep that for two years, then follow with vegetables. We don't have a fixed rotation among the vegetables since all fields are different in terms of nutrients, weeds, and moisture, and these factors determine which vegetable goes where each year. After about three years of vegetables, we'd plant a small grain that was then under-sown to a legume and the rotation starts again. This mixture of grains and legumes in rotation is the key to enhancing soil structure."

"Of our 60 tillable acres I think about 15–20 acres of vegetables should be the limit. In the past we have been too busy trying to generate cash to do this. A few years ago we rented even more land to increase the vegetable acreage, and it was chaos; we had all kinds of problems and I'm getting too old for that. I think that 30% of your land is a

"We try to use green manure crops as our primary source of fertility, complemented with compost. With this approach, it should be possible to meet most crop fertility with on-farm resources, once initial mineral deficiencies are corrected."

good goal to have in production, and up here land is still relatively cheap so that may be feasible, whereas in higher-priced areas it may not be. On the other hand, a well-prepared field with good fertility, good weed control, and good management will improve quality and yields, so less land may be needed to make the same amount of money."

"One thing I am concerned about is marketing, and how strong California is getting in our markets here in the Northeast, in the organic market in particular. We have to get more creative in our marketing to survive, regardless of how well we recycle nutrients on the farm. You need to have the profitability to buy you the time to be a good manager. The whole thing rotates around money, unfortunately: a good market makes for good farms."

Chapter 6

On-Farm Composting

Composting is the managed decomposition of organic residues to produce a biologically stable material. Since most organic residues will decompose in the soil without management, it is important to weigh the benefits of making compost against the time, labor, and expense associated with its production. Generally, greater management inputs (e.g., collecting and mixing ideal ingredients; monitoring temperature and moisture; and turning, moistening, or covering the compost pile when necessary) increase the speed of compost production and the quality of the finished compost. The anticipated end use of compost determines the level of quality required. For example, only the highest-quality composts should be used to make potting mixes, although lower-quality compost may be suitable for field application.

Benefits and Drawbacks of Composting

Well-made, mature compost is probably the ultimate soil amendment. High-quality compost offers the benefits of being a source of slow-release nutrients that does not introduce weeds or pathogens. It improves soil structure and thus the capacity of the soil to hold water and nutrients. Compost is also a means of recycling organic wastes for on-farm use or off-farm sale. On farms with highly dispersed fields, composting can reduce the bulk of raw manure and thus reduce transportation costs. There is also some evidence that composts can suppress plant pathogens and reduce crop disease.

The primary drawbacks of composting are the management inputs required to make it. In addition, because composting is a biological process affected by environmental conditions and because compost is composed of variable ingredients, consistently high compost quality is hard to achieve. Composts that have not achieved sufficiently high temperatures may contain viable pathogens or weed seeds. Immature compost can continue to decompose, and the decomposition process can tie up existing soil nutrients or create compounds harmful to plants.

For field use, making high-quality, mature compost, rather than partially finished compost, may not be cost-effective. Fully mature compost usually has low short-term availability of nutrients compared to less-finished compost, since the nutrients have been converted to stable forms that decompose slowly. And although it is necessary to add organic residues to the soil in order to sustain soil fertility, using cover crops and/or animal manures in addition to, or in place of, compost may be a more practical choice on many vegetable farms than relying exclusively on compost.

On-farm composting makes the most sense when
- Free or low-cost, "clean" organic residues are available on-farm or locally.
- There's an appropriate site for stockpiling materials and making compost.
- Equipment for compost production and handling is available.
- A person with enthusiasm and compost knowledge is on the farm to provide labor.
- Regulations, and possible objections from neighbors do not pose serious obstacles.

If you decide to compost on your farm, consult the references (page 260) for additional information.

The Composting Process

Composting is akin to farming microorganisms that are decomposers. A process that promotes the number and activity of these microbes is called *hot composting*, since extensive microbial activity generates heat while it breaks down organic residues (figure 6.1).

At its fastest, hot composting usually requires a couple of months to make high-quality compost, although six months is typical when compost piles are turned infrequently. A slower composting process, sometimes called *cold composting* or *passive composting*, is acceptable in many situations, although weed seed and pathogen kill will be reduced. In cold composting, conditions are less optimal for microbial activity, and thorough decomposition takes a year or two. With either hot or cold composting, there may be no rush to make compost once several batches at different stages of completion are established—one ready for use that season, and others "in the pipeline."

Hot composting is primarily an aerobic process, and oxygen is necessary to maintain the aerobic conditions that generate heat and accelerate decomposition. One of the principal goals in managing composting is ensuring adequate porosity for oxygen movement in the pile. The process of passive air movement will ideally replenish the air in the pile several times an hour. See sidebar 6.1 for a summary of conditions that promote rapid, "hot" composting.

Cold composting may initially be anaerobic, which in addition to being slower, can generate foul odors. These odors escape when the pile is opened or turned, so if odors are a concern, anaerobic piles should not be turned or opened until decomposition slows and oxygen can slowly diffuse back into the pile.

The ingredients, pile shape and size, turning regimen, and location of the compost should be optimized only so far as makes economic sense. Composting on vegetable farms thus ranges from simple, remote piles with very low management to highly managed systems with dedicated equipment and structures. Most on-farm composting falls somewhere in between these extremes.

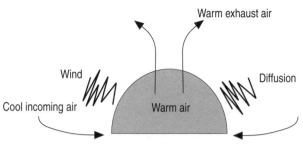

As an actively composting pile heats inside, the warm air rises, pulling cooler, fresher air inward from the sides and bottom.

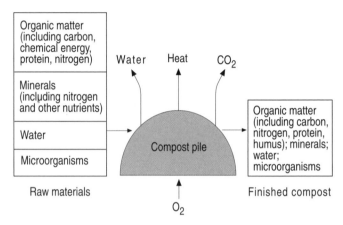

Figure 6.1 The composting process

Source (top): *Field Guide to On-Farm Composting*, NRAES–114; (bottom): *On-Farm Composting Handbook*, NRAES–54

Sidebar 6.1 Conditions That Promote Rapid, "Hot" Composting

1. A carbon-to-nitrogen ratio (C: N) of 25 or 30 to 1 on a dry-weight basis

2. Sufficient but not excessive moisture, about 50–60% water by weight

3. Oxygen concentrations over 5% (although a steady level of 3% may be adequate to limit odorous anaerobic activity)

4. A pH between 6.5 and 8.5

5. Internal temperatures of 130–140° F

6. Particle size of 1/8–2 inches in diameter, which provides porosity for oxygen movement and abundant surface area for microbial decomposition

7. Ingredients are well-mixed and piled high enough to retain heat without compacting the pile internally

Composting Systems

Composting systems on vegetable farms are usually small-scale, using a bucket loader and manure spreader to form, turn, and re-form windrows (figure 6.2). Livestock manure is often a key ingredient in the compost, but is not required if other organic residues with acceptable characteristics are available. Besides manure, commonly used residues for composting include waste hay, sawdust, yard wastes, and vegetable culls.

The frequency of turning depends on the need to homogenize ingredients and aerate the pile and on the availability of labor on the farm. Well-constructed windrows that are highly self-aerating require little turning to produce good compost. Such windrows usually contain lots of straw or other "bulking" materials that keep the pile fluffy; are not built too tall, so that the interior remains aerobic; and are maintained at an appropriate moisture content to avoid saturating the pore spaces.

Large-scale composting is most feasible where there is an extensive supply of free or low-cost organic residues. An off-farm supplier may even pay the composter tipping fees to haul away unwanted materials, and these can be a key factor in determining the economic feasibility of a large composting operation, whether for on-farm soil improvement or sale off the farm. Even when such organic residues as waste from breweries, food processing plants, lumber mills, or livestock operations are free for the taking, the cost of trucking, handling, and stockpiling them may be considerable. In addition, contaminants such as plastic, glass, and metal, or materials such as salts or petroleum products that could cause plant injury can be a problem with off-farm organic residues. However, there are vast quantities of clean organic wastes that are appropriate to composting if transportation and quality control can be dealt with. People in the solid waste sector have long been interested in on-farm composting as a means of diverting from landfills such clean wastes as leaves and grass clippings.

1. Loading mixed compost ingredients into a manure spreader

2. Using a manure spreader to form compost windrows

Figure 6.2 Using a bucket loader and a manure spreader to form windrows
Source: Adapted from *On-Farm Composting Handbook,* NRAES–54

Regulation of Composting

Permitting for on-farm composting may be required by state or local agencies. Specific regulations and permit requirements vary among states and localities. Regulatory concerns include water quality protection, odor control, traffic, and levels of potential contaminants such as heavy metals. The permit process usually requires submitting written compost management and utilization plans that provide for specific setbacks from waterways and monitoring pile conditions and levels of contaminants. In most states, this permitting process is extensive only if materials to be composted are brought in from off the farm. Regulatory requirements also tend to increase if very large volumes of materials other than farm or yard wastes are being composted.

Due to concern about human pathogens and contamination from toxins in the waste stream, composting using sewage sludge bears the greatest regulatory burden. While there are sources of clean sewage sludge that, properly composted and appropriately tested, would make a safe and acceptable soil amendment for most crops, public perception of risk could still pose a threat to vegetable growers. To be on the safe side of public relations, use composted sewage sludge only on non-food crops.

Compost for Greenhouse Use

Organic vegetable farms in particular produce or purchase large amounts of compost for use in greenhouses. Vegetable farms with in-ground greenhouse or high tunnel vegetable production often apply considerable amounts of compost to the soil before planting. High yields of vegetables can be obtained using well-made, minimally supplemented compost as a growing medium, either alone or as an amendment to fertile soil. Compost is often top-dressed on greenhouse crops as well, as a source of additional nutrients and as a medium for adventitious rooting of stems with crops such as tomato. Organic growers also rely on compost as an ingredient in potting mixes. Only stable, mature compost should be used for the production of potting mixes to grow bedding plants or vegetable transplants. Many growers, even those with experience in making such mixes, have had problems using compost-based mixes to produce seedlings in some years. (See "Potting Mixes for Starting Transplants," pages 101–104, for a discussion of recipes and potential problems.)

Compost for Field Use

Although compost for greenhouse or high tunnel use should be stable and mature, compost for field use is buffered by the soil and may be applied within a few months after only a turning or two, depending on the crop to be planted. Some crops, such as corn, tolerate very raw compost as a field soil amendment. In many cases, so-called compost used for field production may be little more than slightly aged manure, managed only enough to improve handling and avoid the likelihood of burning plants.

The maturity of compost affects how much can be applied to the field, because care must be taken to not apply excessive amounts of available nitrogen. Although it may be expensive, mature compost may more safely be applied in larger quantities than immature compost. Generally, compost application rates are similar to dairy manure, in the range of 10–30 tons per acre. Because mature compost contains nutrients in a highly stable form, they are only slowly available to plants. Thus even when high rates of mature compost are used, supplemental fertilization may be needed on low-fertility soils.

Composting Equipment

Composting equipment ranges from common farm machinery, as described above (page 65), to specialty tools such as compost turners, grinders, screeners, and sometimes bagging lines, although the latter tend to be associated with municipal or large commercial compost operations. Compost tools that may be a worthwhile investment for most vegetable growers include a compost thermometer and maybe a composting pad to facilitate operations when the ground is soft. If finished compost is to be stored for some time, covering with heavy tarps or storage in a shed will help maintain its quality.

Testing Compost

Compost testing can be simple, especially if the end-use is field application rather than sale or greenhouse use. The first step is observation. If the answers to the following questions are all yes, the compost is probably mature: Has the pile stopped heating up, even after it is turned? Is it free of off odors? Does the compost appear earthy and uniform in texture?

If the compost appears to be mature, the next step is to send a sample to a lab. Although compost maturity per se is difficult to determine through testing, such aspects as C: N ratio, pH, and ammonium-N levels give some indication of maturity. A high C: N ratio (greater than 25: 1) in a finished compost indicates potential for N immobilization, a characteristic of immature compost that can interfere with plant growth. A compost with an extremely high C: N ratio can be improved by further composting with added N sources or by adding N fertilizer at the time of application. High levels of ammonium can also indicate immaturity and the need for further curing time to allow conversion to nitrate to take place. Since a finished compost should have a pH of close to neutral, significant deviation from this may indicate immaturity.

Most agricultural testing labs offer a manure analysis, and many offer a specific compost testing package. Woods End Lab in Mt. Vernon, Maine, offers specialized compost tests aimed at measuring relative maturity based on respiration rates (see the supplier contact information, page 244).

On-Farm Composting— A Grower Profile

Steven Wisbaum
Champlain Valley Compost Company
Charlotte, Vermont
Steven Wisbaum has worked in a variety of agriculture-related jobs—as a market gardener, an organic farm inspector, and an employee with a

composting business in California. That company transported agricultural by-products to the composting site, turned them with a bucket-loader and a truck-mounted manure spreader, and sold the finished product to farmers and gardeners. "Moving raw ingredients from one place to another proved to be very costly, and it took an excessive amount of time to manage so much material and turn the compost using this method.

> *"A typical problem I see is that vegetable farmers go to the trouble of obtaining raw materials to compost, but then don't manage them properly— primarily because they don't pay enough attention to pile moisture and temperature."*

"I realized that if I ever started my own composting business, it had to be a different model, one that would focus on composting the materials at or near their source in order to minimize hauling of raw ingredients. Working with farmers here in Vermont, I saw widespread interest in composting and lots of good-quality raw materials. But the information they were obtaining from books was not enough; they needed access to someone with practical experience, and a method to turn the compost efficiently and economically. My business now provides custom compost turning, Compostex® compost covers (see the supplier contact information, page 244), and the guidance needed to develop low-cost, environmentally-sound composting operations. In four to six months, my clients can produce a high-quality compost that is weed-seed- and pathogen-free and has lost a minimal amount of nutrients from leaching and volatilization."

"The turner I'm using is an 80-horsepower, self-propelled, straddle-type unit capable of turning windrows up to 8 feet wide and 4.5 feet tall. This seems to be an ideal pile size to optimize passive aeration between turnings, especially with wet and dense materials such as cow manure. I put the turner on a trailer and take it from farm to farm, usually turning piles three to four times over a three-month period. I have an hourly turning rate and an hourly travel time fee, which is shared by the sites being visited on any particular trip. The cost to the farmer ranges from $1 to $3 per finished yard for the custom turning, depending on the volume and total number of visits. I also help clients locate and transport raw materials if they need them."

"To me, the ideal on-farm composting model is a vegetable farm that has a source of bedded livestock manure produced either on or near the farm, perhaps by a tenant or a neighbor. That keeps the cost down, even if there is augmentation with imported materials from further away. Another option would be to collect or accept materials such as leaves or food waste from a nearby community, which may even pay the farmer to take them. Otherwise, if materials come from quite far away, the trucking costs can be excessive."

"A typical problem I see is that vegetable farmers go to the trouble of obtaining raw materials to compost, but then don't manage them properly—primarily because they don't pay enough attention to pile moisture and temperature. For example, rather than keeping dry materials such as bedded horse manure or leaves in one large pile that sheds rain, these materials could be put into an elongated windrow with a flat top that will capture the moisture essential to the composting process. On the other hand, materials can easily become saturated by rainfall during or after composting. Excess water not only displaces oxygen and limits passive aeration within the pile but also leaches out valuable nutrients. Pile size and shape, the use of breathable compost covers, and/or the addition of dry bulking materials like mulch hay or straw are all used to eliminate this problem."

"During the active heating phase, farmers need to consider that water will be evaporated out of the pile. While this is a good thing if the materials are too wet initially, it can also be a problem if they are too dry. The only way to know is to dig into the pile with a pitchfork to evaluate moisture levels. If too dry, you can shape the pile to absorb

more rainfall or add water manually. If excess moisture is an issue during or after composting, piles can be covered, ideally with a breathable cover. It's also OK to cover the pile with a plastic tarp during a rainfall event, then take it off as soon as it stops raining so that air exchange will not be inhibited. This approach is less expensive than buying a compost cover, but it requires more time to take the plastic on and off. Plastic tarps are also much more difficult to secure against wind."

"For vegetable farmers, it is especially important to achieve a sustained elevated temperature to kill weed seeds and plant pathogens, as well human pathogens like *E coli* and salmonella. For this reason, farmers should have a compost thermometer in order to know whether the pile is above the minimum temperature of 125 degrees needed to kill most pathogens and weed seeds. On the other hand, temperatures above 155 degrees will kill beneficial compost microbes and cause excess nitrogen losses. How well the materials are mixed during the compost process will also make a big difference in pathogen and weed seed reduction. Most piles will have a temperature profile with the hottest point either in the center or the outer layers of the pile, depending on the porosity of the materials. In either case, some locations won't get hot enough unless the pile is turned to remix the ingredients.

"Depending on the types of materials used and the initial mixing process, some piles can be turned as little as two times. In other cases, three to four turns are needed to get a homogenous product that has been uniformly heated. Farmers will also discover very quickly whether using a bucket loader by itself or with a manure spreader is sufficient to turn their piles, or whether they'd be better off using a compost turner."

"It's encouraging that more farmers are exploring composting as a method of building soil fertility and providing supplemental income. Again and again, I see composting proving to be an integral part of healthy and successful farms."

Chapter 7

Crop Rotation

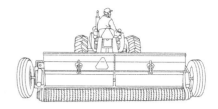

Crop rotation is a fundamental practice of sustainable agriculture. Crop rotation is a planned system of growing different kinds of crops in recurrent succession on the same land. Rotation, or lack of it, can have a profound effect on the marketable yield of vegetables because location of crops around the farm over time influences insect, weed, and disease pressure as well as soil nutrient status and physical condition. To achieve an effective crop rotation, it is critical to have a systematic plan for the arrangement of cash crops and cover crops that looks ahead three or more years.

In general, it is easier to design and implement a crop rotation plan when growing few crops, as on farms producing grains or forages, than it is with diversified vegetable production. On vegetable farms, the area of land needed for different crops can vary tremendously, and the size or combination of crop plantings may change from year to year. In addition, the location and date that a given crop is planted may be decided on short notice due to weather conditions, soil moisture, labor availability, or market demands. Although vegetable crop rotations are unlikely to be fulfilled *exactly* as planned, it is still advisable to develop a written plan and to follow it up by writing down what was actually planted where. Such record keeping is key to improving rotations over time, since it helps track what worked and what didn't—information that should be the basis of future plans.

The benefits of crop rotation are widely recognized although specific sequences of vegetable crops for optimizing them are not well documented. Often, rotations are designed with the general goals of minimizing pest pressure and enhancing soil fertility. However, if there is a dominant concern in a field or on the farm, such as control of a noxious weed, suppression of a prevalent disease, amelioration of soil compaction, or the need for significant amounts of nitrogen from legumes, then the rotation should be designed to address the priority need.

Rotation Groups

Crop rotations often enhance the convenience or efficiency of field operations because they are based on grouping crops by common features that predispose them to being managed as a unit in the field. These common features include botanical family, harvested anatomical structure, planting arrangement, cultivation practices, and timing of planting and harvest (table 7.1, page 70). Rotation groups may have similar nutrient needs, pest complexes, growing seasons, or tillage requirements. The more similarities there are in a rotation group, the better, in terms both of labor savings and of effective use of land and equipment.

Rotation by Botanical Family

Rotation by botanical, or "crop," family is a simple and useful rotation strategy. Often, crops in the same family have in common many of the features listed in table 7.2, page 71. For example, most crucifers are cool-season crops with high nutrient demand and similar moisture needs and are prone to common insect problems, such as flea beetle, cabbage root maggot, and cabbageworms. Grouping them together allows the entire area to be fertilized uniformly, prepared, and planted in a short time frame, irrigated at the same time, and

Table 7.1 Crop features that may be the basis for rotation groups

Crop Feature	Examples
Botanical family	crucifers, cucurbits, nightshades
Harvested anatomical structure	roots, fruits, leaves, or grain
Planting arrangement	multiple rows on raised beds, narrow single rows, or wide-row spacing
Cultivation practices	hilled crops, basket-weeded crops, mulched crops
Timing of planting and harvest	early-, mid-, or late-season; once-over or multiple harvest
Nutrient demand	heavy, medium, or light feeders
Cultural practices	drip irrigated, overhead irrigated, row covers applied
Pest complex	fenced for deer, sprayed for Colorado potato beetle, stale seedbeds used for weed control

protected from pests with the same control practices.

The order of rotation among different crop families on many farms is usually planned without specific pest management reasons for deciding which crop follows another. This approach simply relies on diversity to protect against pests. What usually does determine the sequence of crops planted in a field are the production practices required by the various crops. For example, following a heavy manure or compost application, crops with heavy nutrient requirements should precede those with medium or light requirements. In a field with heavy weed pressure, relatively competitive crops or those suited to repeated, aggressive cultivation or those that allow use of an herbicide that is highly effective against the weeds present would precede less competitive crops, crops not suited to cultivation, or those without effective herbicide options.

Sidebar 7.1 provides an example of a long-term crop rotation strategy based on botanical families,

growth habit, and cover crop options. The goal of this plan is to effectively use an alfalfa sod for legume-based fertility by growing a sequence of crops that have decreasing N demands. The rotation has also been planned in anticipation of the additional weeds that will immediately follow the sod crop. The crops in the sequence have a decreasing ability to compete with weeds, and they are also suited to a sequence of more aggressive to less aggressive cultivation equipment.

Inclusion of sod or hay crops in a rotation is desirable to improve soil structure, if economically feasible for the farm. Otherwise, judicious use of cover crops between cash crops can also maintain soil tilth. After legume sods or cover crops, it is logical that crops with high nitrogen requirements should follow. Similarly, if substantial quantities of manure are used, crops need to be rotated so that heavy feeders follow manure applications in order to best utilize the available nutrients. Such a rotation will also prevent problems that are caused in some crops by excess N, such as too much vegetative growth, too rapid growth, or too succulent growth.

Planning a Rotation
Rotational Units

Rotational units, also known as management units, should be defined to fit the sizes of all the fields available. It is much easier to plan a rotation in terms of fields of the same size or uniform strips within a field or fields. For example, dividing the farm into rotational units of 2-acre plots, or into 360-foot rows on 5-foot centers, makes it easier to juggle crops from year to year and to keep records. Obviously, some crops will need more land and thus more management units than others. In the case of crops of which relatively small amounts are grown, families may have to be grouped together in the crop rotation sequence to fill a rotational unit, as with lettuce and spinach or onion and carrot in the example in sidebar 7.1. There may be a unit comprised of many "miscellaneous" crops that are grown on a very small scale, as is often the case with herbs and flowers on a diversified vegetable farm.

Table 7.2 Characteristics of vegetable crops by botanical family

Botanical Classification	Family Name	Example Crops	Harvested Anatomical Structure	Cold Tolerance	Typical Planting	Weed Competitiveness
Amaryllidaceae	lily	garlic	root	hardy	small	low
		onion	root	hardy	small	low
Chenopodiaceae	beet	beet	root and leaf	half-hardy	small	medium
		chard	leaf	half-hardy	small	medium
		spinach	leaf	hardy	small	medium
Compositae	lettuce	endive	leaf	half-hardy	medium	medium
		lettuce	leaf	half-hardy	medium	medium
Cruciferae	crucifer	broccoli	flower bud	hardy	medium	medium
		cabbage	leaf	hardy	medium	medium
		kale	leaf	hardy	medium	medium
		turnip	root	hardy	medium	medium
Cucurbitaceae	cucurbit	cucumber	fruit	very tender	large	high
		muskmelon	fruit	very tender	large	high
		pumpkin	fruit	very tender	large	high
		squash	fruit	very tender	large	medium
Gramineae	grass	popcorn	grain	tender	large	high
		sweet corn	grain	tender	large	high
Leguminosae	legume	bean	fruit	tender	small	low
		pea	fruit	hardy	small	low
Solanaceae	nightshade	tomato	fruit	tender	medium	medium
		pepper	fruit	very tender	medium	medium
		eggplant	fruit	very tender	medium	medium
		potato	root	half-hardy	medium	high
Umbelliferae	carrot	carrot	root	half-hardy	small	low
		parsnip	root	half-hardy	small	low
		parsley	leaf	hardy	small	low
		celery	leaf	half-hardy	small	low

Sidebar 7.1 Example of a Long-Term Vegetable Rotation Plan

Year	Crop	Family	Production System	Subsequent Cover Crop
1–3	alfalfa hay	legume	sod, three cuttings per year	—
4	sweet corn	grass	30-inch rows, five cultivations	winter rye
5	squash, pumpkin	cucurbit	8-foot rows, dead rye mulch	inter-seed ryegrass
6	broccoli, cabbage	crucifer	30-inch rows, three cultivations	inter-seed oats
7	lettuce/spinach	lettuce/beet	18-inch rows, raised beds, flamed stale seedbed	hairy vetch plus rye
8	tomato, pepper	nightshade	30-inch rows, raised beds, plastic mulch	winter rye
9	onion/carrot	lily/umbel	12-inch rows, raised beds, flamed stale seedbed	winter rye

Relative Area for Different Crops

The relative land area planted to different families of crops varies among farms, depending on markets, climate, soils, equipment, and other factors. On many vegetable farms with direct markets such as roadside stands or farmers markets, large-acreage crop families are grasses (including corn) and cucurbits (including pumpkins and squashes). Crucifers and nightshade crops are often of intermediate-size plantings. Occupying smaller areas of land in many cases are the carrot, beet, lily, and lettuce families. Legumes such as peas and beans may comprise small plantings, but legume cover crops such as clover, alfalfa, and vetch may take up a lot of a farm's acreage.

Steps to Planning a Rotation

Arranging a diverse combination of crops over time and space to optimize the benefits of rotation is one of the most challenging farm management tasks. Planning a rotation involves the following steps:

1. Identify all crops to be grown and expected acreages based on market demand or other considerations.
2. Group crops based on botanical family, production practices, pest complex, or other features (see table 7.1, page 70).
3. Define the size of the rotational unit.
4. Determine the land area (number of rotational units) needed for each grouping of crops.
5. Make a map of available farm land showing size of fields and location of rotational units, noting significant differences among fields, such as drainage, deer fencing, or weed problems. Make a supply of copies of the map.
6. Using copies of the farm map, compare possible rotations, keeping in mind the following:
   a. timing and type of field operations and equipment required by different rotational units
   b. inclusion of cover crops and their effect on subsequent crops
   c. available supply of manure or compost

and where applications will be most effective

Cover Crop Rotations

Cover crop rotations, and in some cases clean-cultivated fallows, which are discussed in the following section, should be included in the rotational plan to the greatest extent that is economically possible. The benefits offered by various cover crops (such as fast growth, nitrogen fixation, and biomass production) and the conditions they require for growth (such as cool season or warm season) dictate how they will fit into a vegetable rotation. Certainly, winter cover crops should follow most vegetable crops. If enough land is available, a portion of the farm should be taken out of cash crop production each year and planted to a full season of cover crops. For more information on the benefits of cover crops and strategies for using them, see chapter 8, "Cover Crops and Green Manures," beginning on page 78.

Clean-Cultivated Fallows

Clean-cultivated fallows involve leaving the ground bare and cultivating the soil lightly on a regular basis, perhaps every two to three weeks. This is usually most effective during the summer when many weeds are actively germinating and growing. The goal is to deplete perennial weeds of their carbohydrate reserves, and to allow broadleaf annuals to germinate and be killed without bringing up new weed seeds via deep tillage. Of course, soil structure and organic matter levels are depleted by this technique and the land is more subject to erosion. The grower profile of Anne and Eric Nordell (page 74) describes one approach to summer fallowing.

Rotation for Pest Control

Rotation for control of insect, weed, or disease pests is most effective when the pest has a narrow set of hosts and a short dispersal range and is a resident pest that overwinters nearby. Rotation is not as effective in controlling pests that have many hosts or a long dispersal range. Rotation will have no effect on pests that overwinter away from their hosts and are migratory. Initially, rotation plans may not be pest-specific. However, once a certain pest has become a significant problem on the farm, it should be the focus of rotational plans.

To plan a rotation for effective pest control, suppression, or avoidance, it is helpful to know as much about the biology of the pest as possible. What families of plants does it attack? Where does it overwinter—in the field, along the hedgerows, or outside the region? In what form does it overwinter—adult, larvae, egg, seeds, or spores? When does it colonize the crop—in a specific season or under a specific environmental condition? How does it get to the crop—walk, fly, or be carried by wind or insect vectors? What conditions promote its rapid reproduction— certain temperatures, host density, or levels of moisture, light, or nutrients? To find such facts, consult the references for the chapters on insect management (page 264), disease management (pages 264-265), or weed management (page 265). This type of information can help a grower design rotations to interfere with resources, habitats, and behaviors of specific pests that are priority problems. To plan a rotation for pest control, plant crops that

1. are in families unsuitable as pest hosts or food sources
2. require tillage when soil-stage of pest is vulnerable
3. compete with or chemically suppress the pest
4. can be grown using cultural practices that suppress or avoid the pest.

A rotation that results in seven or more years between the same family of plants is likely to avoid disease pressure from most pathogenic organisms. However, inoculum (material, such as spores or virus particles, that can infect plants or animals with a disease) can still be moved around the farm through natural forces such as wind and water and also on equipment and clothing. The disease-avoidance effect of rotation can be "conserved" if equipment and tools are power-washed between fields, and shoes are cleaned. Although this requires a lot of extra time that most growers are not willing to spare, it may be worthwhile after working in a field known to have problems with soilborne diseases such as clubroot or sclerontinia, or a noxious weed such as Galinsoga, which can also be spread around a farm by equipment.

On farms with sufficient available land, an effective rotational strategy may simply be the alternation of cash crops and cover crops. By taking a major portion of the farm out of vegetable production each year, or "resting" the land from row crops, not only can fertility be enhanced, but pest pressure is likely to be reduced. Ideally, at least one-fourth of the cropland should be fallowed in cover crops every year. Following this rule, any one field would be in continuous vegetable production for a maximum of three years. While there are cases of continuous vegetable crop cultivation without pest epidemics, there are also abundant examples of farm fields that have severe pest pressure that has been exacerbated by the lack of rotation.

Rotation with Livestock Operations

Rotation with livestock operations has proved useful to some growers as a way to rotate crops without having to deal with the cost of taking land out of production or the management requirements of growing forage sod crops to improve the soil.

For example, a grower in southern Vermont has successfully swapped land with a neighboring sheep farmer. About 10 acres of land is cropped to vegetables each year, and every three or four years about a third of this land is seeded down to alfalfa to be used by the sheep farmer for intensive grazing. At the same time, a similar area of mature alfalfa on which sheep have been grazing is turned under and put into vegetables. In another case, an area of a vegetable farm is planted to forages as part of a rotation, and this area is managed by a nearby dairy farm in exchange for manure, or services such as plowing.

Crop Rotation—
A Grower Profile

Anne and Eric Nordell
Beech Grove Farm
Trout Run, Pennsylvania

Anne and Eric Nordell's farm sits on 90 acres of silty hilltop soils in north-central Pennsylvania. They manage 30 acres of woodland, 50 acres of pasture, an acre of "house gardens," and a 6-acre field of vegetables, half of which is devoted to cash crops in a given year, the other half to cover crops. They rely on horse-drawn equipment and hire no outside help. Most of the vegetables are sold to restaurants or at farmers market, but a few crops, such as onions, are grown in sufficient quantity to sell wholesale to organic growers' co-ops and small-scale distributors. Due to their climate and markets, the Nordells focus on cool-weather crops such as lettuce, carrots, and onions and grow only very small areas of cucurbits and solanaceous crops.

The Nordells have developed a systematic vegetable cropping system that integrates crop rotation, cover cropping, sheet composting, and summer fallowing. Their system results in very effective management of weeds, soil fertility, and labor. While their scale of production and reliance on animal power distinguishes them from many other commercial growers, some of the rotation practices they use have been adapted from large-scale grain and livestock operations and could also be used on large vegetable farms.

The 6-acre field is divided into twelve half-acre strips. In a given year every other strip, or 3 acres, is put into cash crops, and the alternating strips are cover cropped in preparation for vegetables the following year. "For convenience sake, we group plants with similar planting and harvesting dates into the same vegetable strips. This allows us to rotate the type and timing of tillage and winter cover crop species as well as the vegetables themselves. With the many types of vegetables typically grown in our market garden, grouping them by timing continues to keep us on track in terms of a meaningful rotation. Rotating the type of tillage and cover crops is really the key to organizing our vegetable rotation. Just as some livestock farmers now see themselves as grass farmers, we market gardeners can see ourselves as cover crop farmers, developing crop rotations around them rather than the wide diversity of vegetables we grow.

"Devoting the same amount of ground to cover crops and cash crops might at first seem both expensive and wasteful, but the gains in crop health and savings in weed control have more than offset our costs. We feel that by separating cash crops with cover crops we reduce the incidence of insect pests and diseases while providing habitat for beneficial insects. By alternating row crops with cover crops, weed pressure remains low, in part because we consistently utilize a 'summer fallow' in the cover crop strips."

"We first used summer fallowing to clean up fields infested with quack grass. After breaking the sod in the spring, we simply harrowed the bare ground every two to three weeks to deplete the grass of reserves and bring roots to the surface to dry out. A heavy seeding of rye at the end of August smothered the remaining quack over winter. This practice not only eliminated the quack, but also minimized the number of broadleaf weeds the following season." Now, the Nordells use a summer fallow in the year prior to growing any vegetable, including it as part of the rotation plan for the cover crop strips.

"The length of the summer fallow depends on the type and degree of weed pressure. In our first year, the bare fallow lasted twelve weeks in order to knock back quack grass and several generations of broadleaf weeds. With the quack grass under control, we reduced the bare fallow period in subsequent fallow years to six to eight weeks midsummer to coincide with that time of year when most annual weeds set seed. For the past five years, with greatly reduced weed pressure, the period of open ground between cover crops is often just a couple of weeks, and rarely more than a month. We don't think it would be a good idea to continuously use an extended bare fallow, even in alternating years, because of the potential to burn up soil organic matter.

"Summer fallowing still allows enough time for growing lush spring and fall cover crops, which produce the most consistent and competitive growth at our site. These cover crops help suppress weeds, and they contribute organic matter that compensates for the negative effects of frequent tillage during the summer fallow. Our experience has been that a poor cover crop is worse than no cover crop. The weed-suppressing effects of summer cover crops like buckwheat, for example, have been unpredictable because of less dependable weather and soil moisture supply in the summer.

"We tried several types of cover-cropping sequences the year before growing vegetables but the use of a summer fallow consistently produced the best weed control. A full year of clover sod greatly improved the tilth of the soil, but even with frequent mowing, weed populations would increase subsequently. Grubs, wireworms, maggots, and slugs were also a nuisance after even one year of clover sod. We observed that growing small grains the year before vegetables tended to create a broadleaf weed problem. Even after a very clean field of oats, annual weeds appeared the following season. It seemed that the few weeds present always set seed about the same time the small grains ripened, and that would be enough to make weeding next year's carrots or onions a royal chore.

"In addition to summer fallowing to control weeds, we target the timing of tillage to coincide with the weakest point in the life cycle of weeds. A plow-down of a cover crop at the end of June or early July seems to effectively suppress quack grass, and it buries lamb's-quarters and pigweed just before they set seed. In fields where these weeds are no longer a problem but we face dandelion and chickweed, a more effective tillage date is early May."

Over time, the Nordells have continued to improve the integration of cover crops, tillage techniques, and vegetables into their rotation system. "We learned that incorporating the cover crops as shallowly as possible was important for getting the ground ready for vegetables in our cold location. Shallow tillage speeds up the decomposition of the cover crop residues while reducing erosion, leaving enough roots intact to preserve soil structure; and it does not bring up a new batch of weed seeds from down deep."

"Devoting the same amount of ground to cover crops and cash crops might at first seem both expensive and wasteful, but the gains in crop health and savings in weed control have more than offset our costs. . . . by separating cash crops with cover crops we reduce the incidence of insect pests and diseases while providing habitat for beneficial insects."

"We found that lightly disking and field cultivating winter-killed cover crops like Canada field peas and oats made the most sense before early-planted vegetables, allowing us to work the ground early in the spring. An additional advantage to winter-killed cover crops for early vegetables, like onions and spinach, is that the dead and dried residues do not attract maggots as do the succulent over-wintering covers. Before late-planted vegetables, we found that we could get away with skim-plowing live covers like rye and vetch."

"Including deep plowing in the rotation to begin the summer fallow during the cover-cropping year helps create a deeper zone of moisture and fertility for shallow-rooted vegetables to draw on in times of drought. We used to chisel-plow rye at the start of the summer fallow period; and even though it added diversity to the tillage rotation, we no longer do that because it's too time consuming with our two-horse equipment."

"As a result of all this we have ended up with two distinct annual vegetable cropping sequences based on two types of tillage:

1. Surface-tilled oats and peas ⇒ *early*-planted vegetables ⇒ clover

2. Skim-plowed rye and vetch ⇒ *late*-planted vegetables ⇒ rye

The two different vegetable sequences are tied together by the cover crop sequences used in the alternating fallow years. The result is a four-year rotation that repeats itself three times over the twelve fields of the market garden (figure 7.1).

"This rotation gives us a lot of flexibility in terms of which vegetables we grow as we try to adapt to weather conditions and changing markets, but it also provides us with built-in diversity regarding the types and timing of cover crops and tillage. We even rotate compost applications, spreading about 5 tons per acre of compost before planting the oats and peas, which will winter-kill ahead of early vegetables, and incorporating a similar amount of compost with the rye-vetch cover before late vegetables are planted. Combining the compost with cover crops amplifies the soil-building effect of the limited supply of compost we make from our four workhorses, so that we do not have to import organic matter or fertilizer, other than rock phosphate and lime, into the market garden."

The Nordells employ sheet-composting as part of their soil fertility management. The rye and clover are clipped to promote maximum biomass production, and the clippings are left to decompose on the soil surface before being added to the soil. In the spring, rye is mowed whenever it reaches 12–18 inches in height. The clippings become a fine mulch that is incorporated prior to the summer fallow. The clover cover crop, a mix of sweet, red, and Dutch white clovers, is usually clipped twice before being deep-plowed in July, before many weeds start setting seed.

"It is important to note that experienced farmers consider the positive effects of crop rotations to be cumulative, not immediate. That is, progress can be measured over four- and five-year cycles, rather than from season to season or field to field. A rotation that really suits your farm will create a structure that actually allows for a lot of options and flexibility. What's really remarkable is how many aspects of a market garden can be rotated and integrated in an organized fashion."

(The Nordells have produced the video *Controlled Rotational Cover Cropping in the BioExtensive Market Garden.* See appendix B, page 240, for contact information.)

Figure 7.1 The Nordells' rotation plan for vegetables, cover crops, and tillage

1998

Season	Strip 1	Strip 2	Strip 3	Strip 4	Strip 5	Strip 6	Strip 7	Strip 8	Strip 9	Strip 10	Strip 11	Strip 12
	Deep plow	Early harrow	Deep plow	Skim plow	Deep plow	Early harrow	Deep plow	Skim plow	Deep plow	Early harrow	Deep plow	Skim plow
Spring	Rye	Oat/ pea residue *Early* Crops (onion)	Clover	Rye and vetch*	Rye	Oat/ pea residue *Early* Crops (herbs, flowers)	Clover	Rye and vetch*	Rye	Oat/ pea residue *Early* Crops (lettuce, spinach, peas)	Clover	Rye and vetch*
Summer	Bare fallow		Bare fallow	*Late* crops (fall lettuce, spinach, coles)	Bare fallow		Bare fallow	*Late* crops (potato, carrot)	Bare fallow		Bare fallow	*Late* crops (celery, coles, squash, tomato, pepper)
Fall	Oats and peas*	Clover	Rye and vetch	Rye	Oats and peas*	Clover	Rye and vetch	Rye	Oats and peas*	Clover	Rye and vetch	Rye

*Compost applied

1999

Season	Strip 1	Strip 2	Strip 3	Strip 4	Strip 5	Strip 6	Strip 7	Strip 8	Strip 9	Strip 10	Strip 11	Strip 12
	Early harrow	Deep plow	Skim plow	Deep plow	Early harrow	Deep plow	Skim plow	Deep plow	Early harrow	Deep plow	Skim plow	Deep plow
Spring	Oat/pea residue *Early* crops (onion)	Clover	Rye and Vetch*	Rye	Oat/pea residue *Early* crops (herbs, flowers)	Clover	Rye and Vetch*	Rye	Oat/pea residue *Early* crops (lettuce, spinach, peas)	Clover	Rye and Vetch*	Rye
Summer		Bare fallow	*Late* crops (fall lettuce, spinach, coles)	Bare fallow		Bare fallow	*Late* crops (potato, carrot)	Bare fallow		Bare fallow	*Late* crops (celery, coles, squash, tomato, pepper)	Bare fallow
Fall	Clover	Rye and vetch	Rye	Oats and peas*	Clover	Rye and vetch	Rye	Oats and peas*	Clover	Rye and vetch	Rye	Oats and peas*

*Compost applied

Chapter 8

Cover Crops and Green Manures

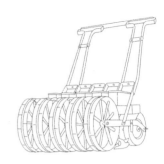

Cover crops are so called because they protect otherwise bare soil against erosion; green manures improve soil fertility. Because a cover crop is inevitably added to the soil, it becomes a green manure; so the terms are reasonably interchangeable. Cover crops and green manures are grown for reasons other than short-term economic gain. In other words, they are not produced for sale but for the benefits they provide to the production of subsequent cash crops.

Potential Benefits of Cover Crops

Farmers grow cover crops for the following reasons:
1. Cover crops that lessen the impact of wind and water passing over the soil surface can reduce erosion.
2. Cover crops that add a lot of organic matter to soil can improve its structure and help absorb and conserve moisture.
3. Cover crops competing for light, water, and nutrients may suppress weeds.
4. Legume cover crops (such as clovers, alfalfa, and vetch) add symbiotically fixed nitrogen (N) to the farming system.
5. Cover crops growing late in the season can capture and "recycle" soluble nutrients that might otherwise be lost by leaching.
6. Enhancing cropping system diversity by using cover crops may attract and create habitats for beneficial insects.

Since a single cover crop planting cannot provide all of the benefits listed above, a grower must prioritize the desired benefits before deciding what to plant. For example, only legume cover crops will fix N from the air, but they are not very fast growing and thus compete poorly with weeds during establishment. For the field in question, what are the N needs of the subsequent crop, and how heavy is the weed pressure? The identification of a cover crop priority, combined with a cover cropping strategy that fits a rotational plan with cash crops will narrow the choices of cover crops. Other factors to consider include seed cost, heat or cold tolerance, suitability to soil conditions, tillage equipment, and the crop to follow.

Cover Cropping Strategies

Strategies for using cover crops are chosen depending on how the cover crop fits into the overall crop rotation plan. A fundamental goal of cover cropping is to avoid bare soil between cash crop plantings. This not only protects soil, but captures sunlight and produces biomass that eventually enhances soil quality. Numerous side benefits accrue from this approach, such as improved trafficability of fields and reduced compaction, enhanced aesthetics, and potential for animal feed production.

There are four general categories of cover crop uses:
1. Fallow cover crops that require taking land out of cash crop production for all or part of a season.
2. Winter cover crops that are sown after vegetable harvest in late summer or autumn and remain in place until the following spring.
3. Smother crops that are grown during a spring, summer, or fall window between cash crops.
4. Inter-seeded, or "under-sown," cover crops that are established alongside a vegetable crop

and may remain in place for varying amounts of time.

Fallow Cover Crops

Of the four uses, fallow cover crops may provide the best benefit in terms of resting the land from vegetable production and adding organic matter to the soil. However, fallow crops can be uneconomical because they are grown in lieu of a cash crop. The availability and cost of land, the volume of crop production needed to meet market demands, and the seriousness of problems in a field (such as weeds or poor tilth) must all be considered when deciding whether to fallow cover crop.

Certainly, an intentional fallow cover is far better than letting weeds take over and/or leaving some soil bare and exposed to erosion. Fallows can be accomplished with a yearlong cycle of cover crop planting and incorporation, such as the cycle field pea–buckwheat–winter rye; or with a single sowing, such as red clover plus an annual grass like oats. A longer-term fallow might utilize a perennial grass like ryegrass or orchard grass, and a legume such as alfalfa that might be left in place for several years.

Winter Cover Crops

Winter cover crops are usually sown after the cash crop is harvested and residues are plowed or disked in. A popular winter cover crop after vegetable crops is winter rye because it can grow as long as the temperature is above 38°F. Oats or other small grains can also be sown late, although they can't match rye's ability to put on growth in cold weather. These grasses are good at mopping up available N that may be left over from fertilizer, manure applications, or mineralization of soil organic matter. Besides the ability to grow at low temperatures, the ability to overwinter is a major consideration. Rye will reliably grow the following spring, while oats will reliably winter-kill in cold climates such as New England. There are advantages and drawbacks to either scenario, the main issue being the amount of residue that will have to be dealt with come spring.

Smother Crops

Smother crops are grown to suppress weeds. Because they must put on a lot of growth rapidly to do the job, they also tend to be good producers of organic residues that can help maintain soil organic matter levels. Smother crop species can be divided into cool-season or warm-season crops, and planting must be timed to the season in which they make most rapid growth. Weather conditions and cultural practices that encourage good stands and rapid early growth are also essential if smother crops are to effectively win the competition with weeds. The key is quick and thick establishment, which is obtained with high seeding rates and seeding methods that distribute seed evenly and cover it properly.

Traditionally, smother crops have been warm-season summer crops that grow when weeds, especially broadleaf species, are also most plentiful. Summer is also the time when the stored food reserves of perennial weeds are lowest, making them susceptible to suppression by shading. Summer smother species include buckwheat, Japanese millet, and sorghum Sudan grass. These crops require soil to be fully warmed in order to establish well.

Cool-season crops like oats, rye, ryegrass, vetch, and field pea, alone or in combination, can smother weeds and protect and improve soil. Cool-season smother crops may die back as temperatures rise and thus be ineffective at smothering warmer-season broadleaf weeds. If enough residue remains, however, the "dead mulch" can sometimes provide good weed control for a while.

Inter-Seeded Cover Crops

Inter-seeding (under-sowing) a cover crop into a standing cash crop is a way to get a jump on the traditional winter cover crop season. This can lead to an increase in cover crop biomass production, and, presumably, better erosion control and soil organic matter enhancement because the cover crop is in place longer. Earlier establishment of inter-seeded covers also increases the farmer's choice of cover crops over those that could only be sown after a full-season vegetable crop. Also see "Intercropping for Weed Suppression," page 164.

In the case of very late vegetable harvest (as for a crop such as kale), it may even be too late for winter rye to put on enough growth to protect the soil over winter. That's where inter-seeding can be an advantage by assuring that some winter protection gets established and the soil is not left bare.

To successfully inter-seed cover crops, the timing of the two crops must be right. Sowing of the cover crop must be delayed enough to minimize competition with the vegetable crop, but early enough so the cover crop can survive competition with the vegetable and then withstand the harvest traffic. The best timing depends on the vegetable-cover crop combination, and, of course, the location. Right after last cultivation (or "lay-by") is a good time to inter-seed a cover crop. There's a nice seedbed; weeds have just been beaten back; and the vegetable canopy is not fully closed, so there's still enough light available to help get the cover crop going.

Small, slow-growing vegetable crops are poor candidates for inter-seeding. Carrots, onions and the like will suffer from the competition. Vigorous vegetables, such as winter squash and sweet corn, are more suitable. Inter-seeding requires good soil-seed contact, sufficient irrigation or rainfall, and good weed control early in the season so that the cover crop has a chance to establish well. High seeding rates help assure establishment of a dense stand. See sidebar 8.1 for general guidelines for avoiding competition from inter-seeded cover crops.

Inter-seeded cover crops can be broadcast over the whole field, using spin seeders, or seeded only between the crop rows, using seed drills. Tractor-mounted seeders, push-seeders, and hand-cranked seeders can also be used. For example, one grower uses an electric spinner-seeder, rear-mounted on the tractor, to apply red clover seed during final cultivation of corn. Other growers

Sidebar 8.1 Avoiding Competition from Inter-Seeded Cover Crops

To avoid competition from inter-seeded cover crops
- Intercrop only with vigorous cash crops such as corn, cabbage, or squash.
- Use only moderately competitive cover crops, such as low-growing clovers or ryegrasses.
- Sow the cover crop after the cash crop is well-established, usually at last cultivation.
- Provide irrigation as needed.
- Maintain good weed control prior to sowing the cover crop.

have used a grain drill to plant ryegrass between wide-spaced rows of winter squash just before the vines "run." In a few cases, custom-seeders have been fabricated for dropping seed between crop rows and then cultipacking with narrow rollers that firm the soil and assure good soil-seed contact (figure 8.1). Also see "Direct-Seeding," pages 96–100.

Some growers have tried inter-seeding with crops such as nearly mature cabbage and found that the broadcast seeds get caught in the leaves, sprout, and interfere with cash crop production. To avoid this, one grower has his crew use 5-gallon buckets to hold the cover crop seed, then walk down the rows hand-broadcasting the rye or oats under the leaves of the crucifers. In smaller fields, the process is not very time consuming.

A concern with inter-seeding is the possibility of promoting disease, since crop residues are not plowed under at the end of the growing season. Hence, inter-seedings are not advisable if there are serious disease problems in the crop. It would then be better to plow or disk the field and plant a winter cover crop. Another concern with inter-seeding is yield reduction due to competition for water. In dry years, this could really be a problem. Inter-seedings are risky unless irrigation is available. It's important to start small as you experiment with a new cropping system such as inter-seeding.

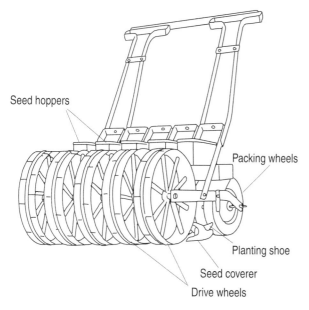

Seed hoppers

Packing wheels

Planting shoe

Seed coverer

Drive wheels

a. Hand-push unit with individual one-row seeders bolted together

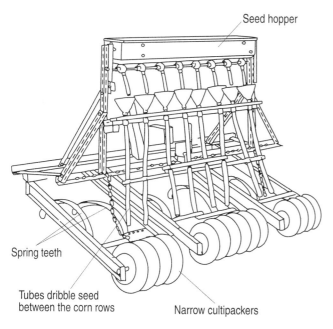

Seed hopper

Spring teeth

Tubes dribble seed
between the corn rows

Narrow cultipackers

b. Tractor-pulled unit to deliver seed between rows of corn and press it into the soil

Figure 8.1 Custom-made cover-crop inter-seeders

Source: (a): "Single-pass seeder" made by Eliot Coleman, adapted from photo by Grace Gershuny in *The Real Dirt: Farmers Tell about Organic and Low-Input Practices in the Northeast*

Seed for Cover Cropping

Certified seed may increase the cost of cover cropping, but the investment is often worthwhile. Uncertified seed is more likely to be variable in performance and to contain noxious weed seeds that may be a problem for years to come.

Cover Crop Species

Cover crop species can be divided into four main categories: grasses, other nonlegumes, legumes, and mixtures. Some species commonly used for cover cropping are described below.

Grasses for Cover Cropping

Grasses are generally used when N contribution to the soil is not a priority. They tend to grow rapidly and thus are better at short-term weed suppression than are legumes, which establish slowly.

Winter Rye

Winter rye is a common winter cover crop, sown after cash crops are harvested in the fall. It is very hardy and adapted to a wide range of conditions, and seed is inexpensive. The latest-sown cover crop, it can be planted from late summer to late autumn in most northern areas. Rye produces a lot of biomass in the spring. This helps maintain soil organic matter levels, but delayed spring plowing may make rank growth difficult to incorporate. Partial incorporation may leave rye as a weed. Sow 90–160 pounds per acre if broadcasting seed and 60–120 pounds per acre if drilling seed.

Oats

Oats as a winter cover crop can protect the soil without requiring intensive management in the spring, because in northern climates all that remains is the winter-killed residue. Shallow incorporation of residues is still necessary before crop planting. Enough growth is needed before first frost to adequately protect the soil, so plant from late summer to mid-autumn. Broadcast 110–140 pounds per acre, or drill 80–110 pounds per acre. Oat residues left on the soil surface may chemically suppress weed growth (a process called allelopathy), in addition to acting as a physical barrier. Oats may also be used as a spring cover, usually in mixture with a cool-season legume such as Canada field pea or hairy vetch.

Other Small Grains

Other small grains such as winter wheat, barley, and triticale (a rye/wheat hybrid) have been successfully used as winter and early spring cover crops. Some growers find them easier to incorporate than winter rye because they are less vigorous. All the small grains provide good rotation crops with vegetables since they tend not to host vegetable diseases. In addition, mature grain can be harvested for a cash crop, and the straw and stubble are an excellent soil conditioner. Seeding rates are similar to rye.

Ryegrass

Ryegrass is a cover crop that produces an extensive root system good at capturing leftover N late in the season after cash crops have been harvested. It is well suited to under-sowing after last cultivation of a vigorous vegetable such as sweet corn, squash, or many crucifers, in order to establish a winter cover prior to harvest. Annual (Italian) ryegrass seed is less expensive than perennial ryegrass and is more likely to winter-kill; however, it may overwinter in milder areas, and perennial ryegrass may winter-kill in harsher zones. Mowing ryegrass before it sets seed is important to prevent it from becoming a weed. Ryegrasses can form a dense sod that reduces erosion. Sow from midsummer to mid-autumn by broadcasting 15–30 pounds per acre or drilling 5–10 pounds per acre.

Sudan Grass and Sorghum-Sudan Grass Hybrids

Sudan grass and sorghum-Sudan grass hybrids are fast-growing, warm-season crops that require good fertility and moisture to perform well. Under such conditions, their tall, rank growth provides excellent weed suppression. However, the heavy growth can be difficult to cut and incorporate. Mid-season mowing allows for regrowing before the crop winter-kills. Sow from late spring to late summer; broadcast 40–50 pounds per acre, or drill 35 pounds per acre.

Japanese Millet

Japanese millet is also a warm-season crop that puts on rapid growth if planted after early summer. Not as tall or coarse as sorghum-Sudan grass, it can be easier to incorporate come fall or the following spring, when a heavy disking of the dead stalks can sometimes be sufficient to prepare a seedbed. Seed at 30–40 pounds per acre when broadcasting, slightly less when drilling.

Other Nonlegumes for Cover Cropping

Other nonlegumes used as cover crops include buckwheat and forage brassicas.

Buckwheat

Buckwheat is a fast-growing summer annual that can be used to protect the soil and suppress weeds in between spring and fall cash crops. It has a reputation for growing well on acid and low-phosphorus soils, but these soil conditions are not common on vegetable farms. It decomposes rapidly, so is easy to incorporate but does not contribute much organic matter to the soil. Seed matures in seventy-five to ninety days, and the crop can be disked after re-seeding, mowed early and allowed to regrow, or incorporated at flowering prior to setting seed. Sow in late spring to midsummer at 60–100 pounds per acre when broadcasting, 50–70 pounds per acre when drilling. To smother weedy fields, some growers plant a fallow cycle of two successive crops of buckwheat followed by winter rye.

Forage Brassicas

Forage brassicas include the varieties of several species of mustard-family crops that have been developed primarily for animal feed, including rape, turnip, and oilseed radish. These cool-season crops can establish quickly, and they have value for dual use as livestock forage and as cover crops. There is also some evidence that forage brassicas have nematode-suppressing properties. However, their susceptibility to diseases and pests common to cruciferous vegetables must be considered in terms of a whole-farm crop rotation plan. Sow at 5–12 pounds per acre, depending on the seed size of the cultivar (small seeds are sown at lower rates), and whether broadcasting or drilling.

Legumes for Cover Cropping

Legumes are usually sown as cover crops when the subsequent cash crop will have a high N demand. Legumes require good drainage and fertility. Seed should be drilled for best stands, and inoculation with the proper rhizobium strain helps assure nodule formation and good N fixation (see "Seed Inoculation," page 97). Sowing with a nurse crop, such as oats, or in mixes with perennial grasses is common. Be aware that legumes provide good habitat for tarnished plant bug, a major pest of many vegetable and berries, and that after mowing or plowing, these pests may move into adjacent cash crops.

Red Clover

Red clover is short-lived perennial that is somewhat tolerant of soil acidity or poor drainage. Mammoth red clover produces more biomass for plow-down than medium red clover but does not regrow as well after mowing. Mammoth will often establish better than medium in dry or acid soils. Sow in early spring or late summer. Red clover can be under-sown in midsummer into corn, winter squash before it vines, and other crops if soil moisture is plentiful. Sow at 10–15 pounds per acre when broadcasting, 8–10 pounds per acre when drilling.

White Clover

White clover is a low-growing perennial, tolerant of shade and slightly acid soil. Ladino types are taller than the white, wild white, or Dutch types, which are all low-growing strains. The clovers do not compete well with weeds unless mowed, in which case their ability to grow laterally and low to the ground by producing runners, or stolons (which are horizontal stems), gives them an advantage. Thus, white clovers are suitable for use in mowed walkways or alleys. Seed tends to be expensive, although stands can last for many years, especially if mowed or grazed, since the lateral-growing stolons continue to root. Sow in spring or fall at 10–14 pounds per acre when broadcasting, 3–9 pounds per acre when drilling.

Sweet Clover

Sweet clover is a biennial crop, except for the annual type called Hubam. Sweet clover is deep-rooted and adapted to a wide range of soils. It is a good soil-improving crop, because of its ability to fix a lot of N and to penetrate deep into the soil. Yellow sweet clover is earlier maturing and somewhat less productive than white sweet clover. Sow in early spring or late summer at 15–20 pounds per acre when broadcasting, 6–10 pounds

per acre if drilled. Heavy growth is produced in the spring after overwintering. The tall, lush growth may be difficult to incorporate without proper equipment. This incorporation should be done in late spring, or by midsummer at flowering, since growth will cease after that. Sweet clover and other deep-rooted crops may deplete soil of moisture, which can be a problem for subsequent crops in dry years.

Hairy Vetch

Hairy vetch is a hardy, winter annual cover crop. It is adapted to many soil types and when properly established has performed well throughout the Northeast. It can fix large amounts of N if allowed to grow until flowering. To ensure winter survival, it should be sown from late summer (in colder areas) to mid-autumn (in warmer areas) in the Northeast. Sow at 30–40 pounds per acre when broadcasting, or mix 25–30 pounds per acre with 1 bushel per acre of winter rye or oats. If drilling, reduce each of these rates by half. The combination is recommended to assure good soil cover over the winter, as vetch puts on little growth in the autumn. Using rye allows the vetch to climb in the spring, which can reduce matting and facilitate cutting before incorporation if desired. Some growers find vetch grown with oats, rather than rye, easier to incorporate in the spring.

Close mowing, undercutting, or rolling and crimping with a rolling stalk chopper at flowering will also kill the vetch and leave a weed-smothering residue (see the grower profile of Steve and Cheri Groff, page 93). Vetch can be spring-planted and used as a fallow, as it will provide good cover through late summer in the cooler parts of the Northeast. Use "pea" type inoculum to assure nodulation.

Alfalfa

Alfalfa requires deep, well-drained soil with a pH near neutral for good growth. Slow to establish, it is often mixed with a grass as a "nurse" crop. It is a long-lived perennial that is probably not worth the expense in a short-term rotation. It fixes large amounts of N once established. Drill seed in early spring or late summer at 10–20 pounds per acre, or 5–10 pounds per acre if mixed with a grass crop. Tarnished plant bug can damage nearby crops when it leaves alfalfa that is mowed.

Canada Field Pea

Canada field pea is a cool-season, frost-tolerant crop used to provide spring or fall N fixation and ground cover, usually in combination with a grass nurse crop such as oats or triticale. It is not winter hardy in most of the Northeast. Plant as early as possible in the spring, on well-limed, moist soils, broadcasting at a rate of 90–100 pounds per acre, or drilling at 50–80 pounds per acre. Soil-seed contact is important, so cover seeds well after broadcasting or drill several inches deep. Incorporate at flowering, five to eight weeks after planting.

Cowpea

Cowpea is a warm-season, traditionally southern cash crop that can be grown as a summer cover crop to provide N fixation and some weed suppression during the warmest summer months in the Northeast. Cowpeas are very frost sensitive. Forage cultivars may be better cover crops as they produce more biomass than horticultural varieties. Drill at 30–90 pounds per acre, or use 70–120 pounds per acre if broadcasting. Good soil-seed contact and well-drained soils are needed to establish strong stands. Nitrogen fixation rates can be substantial. Use cowpea/peanut type inoculum.

Soybeans

Although they are sensitive to frost and drought, when soybeans are grown as a cover crop, the late-season effect of drought on pod fill is not of concern. Short-season varieties that set seed early are probably not best for extended cover cropping, since foliage begins to decline once pods are near maturity. Care should be taken to avoid damaging seed when handling, and planting must place seed deep enough and firmly enough into soil to assure that seed is in contact with enough moisture to result in good germination. Broadcast 50–75 pounds per acre, or drill at about half that rate. Inoculate with soybean-type Rhizobium.

Under-Sowing Cover Crops— A Grower Profile

David Stern
Rose Valley Farm, Rose, New York
Located in the northern Finger Lakes region of New York, Rose Valley Farm includes about 30 acres of diversified vegetables and cover crops, along with some small fruit and nut trees. The farm has two distinct soil types, a sandy loam on lower ground, and a heavy loam on higher ground. Based on these soil types, there are two different crop rotations. The early and late crops are rotated on the sandier soil, and the mid-season crops go on the heavier ground. More compost is applied to the sandy soils, and it is cropped more intensively. Marketing is through a 150-member CSA, urban farmers markets, food co-ops, and on-farm sales.

"I like to keep the soil green, keeping it covered after we are done with vegetable crops, building organic matter and protecting against erosion. The only erosion we ever have on the farm is in the roadways, and even that really bothers me. Under-sowing is a good way to get cover crops going and have them in place after crops are harvested. I hear about the competition for sunlight, water, and nutrients from intercrops, but I didn't really see it except once, when we cut strips into an existing white clover sod with a multivator for transplanted broccoli. The clover really came back in and caused problems. However, that wasn't really under-sowing but more like a living mulch.

"For a lot of our under-sowings we use a 'barrow seeder.' This unit has one large wheel like a wheelbarrow, without the usual container. Instead, it has a lightweight 16-foot-wide pine box. The wheel revolves and a piece of metal is moved by the spokes, causing a chain in the box to slide back and forth, which shakes the box from side to side making the seed drop out the holes in the bottom. It's adjustable, so that the chain will move more or less depending on which numbered setting is selected. The numbering is helpful so you can record how much action is appropriate for different size seed. These are rather ancient units and the only place I ever see them is at auctions, usually in disrepair. I think they were mainly used for frost-seeding, probably until the 1930s. The barrow seeder causes no compaction, so seeding can be done in a lot of conditions. Maybe an electric seeder on an all-terrain vehicle (ATV) would be similar, but on our scale it's not really necessary. The other seeders we use are an over-the-shoulder, hand-cranked spinner-seeder and a small hand-held spinner. Spinning-on seed does cause some to lodge in the leaves of crops like cabbage and broccoli, but there really isn't much of a problem in these or other crops.

"We under-sow all of the large-sized crops; we don't under-sow any small crops like carrots and other roots, or short-season crops like greens and lettuce. We also don't sow any cover crops into potatoes since they require regular hilling. Sweet corn is where we got started on inter-cropping. We use red clover, and, since we have a clover seed producer near here that supplies inexpensive noncertified seed, we can afford to put it on pretty heavy. At the last cultivation, when the corn is scraping the bottom of the tractor, we follow with the barrow seeder and just lay the clover seed on the loose soil surface. All the cracks and crevices following cultivation create a pretty good seed-bed. A good rain soon after helps with stand establishment, if you can time things that way. The clover germinates in low light and takes the trampling at harvest OK; and afterwards I go in with a 5-foot rotary mower to shred the stalks. It's impressive that two weeks later the whole field is green, as the released clover is up above the shredded stalks. The clover is then left for another whole year. We don't put clover in unless it's going to be there at least one full year."

"When we plant peas in the spring, after the second cultivation we seed millet in early May. By the time the peas are harvested, the millet is just heading up, and we disk in everything. Until then, the millet makes a nice cover while the peas are growing. The pea rows are 5 feet on center. A couple of disk hillers on a tool bar are used to make a 10-inch mound in the row, into which we

plant. This settles down to about 6 inches by the time the peas are growing. The mound helps the soil warm and minimizes seed rotting. After the peas are up we go through twice with an Allis Chalmers "G" one-row cultivator before it's time to trellis. We seed the millet and then put up the trellis, and the traffic during trellising actually packs the millet seed in. We just throw on the millet by hand out of a bucket. We don't want it growing on the pea mound. It takes a couple of hours to seed a half-acre or so, and we like to have about one seed per square inch. The millet can really take trampling during frequent pea picking, and it seems to do fine. Even though some of it heads up, it hasn't been a weed problem later. We've used the same procedure with other grains—feed-grade wheat, oats, and rye—and all do well."

"With eggplant and peppers we often seed oats between the rows using the cyclone seeder, putting it on thick. These crops are planted on a 20- by 20-inch spacing; that's the smallest setting we get with our one-row mechanical planter. We put on the cover crop after we have done a good job at weed control and the plants have gotten big enough to shade the weeds. Since we don't have any way to incorporate the cover crop, we put it on after a last cultivation and use noncertified, feed-grade oats so we can afford to seed heavily. We get the oats at three cents a pound from neighbors and it's pretty clean seed. The seed is trampled in during harvests, and the oat and crop residues are left in place over the winter. We've also done this with rye, if we want the cover to be alive next spring. However, if the field will be

> *"I like to keep the soil green, keeping it covered after we are done with vegetable crops, building organic matter and protecting against erosion. The only erosion we ever have on the farm is in the roadways, and even that really bothers me. Under-sowing is a good way to get cover crops going and have them in place after crops are harvested."*

needed for early use, we go with oats so it will be easier to prepare the ground come spring. Rye seems to establish a little better if it's a really wet fall."

"With tomatoes, we plant in 7-foot-wide rows and plant white clover in between the rows, using the barrow seeder. We set the disks on our adjustable tool bar to mound and cut two furrows for the edge of the black plastic mulch; then we lay the mulch and pull soil back with hoes or shovels to secure the edges in the furrows. The black plastic not only warms the soil, holds moisture, and controls weeds, but also keeps the cover crop from establishing in the row because seed rolls off the plastic. It does set a little heavier at the edge of the plastic, but that's OK. We sow the clover using the barrow seeder just before it's time to put in the stakes. The seeder covers two walkways at a time. If the tomatoes are staked before we get a chance to cover crop, then the hand-held spinner is used to spin on a swath of clover seed in each walkway."

"In the wider-spaced vine crops like winter squash and melons, we under-sow after the last tractor cultivation, just before the vines start to run. Again, we lay the red clover seed in; it germinates and then grows slowly in the low-light situation under the crop canopy. After harvest (or frost) the clover explodes with growth and provides excellent cover going into the winter. Between rows of sweet potatoes we put down buckwheat, which provides good weed control. Just prior to the buckwheat setting seed, when the sweet potato crop is starting to spread laterally, the buckwheat is mowed. It lies down flat and becomes a dead mulch."

"Once in a while an intercrop does become a problem in terms of competition, weed infestation, or undesirable seed production. In that case we go in and mow it down using a self-propelled, walk-behind, sickle-bar mower."

Chapter 9

Tillage Equipment and Field Preparation

Preparing a field for planting a vegetable crop entails moving soil by using tillage operations. Primary tillage operations first loosen the soil and incorporate organic residues. Under some conditions, a field will also need secondary tillage to prepare an adequate seedbed for planting. In secondary tillage operations, the top several inches of soil are further worked to smooth it out, break up crusts and clods, or kill weeds. In other situations, no-till production is an option. How much tillage is necessary depends on soil conditions—including the amount of residue on the field—and on the needs of the particular crop and planting equipment.

Soil and Crop Considerations

The extent of tillage should be matched to the crop and cultural practice requirements. Fine seedbeds are required for sowing small-seeded crops or for laying plastic mulches. Rougher seedbeds may be tolerated with large-seeded crops or transplants, saving on labor and soil structure. Thorough incorporation of cover crops, weeds, or soil amendments such as lime and manure may call for several tillage passes over a field.

Unnecessary tillage of any sort is to be avoided, as tillage is generally harmful to soil structure because it breaks up soil aggregates and earthworm channels and promotes compaction. The minimum soil disturbance to get the job done should be the goal.

Since annual vegetable production generally requires a significant amount of tillage, compen-

sating stewardship practices are necessary to maintain soil health. These include regular additions of organic residues via animal manures, cover crops, and compost, and rotation by sod crops. For more information, see the chapters on soil fertility management (beginning on page 46), on-farm composting (beginning on page 63), crop rotation (beginning on page 69), and cover crops and green manures (beginning on page 78).

Tractors

On most vegetable farms, tractors provide the power to push and pull a wide variety of tillage implements as well as operate pumps, mowers, spreaders, and other equipment with a PTO (power-take-off). A few vegetable farmers use horses exclusively, or in addition to tractor power. It can be argued that this is more sustainable, reducing dependence on fossil fuels and energy-intensive industrial manufacturing, as well as enhancing soil stewardship by providing manure, reducing compaction, and encouraging rotation between forages and vegetable crops. However, the skills, equipment, and motivation for horse-powered agriculture are not widespread.

Tractor Options

Many small-scale vegetable growers use two-wheel *walk-behind tractors*, either fixed-unit rototillers with the sole role of soil disturbance, or units like that have interchangeable attachments for tilling, plowing, mowing, spraying, and other operations. Wheeled *sulkies* allow the operator to ride behind the power unit, which is generally 8–12 horsepower.

Cultivating tractors used primarily for weed control are described in "Tractors for Post-Emergence Cultivation," page 166–167. These are generally 25 horsepower or less. Some types can be used for other activities on the farm that do not involve heavy lifting or towing, such as pulling small wagons or mowing. Most vegetable farms of about 5–10 acres and up will be using bucket loaders, multi-bottom plows, heavy disks, chisels, or large wagons, requiring *utility tractors* with about 40–60 horsepower. On farms with large acreage, heavy soils or hardpans (compacted layers of soil) that require deep tillage, large volumes of crops to move around, big PTO-powered irrigation pumps to run, or specialized activities like large-scale composting, a tractor with 80 horsepower or more is justified. Vegetable farms with a couple dozen acres or more usually have three tractor sizes: cultivating, small utility with bucket, and large utility. Having at least one four-wheel-drive tractor can come in handy, too.

Used Tractors

New tractors are expensive, so used tractors are in demand. A well-cared-for tractor can last many decades. When shopping for a used tractor, consider the following: A three-point hitch is essential for attaching most modern implements. Tractors built in the 1950s and earlier may not have this feature, although conversion kits are usually available for several hundred dollars. *Wide front-end tractors* are preferable to *tricycle-type tractors* because they have greater stability and are more suited to vegetable farms, where it is necessary to straddle beds or crop rows.

When buying a used tractor, also keep in mind that about 50% of fatal farm labor accidents involve tractor overturns. To help protect yourself and those who work with you, look for a wide front-end tractor with a certified Roll-Over Protective Structure (ROPS). ROPSs have been available for many tractor models since the 1960s.

Examine the underside of used tractors for evidence of leaks or welds that indicate previous repair. Beware of new paint that may be covering up rust or repair. Check filters and fluids, wires, and plugs for condition as an indication of maintenance. Look at the extent of wear on treads and of sidewall cracking or cuts on tires. Take a drive, and preferably put the tractor under a heavy load to test performance. Ask owners if they have maintenance records and an owner's manual (the latter can often be obtained from the manufacturer).

Talk to nearby farmers, agricultural parts dealers, and repairmen to find out what makes of tractor will be easiest to find parts for and service locally; but otherwise keep an open mind with regard to brand, and look for a good deal on a well-maintained, safe tractor. Also see "Cautions on Buying Used Equipment," page 18.

Equipment for Primary Tillage

Primary tillage incorporates residues and loosens the soil to make it more suitable for crop production. This can be done with moldboard plows, heavy disks, heavy field cultivators, chisels, subsoilers, rototillers, rotavators, or spading machines. The choice depends on the desired seedbed characteristics, the amount of surface residue to incorporate, soil texture, the extent of soil crusting and compaction, and available tractor horsepower. Tillage implements vary in ability to bury or mix in crop residues, manures, and amendments; break up crusts; pulverize clods; cope with compacted or rocky soils; aerate; and level-off the soil. Heavier soil textures, thick sods, and extensive surface residue usually increase the tractor horsepower required and the aggressiveness of the tillage tools used.

Moldboard Plows

The *moldboard plow* is a large and heavy curved piece of metal that, when set down into and pulled through the soil, cuts and flips over a slice of the plow layer 12–18 inches wide and 8–12 inches deep, depending on plow size and orientation (figure 9.1). Moldboard plowing inverts the soil surface, completely burying residues in most cases. Depending on soil conditions and equipment adjustment, surface residues can be partially buried by plowing. Multiple plows are usually mounted on a metal frame, and the individual plow is called a *bottom*. Plows come in various shapes that affect how deep they go and how they move the soil. Approximately 10–15 tractor horsepower is required per bottom, depending on conditions, so two- to four-bottom plows are common on vegetable farms in the Northeast. *Coulters* are metal disks mounted ahead of the plow to cut the soil and assure that it breaks cleanly and flows smoothly over the plow. Extension bars are often mounted behind the plows to insure that the soil is flipped over completely. This is especially helpful to fully bury crop residues, weeds, or cover crops and to leave a more level surface. However, rough plowing without smoothing the surface helps reduce winter erosion if the soil is to be left bare after fall tillage. (A winter cover crop is the best option for protecting soil from erosion. However, leaving soil bare can make it easier to get onto fields in early spring, since less residue may promote soil drying and save on tillage time. This allows for earlier planting. Growers have to balance the need for early planting with the desire to protect against erosion.)

Plowing, because it flips over the soil without pulverizing it, is a good way to bury residues, but it does not thoroughly mix them into the soil or fluff up a seedbed as a rototiller does. However, rototilling can be more deleterious in terms of the soil's physical condition.

Chisel Plows

Chisel plows are heavy metal curved shanks that are pulled through the soil to break up the plow layer without incorporating much surface residue (figure 9.2). Chisel plowing loosens the soil but leaves a lot of residue on the surface. On sloping soils, chisel plowing may be preferable to moldboard plowing prior to sowing large-seeded crops like sweet corn because more residue remains on the surface to protect against erosion. Chisel plowing should be across slopes, not up and down. Many growers like to chisel plow or subsoil the middle of beds before planting deep-rooted crops like carrots, parsnips or daikon; if soils are heavy or have a pan, all beds may be treated this way.

a. The moldboard plow turns the soil, burying crop residue.

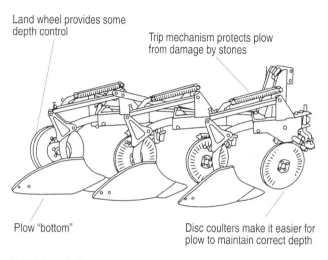

Land wheel provides some depth control

Trip mechanism protects plow from damage by stones

Plow "bottom"

Disc coulters make it easier for plow to maintain correct depth

b. Moldboard plow

Figure 9.1 Moldboard plow with three bottoms
Source (a.): Adapted from Brillion Iron Works, Inc.

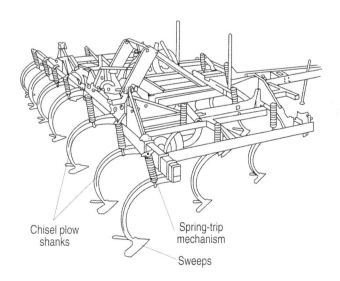

Chisel plow shanks

Spring-trip mechanism

Sweeps

Figure 9.2 Chisel plows
Source: Adapted from an illustration by John Gist in *Steel in the Field: A Farmer's Guide to Weed Management Tools*

Subsoilers (V-Rippers)

Subsoilers, or *"V-rippers,"* are longer and stronger than chisels, with straighter shanks that are pulled deeper, usually 18 inches or so (figure 9.3). Subsoilers are used to open deep drainage channels in compacted soils. There may be an attachment at the bottom to help fracture a plow pan or natural pan, both of which are compacted layers of soil that impede water movement and root penetration. Subsoiling is useful to improve deep drainage, aeration, and root penetration. Each shank requires about 25 horsepower to pull, depending on soil conditions.

Rototillers and Rotavators

Rototillers and rotavators, which are PTO-driven rototillers, have numerous metal tines attached to a rotating shaft that aggressively mix the soil (figure 9.4). The tines are covered by a shield that keeps rocks from flying out and may help level the soil. To adjust tillage depth, some units have metal gauge shoes, or the three-point hitch can be raised or lowered. Rotavators are widely used on vegetable farms because they are so good at preparing a fluffy, fine seedbed. Rotavators come in widths from 30 inches to 8 feet, which require approximately 20–100-horsepower tractors, respectively. It is important to select a tiller that is rated to match the horsepower of your tractor. The tines of rototillers and rotavators are usually independently attached to allow replacement if they break off or wear down, which is not uncommon in rocky soils. Heavier-duty brands with durable tines and drivetrains are recommended for rocky soils.

a. Rototiller

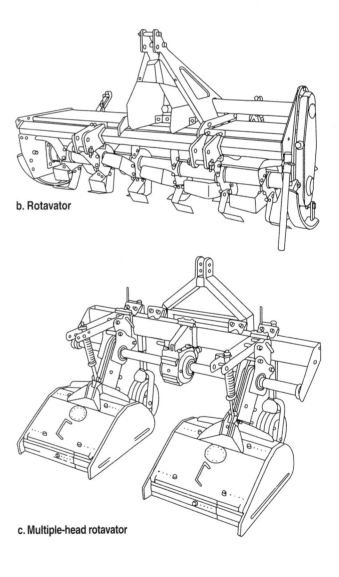

b. Rotavator

c. Multiple-head rotavator

Figure 9.4 Rototiller, rotavator, and multiple-head multivator
Source: (b.): adapted from Howard

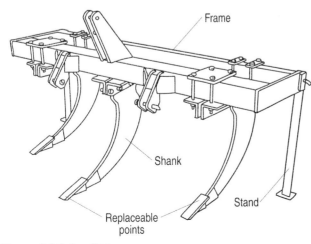

Figure 9.3 Subsoiler

Spading Machines

Spading machines are similar to rototillers, but the tines are wider and rotate more slowly, providing less soil disturbance while incorporating surface materials (figure 9.5). Spading machines are used for primary tillage to loosen soil without compacting or inverting the soil profile. Spading machines also incorporate residues and mix the soil, eliminating the need for secondary tillage in some cases. However, they do not create as fine a seedbed as rototilling. These units are European made, and not widely used in the northeastern U.S. at this writing. Increased availability and interest in protecting soil structure may enhance their popularity.

Disks

Disks come in many sizes, shapes, and configurations that offer different degrees of soil disturbance. They consist of groups of metal disks that rotate freely as they are pulled over the soil, chopping, cutting, and mixing as they go (figure 9.6). Individual disks may be smooth, serrated, or notched; light or heavy; set straight or at an angle; mounted singly or in multiples ("gangs"). Groups of disks may be arranged in one row or multiple rows that may be tandem or offset. Heavy disks, rather than plows, may be used for primary tillage on soils without much residue to incorporate. Lighter disks are used for secondary tillage, as harrows to smooth ("finish") fields after moldboard or chisel plowing. Disks are also used to incorporate broadcast soil amendments such as fertilizer, lime, and modest quantities of manure or compost.

Equipment for Secondary Tillage

Secondary tillage works the top several inches of soil to smooth it out for planting, break up crusts and clods, and kill weeds. Equipment used for secondary tillage includes various types of harrows and various types of field cultivators and bed formers.

Harrows

Harrows (figure 9.7, page 92), are used to smooth and pulverize plowed soil, or they may be used instead of plowing when there are few residues on the soil surface. Harrows are used for shallow tillage to prepare a seedbed, break up soil clods, and remove small weeds. They include disk harrows, chain link harrows, spring-tooth harrows, spike-tooth harrows, and combinations of shanks and roller cages or soil crumblers.

Field Cultivators (Conditioners)

Field Cultivators ("conditioners") are used when the soil is rougher or has more residues on it (figure 9.8, page 92). A field cultivator combines different implements on a tool bar frame. In general, field cultivators are heavier than harrows and have either C-shanks or S-shanks (sometimes called Danish S-tines) mounted on a toolbar frame. Figure 9.9 (page 93) shows types of shanks. There may not be much difference between a heavy-duty harrow and a light field cultivator. Field cultivators come in a wide array

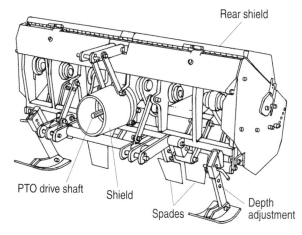

Figure 9.5 Spading machine
Source: Adapted from Celli, S.p.A, Italy

Rear shield

PTO drive shaft Shield Spades Depth adjustment

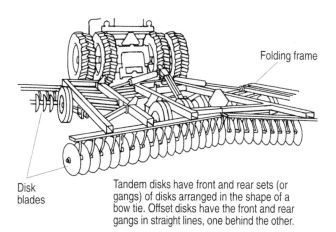

Folding frame

Disk blades

Tandem disks have front and rear sets (or gangs) of disks arranged in the shape of a bow tie. Offset disks have the front and rear gangs in straight lines, one behind the other.

Figure 9.6 Disks
Source: Adapted from an illustration by John Gist in *Steel in the Field: A Farmer's Guide to Weed Management Tools*

of configurations suited for different soil types, field conditions, and residue levels. They may include sweeps, stiff or flexible tines, chains, and rollers.

Bed-Formers (Shapers)

Bed-formers, or *"shapers"* gather, press, and flatten soil to create a raised surface, usually 4–12 inches above field level and 2–5 feet wide (figure 9.10). Raised beds encourage soil warming and drainage, allow for concentration of water and nutrient inputs near the crop, and help guide precision planting and cultivation equipment. After rotavation or disking have loosened the soil, hilling disks, rolling cultivators, or V-plows can be used to push soil into ridges that are then shaped into beds by a metal or wooden pan that presses the top and sides of the ridge. This can be accomplished using either a combination of on-farm equipment and a homemade pan, or a com-

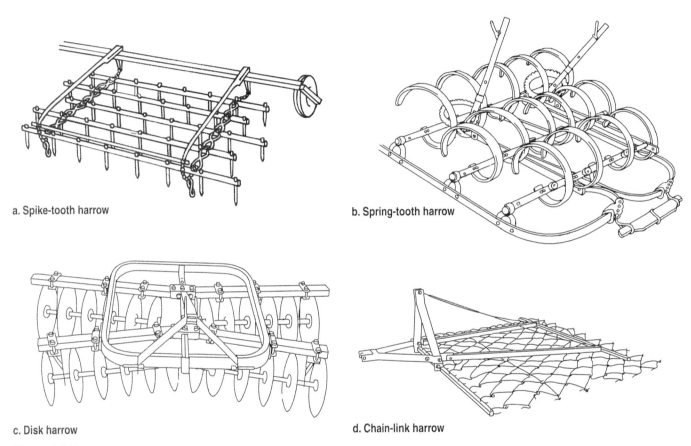

a. Spike-tooth harrow

b. Spring-tooth harrow

c. Disk harrow

d. Chain-link harrow

Figure 9.7 Harrows

Source (a.): Adapted from an illustration by John Gist in *Steel in the Field: A Farmer's Guide to Weed Management Tools;* (d.): adapted from Rem Manufacturing Ltd.

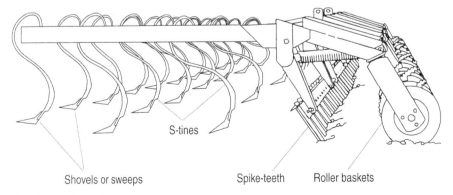

S-tines

Shovels or sweeps

Spike-teeth   Roller baskets

Figure 9.8 Field cultivator (conditioner)

Source (a.): Adapted from Unverferth Manufacturing Co., Inc.

mercial bed-former. Press pan units gather soil and form it into a firm bed. Some bed-forming units can also apply fertilizer and lay plastic mulch, and/or drip tape.

Conservation Tillage (No-Till or Minimum Tillage)

Conservation tillage (no-till or minimum tillage) leaves a significant amount of residue on the soil surface when crops are planted, unlike conventional tillage. Conservation tillage is an option with vigorous crops that do not require a fine seedbed. It should be considered on highly erodible soils. Strip-tillage, which alternates residue-free seedbed strips with high-residue strips, has been used with laterally-spreading crops like pumpkins and winter squash. This allows conventional planting equipment to be used in the tilled strips. No-till corn planters have been adapted to plant pumpkins into a killed-rye sod (see the grower profile of Jim Barber, page 216), and a no-till vegetable transplanter has also been developed in recent years (figure 9.11, page 94) Also see the grower profile of Steve and Cheri Groff (below).

For several reasons, not all vegetable crops and farms are suited to no-till: it requires specialized equipment and herbicides; it does not result in the fine seedbed required for direct seeding of some crops; and it leaves surface residues that may slow soil warming. No-till seems especially suited for transplanted vegetables on sloping land that would otherwise be prone to erosion.

No-Till Vegetables— A Grower Profile

Steve and Cheri Groff
Cedar Meadow Farm
Holtwood, Pennsylvania
Steve Groff, his wife Cheri, and his parents farm 175 acres of rolling land in Lancaster County. They grow 40–50 acres of vegetables on loamy soils, in addition to hay and field crops like corn, soybeans, and small grains. Their markets are mostly wholesale.

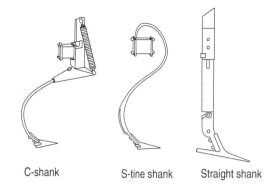

C-shank   S-tine shank   Straight shank

Shanks have a tool (such as a shovel or sweep) attached at the bottom. In general, C-shanks vibrate slightly; S-tine shanks vibrate vigorously; and straight shanks are rigid.

Figure 9.9 Types of shanks

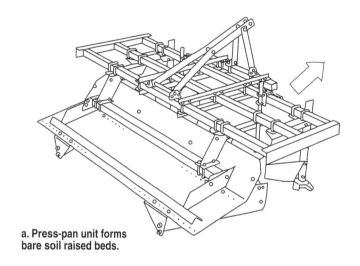

a. Press-pan unit forms bare soil raised beds.

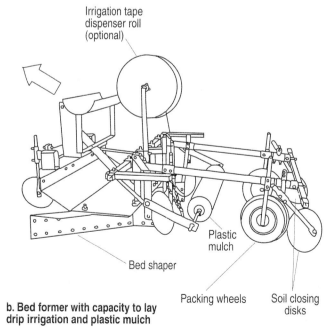

Irrigation tape dispenser roll (optional)

Plastic mulch

Bed shaper

Packing wheels   Soil closing disks

b. Bed former with capacity to lay drip irrigation and plastic mulch

Figure 9.10 Bed-formers ("shapers")
Source (a.): adapted from Buckeye Tractor Co.; (b.): adapted from Holland Transplanter Co.

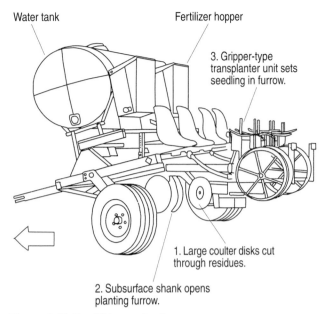

Water tank

Fertilizer hopper

3. Gripper-type
transplanter unit sets
seedling in furrow.

1. Large coulter disks cut
through residues.

2. Subsurface shank opens
planting furrow.

Figure 9.11 No-till transplanter

"Fifteen years ago I started no-tilling with field corn because of soil erosion on the farm. We had to fill in ditches to get machinery in to harvest, and I didn't think that was right. Little did I know all the other benefits I was going to get from it. The long-term effects of no-till are outstanding — I have fields that have not been touched by tillage for 15 years and the tilth is so mellow now that sometimes I have to raise the planter or else the coulter sinks in up to the hubs."

"In 1995 we started to do no-till with vegetables when the Keystone Chapter of the Soil and Water Conservation Society bought a prototype no-till transplanting machine developed by Ron Morse of Virginia Tech and made it available to farmers, in cooperation with NRCS (the Natural Resources Conservation Service). I am grateful to them for doing that, because I wouldn't have paid $10,000 for a planter just to try something I'd never done before. Now we no-till tomatoes, peppers, broccoli, pumpkin, sweet corn, and some minor vegetables, either as transplants using the prototype, or direct-seeded with a Kinze seeder. I store the prototype here on the farm for the district, and they coordinate the dates when other farmers want it. There's no cost for using the planter.

"The first step in my no-till system is sowing a cover crop the autumn before vegetables are to be planted. The cover crop seed is drilled with a no-till seeder in September. I started using rye and hairy vetch, now I use a three-way mixture that includes crimson clover, too. On each acre I use 4 pounds of clover, 25 pounds of vetch, and 30 pounds of rye. Each cover crop has a distinctly different rooting action, and they all complement each other underground and in the residues they leave above ground. That makes a difference in terms of improving the soil and leaving a good cover to suppress weeds. The vetch tends to degrade quickly; the rye hangs around longer and acts kind of like a sink in conserving the vetch nitrogen. The crimson clover germinates quickly and grows right away, while the vetch takes a lot longer to get going. And if the vetch doesn't quite make it, you've got the clover as a backup.

"I started by using herbicides to control the cover crops in the spring before no-tilling into them. I tried mowing or flail-chopping the covers, and that works; but when you have a lot of acreage to do, it is too time consuming, and it also shreds the covers too much and speeds up decomposition, reducing weed suppression. I still wanted to control the covers without chemicals. I don't have an inherent bias against pesticides, but I want to save costs, and my feeling is that avoiding sprays just makes everybody happier.

"Now I use a 10-foot-wide Buffalo rolling stalk-chopper that rolls the cover crop and crimps it. It cost $4,300 plus another $1,000 of my time and materials, welding and adding parallel linkages to get it the way I want it. It has two rows of rollers—four in each row, side by side. The parallel linkage arms allow the rollers to float independently over the soil surface; it jumps over stones and does a better job where there are depressions in the field. It performs somewhere between a flail chopper and a disk. Just rolling the cover crop with a cultipacker won't kill it, whereas stalk chopping does control the cover once the vetch gets to mid-bloom. However, in the planting row or where there's a weak cover spot I still get some weeds. That's why I still use some herbicide to control broadleaves and grasses in a crop like tomatoes."

Steve recently learned about flame weeding in vegetables, and is interested in trying to adapt a system that would work to control weeds in the row without setting the cover crop residue on fire. He's also working on adapting and improving the no-till transplanter. "I see some improvements that could be made to the no-till transplanter that was developed by Ron Morse. I give him lots of credit for what he developed, but it's a Cadillac, and I have in mind to design a smaller and cheaper model, with a smaller water tank, and perhaps even a one-row unit; and I'm working with him on that. The planting mechanism needs to be beefed up and improved for better depth control, too."

"One mistake I've made with direct-seeded, no-till pumpkins was to let the vetch and rye grow because I wanted it to suck up soil moisture in a wet spring; so I didn't roll the cover crop mixture until right before I planted pumpkins. By then the rye was shedding pollen and was very stiff. The soil was so mellow that the rye was 'hair pinning' when the coulter pushed the residue down in the slot. That leaves the rye sticking up vertically, and it can wick the moisture away from the seed so it won't germinate as well. I tried a bunch of different coulters and none of them worked the way I wanted. It's just a little thing, but it can be the difference between a good crop and a great crop."

"No-till is not a miracle, but I'm committed to it, and it's the way I've chosen to go because it works for me. It's good for my bottom line; I'm saving soil; and I'm reducing pesticides and increasing profits. For example, tomato growers had a contest here in Pennsylvania last year, and we won our acreage class. Our tomato pesticide bill was $75 per acre, mostly fungicides because it was so wet; versus $245 per acre for the conventional growers that used a lot of herbicides. Our yields were 32 tons per acre no-till. I don't even consider that very good myself, but I did have yields on one small field of almost 50 tons, which is almost twice the state average of all classes. That field had drip irrigation, and it followed an alfalfa field that supplied N and it had a really good vetch stand with less rye; in other plots the rye may be tying up too much N from the vetch as it gets mature. We continue to learn which cover crops and mixtures of covers are best and how much, if any, commercial fertilizer to supplement with."

"It's time we vegetable growers stop turning our back on soil erosion and saying it's just something we have to live with because of the way we plant. No-till systems have a place on a lot of vegetable farms. There are some drawbacks to no-till. For example, our groundhog holes never get tilled in, so every year we have to take a day and fill in all the holes by hand. Earliness is a major limitation, since the cover crop residues slow soil warming in the spring. I'm exploring ways to overcome that problem, perhaps using floating row covers or different cover crops. Another challenge is the lack of information. Except for Dr. Abdul-Baki at USDA in Beltsville, no-till vegetables does not get a lot of research attention yet. I'm trying to spread information from my web site (http://www.cedarmeadowfarm.com). I want to be proactive and have people see that farmers are doing something good. I've also developed a video that I'm selling called *No-Till Vegetables: A Sustainable Way to Increase Profits, Save Soil and Reduce Pesticides*. (See appendix B, page 240, for contact information.) Marketing this kind of information is just another way I'm diversifying the farm."

> *"No-till is not a miracle, but I'm committed to it, and it's the way I've chosen to go because it works for me. It's good for my bottom line; I'm saving soil; and I'm reducing pesticides and increasing profits. For example, tomato growers had a contest here in Pennsylvania last year, and we won our acreage class."*

Chapter 10
Seeds and Transplants

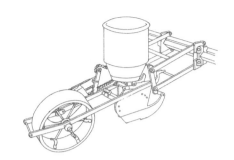

Establishment of the crop is a critical stage of vegetable production. Taking local conditions, markets, and farm resources into consideration, growers must decide whether to establish a particular crop from seed or from transplants. The management of seeds and transplants affects the uniformity and vigor of a vegetable planting, and thus influences crop earliness, quality, and marketable yield.

Direct-Seeding
Seed Quality

Seed quality refers to the ability of seed to germinate and grow vigorously. Seeds are alive, and they continue to deteriorate slowly over time until they either germinate or die. Growers have some control over seed quality and resulting seed performance through the kinds of seed treatments they select, the way they store seed, the seeding methods they employ, and the conditions they create for germination and emergence.

Seed Treatments

Intended to improve seed performance biologically or physically, seed treatments include seed priming, seed coating, hot water treatment, and inoculation. In general (and with the exception of inoculation), growers do not attempt to treat seed themselves, but rely on seed companies to do so.

Seed Priming

Seed priming includes several processes used to enhance the moisture content of seeds, either by exposure to humidified air, incubating in moist media, or placing in water or a mixture of water and other materials for a period of time long enough to cause water uptake but not long enough to allow germination. This controlled uptake of water by the seed stimulates metabolic activity and leads to faster subsequent germination and emergence, especially under less-than-optimal soil temperatures. Priming seed may also speed its subsequent deterioration in storage.

Seed Coating

Seed coating includes pelleting and film coating. Seed pelleting is used to create a uniform size and shape of small seeds in order to improve precision seeding. Pelleting also allows for the addition of fungicides, insecticides, and microbial inoculants to protect seeds from pests. Pelleting is accomplished by tumbling the seeds with a mixture of solid particles and a binding agent. Pelleted or raw seed may be separated into groups with a specific range of seed diameters, or "sized."

Seeds are film-coated by spraying with a polymer, plasticizer, and/or pigment. Coating is done to apply chemical protectants, improve seed visibility when checking seed placement, promote the smooth flow of seed through planters, and minimize dust associated with pelleting. Film coating may be applied after pelleting or priming of seeds.

Hot Water Treatment

Hot water treatment of seed minimizes the spread of certain seed-borne diseases, such as bacterial canker of tomato and black rot of crucifers, by exposing inoculum on the seed surface to lethal temperatures. The process involves the immersion of seed in water heated to a very specific temperature, for a specific length of time. Outside of the recommended range of temperature and time, seed viability or disease control may be seriously reduced.

Sustainable Vegetable Production from Start-Up to Market

Seed Inoculation

Seed inoculants are preparations of beneficial microbes that are usually mixed with the seed just prior to planting. A common practice is to treat legume seed with the appropriate *Rhizobia* bacterium to promote nodulation and nitrogen fixation. More recently, commercial preparations of beneficial fungi (such as *Trichoderma* or *Gliocladium*) or bacteria (such as *Bacillus* or *Pseudomonas*) have been developed as seed treatments to suppress plant pathogens that cause damping-off and other diseases.

Storing Seed

Seed storage conditions must be cool and dry in order to maintain seeds in a viable state. Seed moisture content and storage temperature are the key factors that determine how long vegetable seeds will remain viable. The life of a seed can be cut in half by just a 1% increase in seed moisture content, or by an increase in storage temperature of just a few degrees. A simple rule of thumb is that the sum of the storage temperature (in degrees F) and the percentage of relative humidity in storage should not be greater than 100. Generally, storage just above freezing is best, although 40–50°F is satisfactory under most conditions. If the moisture content of seeds is low, they will not be harmed by freezing. Seed moisture can be kept low by storing in airtight containers, above but not touching some calcium chloride or dried silica gel.

The life expectancy of seeds varies among species and storage conditions. Table 10.1 summarizes the life spans of vegetable seeds that are stored under favorable conditions.

Seed Testing

Seed testing includes evaluating both seed viability (ability to germinate) and vigor (overall health of seedling). In a standard germination test of nondormant seeds, the percent germination of a seed sample under optimal temperature and moisture conditions is measured. Many university and private labs offer such a test, and some also offer a low-temperature germination test for seeds such as peas, onions, cabbage, and corn that may be planted into cool soils.

Table 10.1 Longevity of stored vegetable seed

One to Two Years	Three to Four Years	Five to Six Years
leek	asparagus	beet
okra	bean	cress
onion	carrot	cucumber
parsley	celery	eggplant
parsnip	cole crops	lettuce
pepper	pea	muskmelon
sweet corn	pumpkin	radish
	spinach	
	squash	
	tomato	
	turnip	
	watermelon	

Source: Adapted from 1954 extension leaflet from California, cited in Maynard and Hochmuth, 1997

If you plan on using seed carried over from previous years, it's a good idea to do a germination test. Small-scale plantings or small lots of seed may not warrant a lab test, and a home germination test can be performed as follows. Place from fifty to one hundred seeds between consistently-moistened paper towels in a warm room to see how many sprout in seven to ten days. Wait twice as long for slow-to-germinate crops such as asparagus, celery, parsley, parsnip, and pepper. Keep in mind that seed vigor is more than just the ability to sprout. Seed vigor means that seeds germinate rapidly and uniformly, which is key to good crop performance.

Seeding Considerations

All seeding methods should optimize soil-seed contact to facilitate the uptake of water and to protect against drying out once the germination process is underway. In addition, the depth of seed placement influences soil temperature, moisture, and the physical resistance that the seed encounters, each of which affects the rate of emergence. Accurate and consistent spacing between seeds is also necessary to achieve a uniform stand and minimize the need for subsequent thinning.

Equipment for Seeding

Seeding equipment may be hand- or machine-powered. On diversified farms both are often used. In general, a large acreage of crops like sweet corn and pumpkins is seeded with multiple-row *tractor-mounted planters* while single-row *hand-push planters* are more common for crops sown on small areas or planted in sequential batches. If sufficient labor is available, growers can mechanically mark rows and then hand-plant a rather large acreage of crops. All types of seeders can have fertilizer hoppers added as an option to make banded applications of nutrients.

Low-cost seeders are *drill-type* seeders (figure 10.1), which spout seeds into the furrow from a funnel-like opening at the bottom of the seed hopper. Tractor-mounted or hand-pushed drill seeders can plant small or large seed, depending on the opening size at the bottom of the seed hopper. Different seed disks are used to change the hole size to accommodate seeds of different sizes. Drill planters have little or no spacing adjustment, so their use often requires thinning later.

Plate-type planters or seeders (figure 10.2) have seed plates (rotating metal disks with holes along the edges) that pick up one seed at a time from the hopper above before dropping them into the soil. Plate planters are usually for medium to large seeds such as corn, pumpkin, and beans; and seed plates with varying hole sizes are selected accordingly. Seed spacing is adjusted by changing the spacing gears that turn the plate. Compared to seed drills, plates do a better job of planting individual seeds (singulating), which is important to achieving uniform spacing between seeds.

The uniformity of spacing and depth of planting are increased with *precision seeders* (figure 10.3), which are able to singulate seeds by means of a punched belt, seed cup, or vacuum system. Uniformity of seed size enhances seeding precision, especially with a small-seeded crop, so sized or pelleted seed is often used with precision seeders.

Seed disk

Seed hopper

Dirt scrape

Press wheel   Seed coverer   Drive wheel

Planting shoe
(available in different shapes that
affect depth and width of seed row)

Figure 10.1 Drill-type seeder
Source: Adapted from Powell Manufacturing Company, Inc.

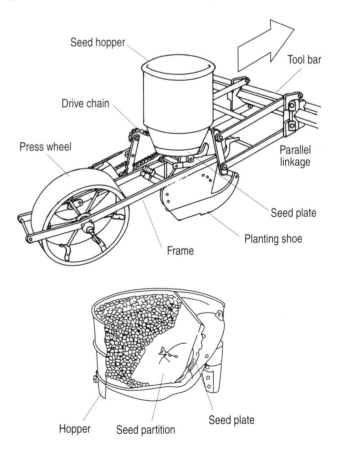

Seed hopper

Tool bar

Drive chain

Press wheel

Parallel
linkage

Seed plate

Planting shoe

Frame

Hopper   Seed partition   Seed plate

Figure 10.2 Plate-type planter or seeder
Source (top): Adapted from "unit corn planter" drawing by John Bartok, University of Connecticut, for Adams and Clark, eds., 1995

Precision seeders are the most accurate planter and the most costly. They can eliminate the need for subsequent thinning when properly adjusted.

Spin seeders (figure 10.4) are used to broadcast cover crop seeds onto the soil surface. They are available as hand-held or tractor-mounted units. The latter may be PTO or electric -powered; front, side, or rear-mounted. After sowing, the seed must be covered by light harrowing or by the impact of heavy rainfall or irrigation to assure good soil-seed contact.

Seed drills (or "grain drills") commonly used for small grain production are also used for sowing cover crops (figure 10.5, page 100). They drop and then cover the seed directly under the planter box. By adjusting seeding depth, dispersing seed evenly and firming the soil, these units usually give uniform results. The roller seeder creates a smooth, firm seedbed with cultipacker rollers and sows seed evenly over soil surface for uniform stands.

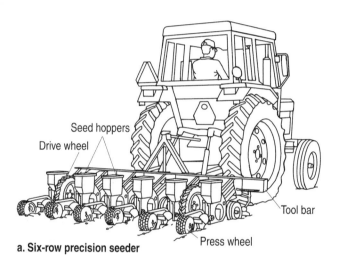

a. Six-row precision seeder

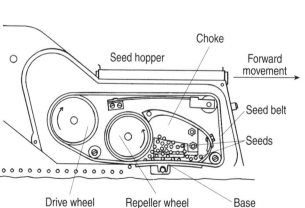

Seeds in the hopper fall past the choke, which regulates the quantity of seed in the chamber. The seed belt rotated by the drive wheel moves the seed to the repeller wheel. This agitates seed in the chamber, and rolls excess seed away from the hole in the belt, allowing only the required amount to drop through at the end of the base. Different chokes, bases, and belts are used to adjust for seed size and spacing.

b. Punched-belt precision seeder mechanism

Figure 10.3 Precision seeder

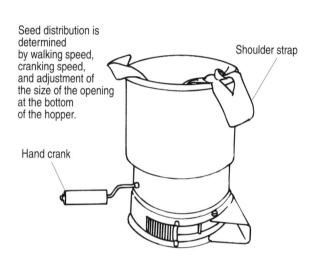

a. Over-the-shoulder, hand-cranked broadcast seeder.

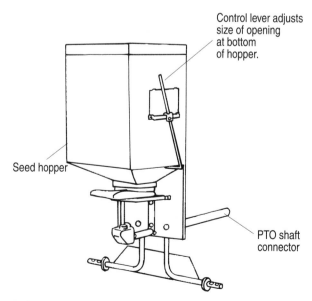

b. PTO broadcast spreader for cover crop seeds

Figure 10.4 Spin seeders

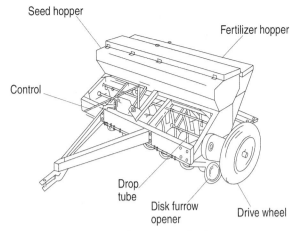

a. Grain drill for small grains that are sown in close rows

Labels: Seed hopper, Fertilizer hopper, Control, Drop tube, Disk furrow opener, Drive wheel

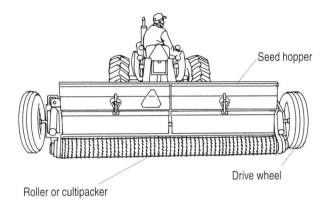

b. Roller seeder for small grains and small legume seeds

Labels: Seed hopper, Drive wheel, Roller or cultipacker

Figure 10.5 Grain drills for sowing small grains
Source (a.): *Fertilizer and Manure Application Equipment*, NRAES–57; (b.): adapted from Brillion Iron Works, Inc.

Production from Transplants

Producing vegetables from transplants often leads to earlier yields, more uniform stands, and better weed control than direct-seeding. Setting out transplants is a way to extend the growing season and harvest period. Long-season crops such as celery or heat-requiring crops such as melons cannot reach maturity from direct-seeding in northern growing seasons and so require transplanting. With other crops, transplanting is key to getting a jump on the growing and marketing season. For example, broccoli and lettuce are often transplanted as well as direct seeded to provide for both early and main-season harvests.

Purchasing Transplants Versus Producing on Farm

Purchasing transplants can save on labor, greenhouse and fuel costs, and aggravation compared to growing your own. However, on-farm transplant production, if efficient, can be less costly than buying them in. Production costs, availability of labor and management, and volume and variety of transplants needed will determine which option a grower chooses. Growing your own allows flexibility in terms of variety selection and timing of production, as well as control over transplant quality and pest management. Use of off-farm transplants involves some risk because quality and timeliness are out of your control.

Developing a good relationship with a competent transplant producer is key to avoiding delivery or pest problems. Try to buy from a producer in your region, so you can check on the quality of plants before they are delivered. Because pests can also arrive with your transplants, upon delivery conduct a careful inspection and if necessary set up a temporary quarantine in a single growing area.

On-Farm Transplant Production

Transplant production greenhouses vary in their climate control and materials-handling sophistication. High tunnels and cold frames can also be used to start transplants if outdoor conditions do not require substantial protection against cold temperatures (see pages 133–134).

Whether you grow them or buy them, obtaining high-quality transplants is critical. Stocky, vigorous, and insect- and disease-free plants are the objective. Transplant production must consider the growth rates and requirements of different crops (table 10.2), and should be based on a schedule that coordinates greenhouse production with field-planting and harvesting plans (figure 10.6, pages 102–103).

Once transplants are ready, proper handling is key to successfully setting transplants in the field. Harden off seedlings by gradually reducing water, temperature, and fertilizer for about a week prior to transplanting. Then put transplants in the ground as soon as possible, but have sufficient storage space available to hold them if weather or labor do not permit immediate planting. Keep them properly watered, protected from wind and heat, and up off the ground if possible. At planting, pre-irrigate if the soil is dry; water plants in as soon as possible; and avoid excessive fertilization that can cause salt injury.

Potting Mixes for Starting Transplants

Potting mixes for starting and growing transplants should optimize germination and growth and minimize nutrient and pest problems. In the greenhouse, most growers use *soil-less or peat-lite mixes*, rather than soil, for growing transplants (see sidebar 10.1, page 103, for a sample recipe). These mixes are well-aerated and retain water well. Soil-less mixes are made of peat moss, vermiculite, or perlite, with fertilizer plus a wetting agent to facilitate watering of the dry mix. Since peat is acidic, lime is included in the mix. Peat is comprised of decomposed plants and is usually free of weed seeds and disease organisms,

as are vermiculite and perlite, which are made up of minerals. It is not advisable to add unsterilized soil to a potting mix since that may increase problems caused by damping-off organisms. Various soil-less mix formulations are available with different fertilizer amendments, grades of peat, and texture. Fine-textured mixes are needed for use in small plug trays and are best for small-seeded crops, such as lettuce and celery.

Compost-based potting mixes are used by organic growers to avoid the synthetic fertilizers and wetting agents in commercial soil-less mixes. Organic potting mixes are made of peat, vermiculite or perlite, lime, and organic sources of nutrients. Sidebar 10.2 (page 103) shows a typical recipe for an organically-approved potting mix. While many growers have had success with compost-based mixes, others have had performance failures with organic potting media, both of their own manufacture and commercially produced.

Table 10.2 Vegetable transplant production

Crop	Greenhouse Temperatures (° F day/night)	Transplant Age (weeks)	Ideal Growth Stage	Frost Tolerance	Field Growth to Harvest (weeks)
Broccoli	65/55	4–6	4–5 true leaves	hardy	6–10
Brussels Sprouts	65/55	4–6	4–5 true leaves	hardy	12–15
Cabbage	65/55	4–6	4–5 true leaves	hardy	7–12
Cauliflower	65/55	4–6	4–5 true leaves	hardy	7–12
Celery	70/60	8–10	5–6 inches tall	moderate	10–12
Cucumber	70/60	2–4	3–4 true leaves	tender	6–8
Eggplant	75/65	5–7	2–3 true leaves	tender	7–10
Leeks	65/55	6–8	6–8 inches tall	hardy	10–14
Lettuce	60/50	4–6	3–4 true leaves	hardy	4–6
Melons	75/65	2–4	1–2 true leaves	tender	10–12
Onions	65/55	10–12	4–5 inches tall	hardy	10–14
Parsley	75/65	6–8	3–4 true leaves	hardy	8–10
Peppers	75/65	6–8	3–4 true leaves	tender	7–10
Squash	75/65	2–4	3–4 true leaves	tender	5–7 (summer) 10–14 (winter)
Tomatoes	75/65	5–7	buds, no flowers	tender	7–12

Source: Adapted from Heiden, Carlson, Heins, Biernbaum, and Ewart, 1989; and other sources

Seeding Date	Crop	Variety	Number of 350' Rows	Plants per Row	Plants Needed*	Number of Trays	Approximate Set-Out Date
3/20	Broccoli	Emperor	6.00	235	1,692	24	4/30
3/20	Cabbage	Blues	2.00	235	564	8	4/30
3/20	Cabbage	Fieldsport	1.00	350	420	6	4/30
3/20	Lettuce	Waldmann's	1.00	350	420	6	4/30
3/20	Lettuce	Two Star	1.00	350	420	6	4/30
3/20	Lettuce	Carmona	1.00	350	420	6	4/30
3/20	Radicchio	Chioggia Red	2.00	350	840	12	4/30
3/20	Kohlrabi	Kohlribi	5.00	350	2,100	29	4/30
3/20	Parsley	Forest Green	1.00	350	420	6	5/10
3/20	Parsley	Gigante D'Italia	1.00	350	420	6	5/10
4/1	Broccoli	Emperor	6.00	235	1,692	24	5/10
4/1	Cabbage	Early Jersey	1.00	350	420	6	5/10
4/1	Cabbage	Sombrero	1.00	350	420	6	5/10
4/1	Radicchio	Chioggia Red	2.00	350	840	12	5/10
4/1	Eggplant	Dusky	2.00	270	648	36	5/20
4/1	Eggplant	Pingtung Long	1.00	270	324	18	5/20
4/1	Eggplant	Neon	1.50	270	486	27	5/20
4/1	Pepper, hot	Early Jalapeno	0.10	235	28	2	5/30
4/1	Pepper, hot	Anaheim	0.40	235	113	6	5/30
4/1	Pepper, sweet	Ace	1.00	235	282	16	5/30
4/1	Pepper, sweet	North Star	2.00	235	564	31	5/30
4/1	Pepper, sweet	Lipstick	1.50	235	423	24	5/30
4/1	Celery	Ventura	6.00	350	2,520	35	5/30
4/10	Lettuce	Two Star	1.00	350	420	6	5/20
4/10	Lettuce	Nancy	1.00	350	420	6	5/20
4/10	Lettuce	Carmona	1.00	350	420	6	5/20
4/10	Tomatillo	Toma Verde	0.10	235	28	2	5/30
4/10	Tomato, cherry	Sun Gold	1.00	235	282	16	5/30
4/10	Tomato, cherry	Super Sweet 100	1.00	235	282	16	5/30
4/10	Tomato, plum	Bellstar	1.00	235	282	16	5/30
4/10	Tomato, plum	Hybrid 882	1.00	235	282	16	5/30
4/10	Tomato, plum	Mankin Plum	2.00	235	564	31	5/30
4/10	Tomato, slicing	Brandywine	1.00	235	282	16	5/30
4/10	Tomato, slicing	Jet Star	1.50	235	423	24	5/30
4/10	Tomato, slicing	Big Beef	1.00	235	282	16	5/30
4/10	Tomato, slicing	Celebrity	0.50	235	141	8	5/30
4/10	Celeriac	Diamante	5.00	350	2,100	29	5/30
4/30	Watermelon	Yellow Doll	1.00	125	150	8	6/1
4/30	Watermelon	Crimson Sweet	1.00	125	150	8	6/1
4/30	Cantaloupe	Earliqueen	3.00	125	450	25	6/1
4/30	Lettuce	Two Star	1.00	350	420	6	6/10
4/30	Lettuce	Slobolt	1.00	350	420	6	6/10
4/30	Lettuce	Vulcan	1.00	350	420	6	6/10
4/30	Broccoli	Saga	4.00	235	1,128	16	6/10
5/10	Basil	Sweet	1.00	350	420	6	6/20
5/10	Cauliflower	Burgundy Queen	1.00	235	282	4	6/20
5/10	Kale	Winterbor	3.00	235	846	12	6/20
5/10	Kale	Judie's	2.00	235	564	8	6/20
5/10	Collards	Champion	1.00	235	282	4	6/20

(continued on next page)

Sustainable Vegetable Production from Start-Up to Market

(continued from previous page)

Seeding Date	Crop	Variety	Number of 350' Rows	Plants per Row	Plants Needed*	Number of Trays	Approximate Set-Out Date
5/20	Broccoli	Arcadia	4.00	235	1,128	16	6/20
5/20	Brussels sprouts	Oliver	2.00	235	564	8	6/20
5/20	Brussels sprouts	Jade Cross	2.00	235	564	8	6/20
5/20	Cabbage	Ruby Perfection	2.00	350	840	12	6/20
5/20	Cabbage	Rio Verde	4.00	350	1,680	23	6/20
5/20	Cauliflower	Candid Charm	3.00	235	846	12	6/20
5/20	Cauliflower	Fremont	1.00	235	282	4	6/20
5/20	Lettuce	Sierra	2.50	350	1,050	15	6/30
5/20	Lettuce	Nevada	2.50	350	1,050	15	6/30
5/30	Broccoli	Green King	4.00	235	1,128	16	7/1
5/30	Broccoli	Saga	4.00	235	1,128	16	7/1
6/20	Lettuce	Sierra	2.50	350	1,050	15	7/20
6/20	Lettuce	Nevada	2.50	350	1,050	15	7/20
6/20	Radicchio	Medusa	3.00	350	1,260	18	7/20
7/10	Lettuce	Sierra	2.50	350	1,050	15	8/10
7/10	Lettuce	Nevada	2.50	350	1,050	15	8/10
7/10	Lettuce	Two Star	1.00	350	420	6	8/10
7/10	Kohlrabi	E. W. Vienna	5.00	350	2,100	29	8/10
7/10	Escarole	Coral	5.00	350	2,100	29	8/10
7/10	Bok choy	Prize Choy	2.00	350	840	12	8/10

*20% extra transplants are grown to assure only high quality plants are set out. Typical tray size is 72-cell, except for warm-season crops, which are grown in 18-cell trays.

Figure 10.6 Sample transplant production schedule spreadsheet
Source: Adapted from Dan Kaplan, Brookfield CSA Farm, Amherst, Massachusetts

Sidebar 10.1 Sample Recipe for Peat-Lite Potting Mix

Peat-Lite Mix "A" for Seedlings or Bedding Plants

Sphagnum peat moss:	0.5 cu yd*
Vermiculite:	0.5 cu yd
Ground limestone:	10 pounds**
Superphosphate (0-20-0):	1–2 pounds
Calcium or potassium nitrate:	1 pound
Fritted trace elements:	2 ounces
Wetting agent:	3 fluid ounces

*   1 cubic yard (cu yd) = 27 cubic feet (cu ft). However, 15–20% shrinkage occurs in mixing; for 1 full yard of mix, use an additional 2 ½ cubic feet of both peat moss and perlite or vermiculite.

**The amount of limestone added depends on the crop for which the mix is formulated.

Source: Adapted from Boodley and Sheldrake Jr., 1982 (revised). *Cornell Peat-Lite Mixes for Commercial Plant Growing.* Cornell Cooperative Extension Bulletin 43. Ithaca: NY

Sidebar 10.2 Typical Recipe for an Organically-Approved Potting Mix

Typical Ingredients Used to Make Organically-Approved Potting Mixes

Mature, screened compost	5 gallons*
Peat moss and/or peat humus	5–10 gallons
Vermiculate and/or perlite	1–5 gallons
Lime	1–2 cups (or 2% wet weight of peat)
Bonemeal (*or* colloidal rock phosphate)	1–2 cups
Blood meal	1–2 cups
Greensand (*or* sul-po-mag ¼ cup)	1–2 cups

*   1 cubic yard = 202 gallons

Caution: Performance varies considerably based on quality of compost and peat used to make mixes. Test all mixes prior to use.

Source: Adapted from recipes in *The Real Dirt: Farmers Tell about Organic and Low-Input Practices in the Northeast,* 1994, and other sources

Potting mix problems can occur with both soil-less mixes and compost-based mixes. The cause may be improper pH, excess soluble salts, insufficient or toxic levels of nutrients, unsuspected contaminants, excessive density, volatile organic acids due to compost immaturity, or improper management (such as overwatering or over-fertilization). Whenever using a new mix or a noncommercial mix, it is advisable to conduct a lab test well in advance of planting seeds. Request a test—such as saturated media extract analysis—that is designed for potting soils and that measures pH, soluble salts, and available nutrients (including nitrogen). See table 10.3 for optimum ranges of saturated media extract analysis results. In addition, a test planting, or "bioassay," is advisable to identify problems before the planting season begins. Sow test plantings of sensitive plants such as cress, cucumber, wheat, or oats, as well as your major crops, a month or more in advance of greenhouse seeding.

If problems with plant growth in the mix do show up, corrective actions can include adding materials that lighten the mix to improve aeration, leaching the mix of excess salts, or adding sources of available nutrients. When using homemade mixes, it is wise to keep careful records of your mix recipes, have mixes tested every year by a lab with appropriate expertise, and test "good" mixes, not just "problem" mixes, so that results can be compared.

Watering in the Greenhouse

Watering requires attention to detail. Potting mixes can be difficult to moisten, and they absorb a lot of water, so they should be thoroughly wetted before any seeds are planted. Some growers moisten soil-less mix and allow it to sit and absorb water for several hours before placing it in trays or pots. This is easier than trying to wet a tray of dry mix, and it allows the mix to fully expand, providing more air space for roots. Because they retain water well, potting mixes require care to avoid overwatering of seeds and small seedlings. Once the plants are actively growing and transpiring, mixes may dry out rapidly, especially if cell sizes are small. Trays may dry out at different rates depending on their location in the greenhouse, due to variation in environmental conditions.

Automated watering systems are used by some growers to enhance the uniformity of watering, and thus transplant growth, and to reduce labor for watering. Ebb and flow benches, trough systems, capillary mats, drip tubes, and overhead sprinklers are methods of automated watering used in greenhouses (figure 10.7).

Containers for Seedlings

Seedling flats hold the growing media into which seeds are planted, and they contain the seedlings until they are transplanted to another container or set out in the field. Flats are made of wood, Styrofoam, or most commonly, plastics of varying thickness and strength (figure 10.8, page 106). They are roughly 2 feet long, 1 foot wide, and 2–3 inches deep, depending on the manufacturer. Using flats of a consistent design facilitates materials handling in the greenhouse and is essential if mechanized filling or seeding of flats is to be used.

Table 10.3 Approximate optimum ranges of test results (using saturated media extract analysis) for soil-less potting mix

Nutrient	Saturated media* (distilled water) PPM in extract
NO_3-N	23–68
NH_4-N	<12
P	5–20
K	150–350
Ca	200–400
Mg	70–200
(EC) Soluble Salts	**Millisiemens/centimeter**
Seedlings	<3.5 mS/cm
Established	<5.0 mS/cm
pH	
pH	5.8–6.2

*Add sufficient distilled water to a 250–400 milliliter substrate sample to create a glistening, slightly flowable paste.

Source: Adapted from *Water and Nutrient Management for Greenhouses*, NRAES–56

Sustainable Vegetable Production from Start-Up to Market

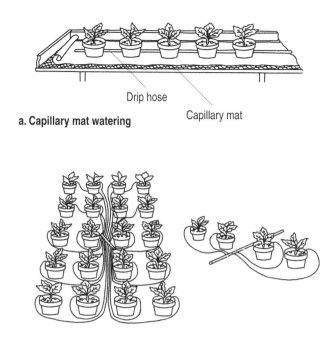

a. Capillary mat watering

Drip hose

Capillary mat

b. Drip tubes

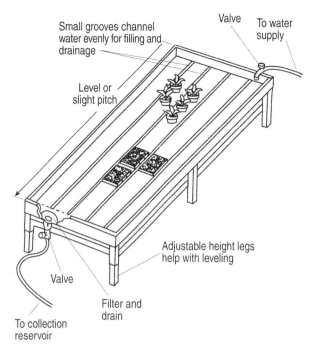

Small grooves channel water evenly for filling and drainage

Valve

To water supply

Level or slight pitch

Adjustable height legs help with leveling

Valve

Filter and drain

To collection reservoir

c. Ebb and flow (or flood) system: Pots or flats sit in standing shallow water; the solution is drained.

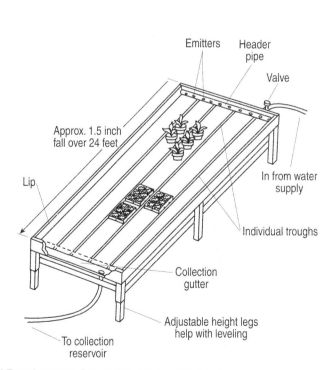

Emitters

Header pipe

Valve

Approx. 1.5 inch fall over 24 feet

Lip

In from water supply

Individual troughs

Collection gutter

Adjustable height legs help with leveling

To collection reservoir

d. Trough system: Pots or flats create resistance to flowing water, allowing time for media to absorb it.

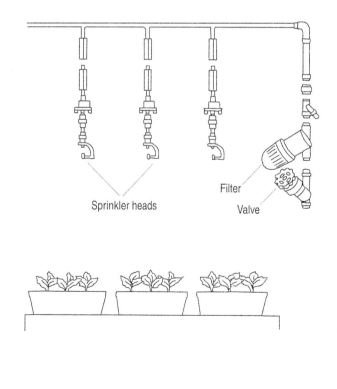

Sprinkler heads

Filter

Valve

e. Overhead sprinklers

Figure 10.7 Transplant watering systems

Source (a., b., and d.): Adapted from *Greenhouse Engineering*, NRAES–33

Seedling trays are used for starting plants that are then set out in the field or transplanted to cell-packs or pots for retail sale. Plug flats come in a variety of cell numbers and shapes and are used for growing transplants for field production. Reusable trays are used to hold cell-pack containers and provide rigidity for movement in greenhouse or during transportation. Cell-packs, or inserts, are used for bedding plant production.

They are named according to the number of individual packs per tray and the number of cells per pack.

Flats may be undivided, or they may be sectioned into individual rows or cubicles. Undivided plastic flats are sometimes called trays, and these may be fitted with so-called inserts, packs, or sheets that come in a wide range of individual plant "cell"

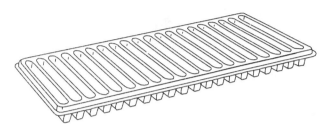

a. Seedling trays for starting plants to be transplanted to cell packs or pots for retail sale

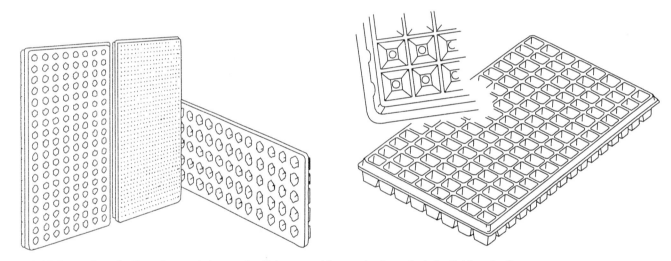

b. Available in a variety of cell numbers and shapes, plug flats are used for growing transplants for field production.

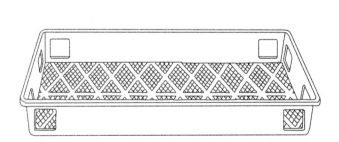

c. Reusable trays hold cell-pack containers and provide rigidity for moving the cell-packs in the greenhouse or during transportation.

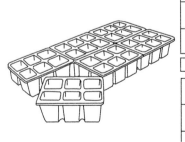

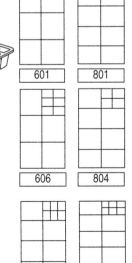

d. Cell packs, or inserts, are used for bedding plant production. They are named by the number of packs per tray and the number of cells per pack. 606 indicates 6 packs per tray and 6 cells per pack.

Figure 10.8 Seedling flats, trays, and inserts

Sustainable Vegetable Production from Start-Up to Market

configurations. Divided plastic flats with many small cubicles are called plug trays or plug flats, which are typically 10 inches wide by 20 inches long and contain 50 to 512 individual "plugs" or rooting volumes. Plugs may be cubical, conical, or cylindrical and have smooth or fluted surfaces.

Selection of a growing container system depends on seed size, desired seedling size, length of growing time in the greenhouse, ability to control moisture and nutrient supply, available greenhouse space, and number of seedlings needed. In general, plants tend to grow faster and get bigger when grown in larger containers. Crops such as tomato that garner a premium for early fruit should be produced in the largest cell size that is practical, since small cells are likely to slow plant growth and delay flower and fruit production.

It is essential that all flats and other growing containers be sterilized before reuse. This involves thoroughly washing out all debris and then cleaning all surfaces with an approved greenhouse sanitizer. Steam sterilization is a possibility for containers made of suitable materials.

Germinating Seeded Flats

Germination of seeded flats requires moisture and warmth—about 70–75°F is ideal for most vegetable species, but some require cooler temperatures (lettuce) or perform best with higher temperatures (seedless watermelon, peppers). Many growers pre-warm flats of soil mix before planting seeds. Heating mats are available that maintain the flats at a consistent warm temperature. A separate grow-room can be constructed or sectioned-off in a greenhouse to save on heating costs.

Lighting for Transplants in the Greenhouse

Most seeds do not require light to germinate, but once the plants emerge from the soil, high light intensity is needed to keep them short and stocky. Short, stocky plants are desirable since they handle better, are more likely to withstand windy conditions, and are better able to capture sunlight for early growth. High light produces shorter

plants than low light, so plants grown under glass or supplemental lighting are often shorter than those grown under polyethylene cover.

Supplemental lighting is an expensive option, so make the most of natural light. Change greenhouse plastic in a timely fashion; clean off greenhouse glazing if necessary; paint interior surfaces white to reflect light; and avoid placing above transplants any hanging baskets or other items that will block the light.

Controlling Growth in the Greenhouse

Controlling growth of well-established transplants may be necessary so that they don't get too big before the weather is right for setting them in the field. This can be done by keeping daytime temperatures cool, about 60–65°F, keeping the night temperature the same or slightly higher, or by holding back on water until just before the plants begin to wilt. Do not reduce light levels, however, as this will weaken the plants and cause them to stretch.

Shaking plants or brushing them several times a day has promise as a transplant height control method with some vegetables such as tomato. Polystyrene foam, plastic plumbing pipe, and wooden sticks have all been used to brush plants. Multiple brushings, about ten or so per day, starting when plants are a couple of inches tall, can result in a shorter, stockier plant.

Equipment for Setting Transplants

Transplanters provide mechanical assistance with setting either bare-root plants or seedlings grown in plugs, cells, or pots. Transplanters are usually tractor-pulled and may also apply fertilizer or water to the plants. They seat one or two people per row, who feed seedlings to the planting mechanism, which can vary widely in speed, sophistication, and flexibility. Transplanters include trays or shelves to hold the seedlings that are to be planted. A shoe, coulter, spiked wheel or spade opens the planting furrow or holes. Packing wheels firm the seedling into place.

The simplest transplanters are *hand-set,* or *hand-plant,* units (figure 10.9) that open a furrow, or, in the case of *water-wheel transplanters,* spiked wheels punch a hole in the soil, or through plastic mulch. Operators set plants into the hole, and water from a tank then "muds" plants into place.

Conventional or *gripper-type* units (figure 10.10) have plant holders that open and shut, which clasp seedlings and deliver them to an open furrow by means of a moving chain or rotating disk. Plant holders are attached to a vertical packing wheel. Holders open and shut to "grip" seedlings and then deliver them to the furrow, where they are released. Different holders are available for various seedling sizes.

In *cell-type* or *carousel* units (figure 10.11) plugs or cells are placed into cones or cups attached to a horizontal rotating table. Cups open one at a time to drop seedlings into the furrow. Several thousand plants can be set per hour per row with these models.

Spade-type units are designed to cut through and set plants in plastic mulch. *No-till transplanters* are a recent development, designed to place plants into soil that has a lot of surface residues (see figure 9.11, page 94).

Planting Arrangement

The way vegetable rows are arranged in the field depends on how much space a crop needs, as well as the seeding, transplanting, and cultivation equipment to be used. Most growers try to minimize the need for changing or adjusting equipment by using a uniform planting system, having rows that are spaced in multiples of a standard row width, or having a separate tractor or cultivation tools all set up for different planting arrangements.

Generally, planting arrangements must be based on tractor wheel spacing, which is usually 60 or 72 inches apart on center (the distance between the midpoints of the two rear tires). So in order for the tractor to pass over the crops, rows are usually spaced 30 or 36 inches apart for large crops such as corn, potatoes, and crucifers; and 15 or 18 inches apart for smaller crops such as lettuce,

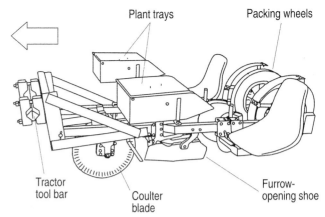

a. Hand-set transplanter

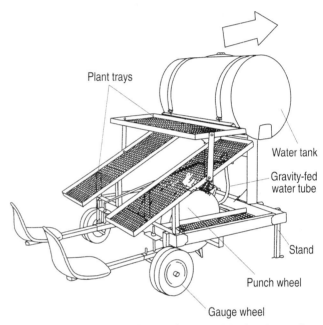

b. Water-wheel transplanter for planting vegetables into bare soil or plastic mulch

Figure 10.9 Hand-set and "water-wheel" transplanters
Source (a.): Adapted from Holland Transplanter Co.; (b.): adapted from Rain-Flo Irrigation

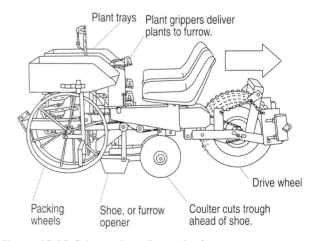

Figure 10.10 Gripper-type transplanter
Source: Adapted from Mechanical Transplanter Company

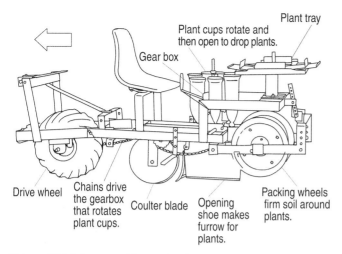

Figure 10.11 Carousel transplanter
Source: Adapted from Holland Transplanter Co.

beets, and carrots. Raised beds must be straddled by the tractor, so they are frequently 4 or 5 feet wide with multiple rows on each bed. Ideally, the arrangement of rows conforms not only to tractor-wheel spacing, but also to equipment used to form beds, set transplants, control pests, and harvest the crop, resulting in a production system that's suited to the farm from start to finish.

Row spacings that give the highest yield for particular crops may not be suitable for cultivating weeds or for promoting air circulation to prevent development of disease. Row spacing aimed at giving the highest yields may not be the best when it comes time to harvest, either. Extension publications list a dozen or more different row spacings that optimize the yield of various vegetables, yet many growers use just one system of arranging plants in order to enhance the efficiency of field operations.

Transplanting Efficiency— A Grower Profile

Bruce Kaufman and Judy Jarvis
Riverside Farm, East Hardwick, Vermont
Bruce Kaufman and Judy Jarvis farm 40 acres of mixed vegetables, cover crops, and medicinal herbs. The couple markets 50% through an organic growers wholesale cooperative and the

other 50% locally: directly to local co-ops, at farmers market, and through a CSA of about 75 members. Their soils are well-drained sandy loams on river bottom land. Bruce has been farming for twenty-one years, ten years at this site. It is a very cold location in the "Northeast Kingdom" of Vermont, so he specializes in short-season cropping.

"Growers have to be practical in terms of efficiency; we have a certain amount of time and money with which to solve a given problem. As a grower that plants about 20 acres of spring transplants (lettuce and cole crops), which require about 400,000 transplants a year with my row spacing, I was looking for a way to be efficient as well as reduce the problem I was having with diseases like rhizoctonia bottom rot. I had heard that some European growers don't have the problem, because they grew their plants in soil blocks. They didn't break any lower leaves off when transplanting, so there were no entry points for the disease, which made sense to me.

"I knew I had to be totally mechanized because of my scale, so if I used soil blocks, there was no way to make them by hand. For about five years I had been doing plugs, so I was used to idea of propagating within the planting block rather than pricking out, which would be way too labor intensive. So after I heard about these companies in Europe that made block machines, I was interested in investing in one. Luckily, in the late 80s there was a nonprofit group called the Working Land Fund that had a program to help farmers identify, try out, and buy innovative equipment. They bought the equipment and let you have it for a one-year trial; then you either bought it with no interest, or you returned it to them and they let another farmer test it. There were three cases, my soil-blocking machine, a Lely tine-weeder, and a German flame-weeder; and all the farmers kept them. We had to promise to publicize the equipment and the program.

"I got a Belgian soil block machine made by Dewa, which cost $4,800 including shipping and was the first one in the United States at the time. It has a hopper that you fill with potting mix, which it meters out to the correct depth, presses down, and cuts into 1 ⅛-inch cubes. Then it makes a dibble hole and puts a seed in it, and the blocks come out on a conveyor. It produces about 10,000 seeded blocks per hour with one person feeding in and one person taking the blocks off. When it first arrived, I did change the motor so it would match the U.S. electric system; I put a 3/4-horsepower GE motor on it. Everything on it is belt-driven and doesn't take much horsepower. I have used the machine for ten years, making five to six million blocks, and I've never done anything else but grease the fittings. This machine is designed by Visser, a Dutch company.

"For the machine to work well, a soil mix is required that is fibrous enough to hold together, and moist enough to form the block. This equipment came with one page of instructions that basically said 'the quality of the mix is the important factor in success.' Period. That's all it told me, so it took some trial and error to figure out what that was. It is a gravity drop planter so the seed has to be uniform in weight and size to get uniform seeding. The manufacturer does make pneumatic planters that can go on these machines, for a lot more money.

"After some experimentation, our basic mix is about 45% compost, 45% horticultural-grade peat moss, and 10% vermiculite; and we add some organic fertilizers depending on the compost quality. I wet the mix to the point that when you squeeze it, only a little bit of moisture comes out between your fingers. This is drier than mixes used for a hand-blockers, but wetter than mixes used for a tray seeding. You should be able to make a ball that holds together, but crumbles when you drop it." (See appendix C, page 245, for supplier contact information.)

"For lettuce we use pelleted seed, for all the brassicas, just raw seed. Some seeds are too small to use the mechanical sower, so you have to put them in the blocks by hand—like basil or celeriac for example. I would pelletize these if we could get small lots. About 95% of my transplants are cole crops and lettuce."

"Using the block machine is only a third of the transplant process. I still needed a way to handle and transplant the blocks that was economical. I tried handling the blocks using trays on benches, but this was a failure since it required too many trays and too much handling; but more importantly, the blocks were up off the ground and would dry out from underneath.

"I love the block system of transplanting, and I think for the farmer with the right size it will pay for itself; so don't be afraid of the up-front cost. I know that with our 20 acres of transplants it has been a good investment for me."

So I built a special greenhouse with a heated concrete slab, so when the blocks come off the machine, we use a flat blocking fork to lay the blocks right on the slab. This is what the Dutch do, except they rototill their clay soil, then pack it down to get a hard surface. The result is you have a very efficient use of space; the greenhouse is filled from one end to the other, with just one aisle: it's like rolling benches with no benches. The one walkway is along an edge of the house, so the machine can be rolled along as you lay down the blocks in rows. Each row contains the same variety ready for the same planting date.

"The blocks have to be organized by first in, first out. The onions are laid down first on the concrete, then lettuce planting 1, lettuce planting 2, etc. From a horticultural point of view this system has many advantages. All the plants are sharing a common floor, which helps keep the water supply uniform, perhaps the most important greenhouse job. Because the blocks are in contact with each other, they wick water amongst themselves; so it is not as critical that every block get exactly the same amount of water. In addition, they don't leach out as much water as when they were on benches, and there is less surface area exposed, so I water a lot less than when they were up on benches; and that has a major effect on nutrient leaching. We use a 'Wonder Waterer' watering wand that can cover 15 or 16 feet, and I also have an overhead sprinkler system that is used mostly in mid-afternoon to lower the temperature of the greenhouse.

"The next step is putting the plants in the field, after the lettuce has grown for four weeks. Due to the shared watering and consistent nutrient supply, the growth is really uniform. We put in 12,000 lettuce plants weekly, and I'm really happy with just about all of them.

"We use the same flat fork to pick up the finished blocks, 108 at time, and put two fork-loads of them side by side in a three-sided wooden flat with a 2-inch lip that holds the blocks tightly together, so we carry 216 plants in a tray to the field. I use a three-row Kennco water-wheel transplanter to set the plants. You cannot use a mechanical wheel or Holland transplanter with blocks because there is too much weight, and when the leaf is held by the planter arm and the root ball is in the air, there is too much breakage.

"A water-wheel makes a hole in the ground and adds water, then the people sitting behind it take the plants and place them in the muddy hole. Because it's wet the hole closes itself up. We built racks so we can hold twenty-four trays on the transplanter, and each person has a tray on his lap as he plants. On bare ground, the transplanter spikes tend to mud-up and you just have to stop and scrape the mud off. We always use a 4-inch-tall by 44-inch-wide raised bed, with three rows on 15-inch centers. I set the plants so that the outer rows are even with each other but the middle row is offset; this diamond pattern makes it is easy to hoe and gives the plants a little more room. The key is to make those plants go into the ground smoothly without operator discomfort, and for that you need a hydrostatic tractor or one with a creeper gear.

"We used to use a John Deere 2510 row-crop tractor, but its lowest gear was 0.8 mph, and that was not slow enough. Now we go about 0.6 mph with an International 656 hydrostatic, which allows us to slow down if the plants are leggy or go faster if the plants are perfect. That is preferable to a creeper gear since there is no gear shifting to adjust our speed. With the Kennco, we have to go slower than if we had a carousel transplanter. We top out at 1,800 plants per hour per row, whereas carousels can go up to 50% faster, but they drop the blocks from about 2 feet up, then rely on a covering shoe to cover them. I would still need someone to walk the field and make sure they are all upright and look good. Our unit cuts down on that extra labor since all the plants go in just right because they are hand set. I don't walk the field any longer. The bottom line is that my stand is excellent and plant quality is excellent.

"The organic matter in the blocks act like a sponge when there is a little bit of rain or a light irrigation. Sometimes you can see that the field has dried but the plant itself is sitting in a moist square, so that sponge effect has had a major impact on my need to irrigate. You never see salts crusting on the block either, since the high organic matter retains the nutrients.

"I love the block system of transplanting, and I think for the farmer with the right size it will pay for itself; so don't be afraid of the up-front cost. I know that with our 20 acres of transplants it has been a good investment for me. People have to ask themselves how much time they want to spend seeding in the greenhouse. When I go into the greenhouse, in an hour I have an acre seeded. In March and April, my labor needs are drastically reduced by not filling trays, and there are no piles of plastic trays on my farm anymore, which is an environmental plus. However, I do use a lot more potting soil than other people. As a result, I work closely with a local compost company to assure that a high-quality, compost-based potting mix is manufactured locally."

Chapter 11

Irrigation and Spraying Systems

Successful vegetable production is highly dependent on a consistent and sufficient supply of water for crop growth. In the Northeast, rainfall during the growing season is usually erratic and often inadequate. Even in years when plenty of rain falls, the distribution of precipitation over the season may be far from uniform, resulting in periods of drought stress. Irrigation is generally a wise investment on a vegetable farm and is certainly wise where high-value crops are grown. In some areas irrigation is not an option, but a requirement, for production of vegetables. For example, an irrigation system is essential on soils with low water-holding capacity that are light in texture and low in organic matter, or in relatively dry microclimates. Irrigation can also be used to protect against frost, incorporate agricultural chemicals into the soil, and apply fertilizers.

Irrigation Systems

Irrigation equipment brings water from a source such as a river, pond, or well to crops in the field. On average, vegetable crops require at least one to two inches of water per week to yield well, and more may be required during the hottest, driest periods of the year. Irrigation is usually necessary to fulfill this requirement throughout the growing season. An irrigation system should be designed to match the water supply, peak water demand, available labor, and other considerations such as frost protection where appropriate. If a natural body of water is not available, it may be worthwhile to construct an irrigation pond or drill a well.

In addition to a source of water, an irrigation system includes a delivery and dispersal system. A pump forces water into a main pipe that carries it

to the field. The pump may be electric or petroleum powered, independent or PTO-driven. The main pipe may be permanently buried, with risers (vertical pipes) at different points on the farm; or it may be movable above ground pipe or tubing. Sub-mains may further divide the water flow until it is delivered to an individual field. There, water is distributed either by *overhead sprinkler irrigation*, or by *drip*, or *"trickle," irrigation*.

Equipment for Overhead Sprinkler Irrigation

Overhead (sprinkler) irrigation can provide a lot of water quickly to a crop, and in many cases the same equipment can be used to deliver water to different fields on a farm. In general, sprinkler irrigation requires an abundant supply of water, such as a river or pond. Sprinkler irrigation systems may be stationary or mobile while water is being delivered. Stationary systems include *solid-set* and *hand move* systems. Mobile irrigation is accomplished with *traveling guns* (hose-reel or cable-tow) or *side-roll* (wheel move) systems. Stationary overhead irrigation can also be used for frost protection, since the formation of a thin layer of ice on crops can keep plant tissues from freezing.

Both solid-set and hand move systems are comprised of main lines to which lateral pipes are coupled at desired intervals. Attached to laterals are risers with sprinklers on top. Lateral pipes and risers should be set up in a field to assure that individual sprinkler coverages overlap sufficiently to completely cover the desired area, accounting for the fact that wind will cause variation in the pattern of water dispersal (figure 11.1). Sprinklers (figure 11.2) vary in characteristics such as re-

Sustainable Vegetable Production from Start-Up to Market

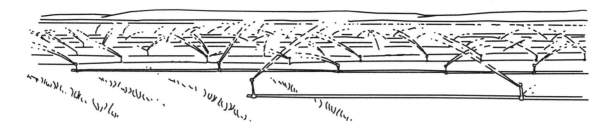

Figure 11.1 Sample layout of lateral pipes and risers

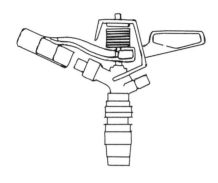

Figure 11.2 Sprinkler
Source: Adapted from Charles W. Harris Co. Inc.

quired water pressure, flow rate, and water distribution pattern.

Solid-set pipes, either above or below ground, are left in place to irrigate an entire field throughout the growing season. Hand move pipes are moved from field to field as needed during the season. Many vegetable farms use a combination of permanent solid-set and portable hand move irrigation in which the main lines, generally PVC plastic pipes, are buried; and the above ground laterals, generally quick-coupling aluminum pipe, are moved to irrigate small sections of land at a time (figure 11.3). Hand move systems, while labor intensive, are designed to be easily configured to accommodate small fields or plantings of irregular shape. Hand move systems are also well-suited to diversified farms where the water requirements of the crops vary over the season.

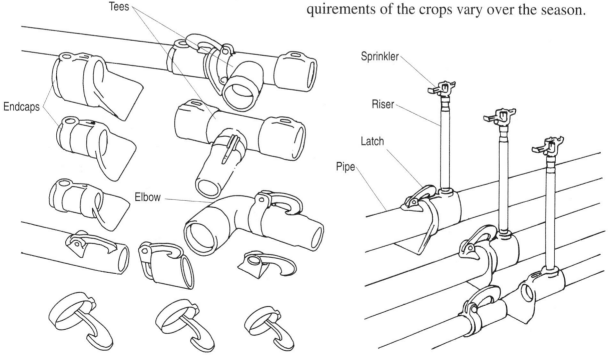

Figure 11.3 Hand move sprinkler irrigation systems include quick-coupling aluminum pipe and fittings
Source: Adapted from Charles W. Harris Co. Inc.

The capacity of a pump or water supply is usually limited to one or a few fields at a time, so hand move systems must be moved around frequently to keep up with irrigation needs on a vegetable farm during dry periods. A wagon facilitates moving pipe around the farm (figure 11.4). Irrigation pipe is rather costly, so moving it often during the growing season may be more desirable than owning a lot of it. However, faced with significant labor costs, some farmers decide to buy a lot of portable pipe, or to install a permanent solid-set system in order to minimize the time spent moving and setting up overhead irrigation.

Instead of using laterals with many small sprinklers, a single *irrigation gun* may be used to dispense water to large areas (figure 11.5). Such guns may be positioned in the field by hand for stationary operation. Traveling guns move continuously through a field on a cart, towed by a cable or by the irrigation hose as it automatically wind up on a reel (figure 11.6). Once fully re-

wound, the system shuts off. Cable-tow and hose-reel units can deliver large volumes of water rather quickly. They are best suited to large, level fields with long, straight rows.

Another type of mobile irrigation is the *linear traveler (side roll)* system. These units have a long, straight aluminum pipe that serves as the axle for wheels spaced 30 to 40 feet apart. Sprinklers are spaced on the pipe midway between the wheels. Side-roll systems require square or rectangular fields that are relatively flat. They are not easily moved from field to field.

Equipment for Trickle (Drip) Irrigation

Trickle, or *"drip," irrigation* is the most efficient means of supplying water to plants, because losses due to evaporation are minimized, and water is applied directly where needed, to the crop root zone. This allows smaller water sources and less energy to be utilized for irrigation purposes than would be the case with sprinkler irrigation. However, only a small volume of water is applied, so drip irrigation systems must be better managed than overhead sprinkler systems. Because of the small water volume, drip irrigation systems cannot be used for frost control. In addition, poor design or management may cause clogging or

Figure 11.4 Wagon for transporting and storing pipe
Source: Adapted from Charles W. Harris Co. Inc.

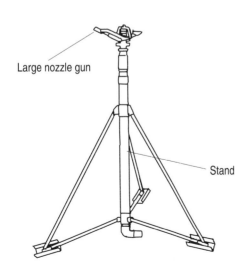

Figure 11.5 Irrigation gun may be used instead of sprinklers.

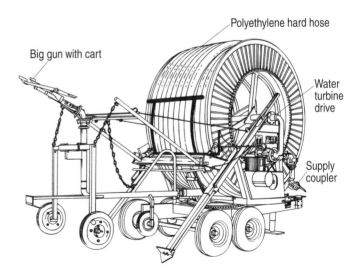

Figure 11.6 Hose-reel (or hard-hose) traveling gun
Source: *Liquid Manure Application Systems Design Manual*, NRAES–89

Sustainable Vegetable Production from Start-Up to Market

damage to lines. Another problem not applicable to sprinkler systems is disposal every year or two of the plastic tubing or row-crop tape used for drip irrigation lines.

Trickle system components include a clean water source, pump and power unit, filters, distribution system, emitters, and monitoring devices (figure 11.7). Fertilizer injection and automated controls are optional. The source of water for trickle irrigation should be clean enough to minimize the need for filtration to prevent clogged emitters. Fast flowing water is often higher in suspended particles than are large, still bodies of water. Suction should be from a point elevated off the bottom of the water supply.

The pump must be properly sized for the system (taking into account changes in elevation, friction due to length of water flow, and pressure required at furthest emitter). Irrigation handbooks or salespeople can provide the information to calculate the required pump size. Always err on the side of extra capacity to assure that all emitters provide the expected flow of water. For a 5-acre system, an electric pump must usually be about 10 hp, or a gas pump about 20 hp. Centrifugal pumps are suited to surface or shallow waters, while submersible pumps are needed when water must be lifted more than 15 feet.

Filters are required with trickle irrigation. Fine mesh screen filters or disk filters are used for well or city water; sand filters are needed for pond or creek water to keep the emitters from clogging. A secondary filter may also be necessary with surface water sources for back flushing.

Main and sub-main pipes may be aluminum, PVC, steel, or reinforced plastic lay-flat hose. The laterals, which actually irrigate the fields, are generally either row-crop tape (tubing) or polyethylene pipe with individual point-source emitters. A row-crop tape has emitters incorporated into the thin-wall tubing at close spacing, so it wets a continuous strip (line source) of ground. Individual point-source emitters can be installed at any spacing and are used for wide-spaced plants, typically fruit and landscape plantings.

Water discharge rates are specified in gallons per hour (gph) for point-source emitters and gallons per minute (gpm) per 100 feet of row for line sources, at a designated pressure in pounds per square inch (psi). Vegetable growers commonly use line sources that operate at less than 15 psi and provide 0.25 to 1.5 gpm per 100 feet of line. Line sources should be used only on level or nearly level fields in order to minimize changes in discharge rates over the field due to elevation. On

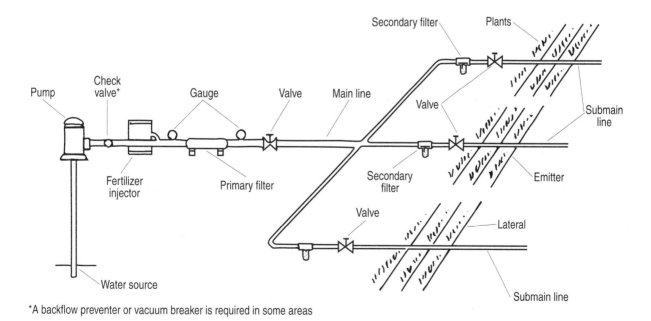

*A backflow preventer or vacuum breaker is required in some areas

Figure 11.7 Trickle irrigation system components
Source: Adapted from *Trickle Irrigation in the Eastern United States*, NRAES–4

sloping or rolling land, pressure-compensating trickle tubing that incorporates uniformly-spaced, pressure-compensating emitters into a thin-wall polyethylene pipe should be used.

Irrigation Scheduling

Irrigation scheduling involves matching the application of water to various crop needs. Soil type, rainfall pattern, stage of crop growth, and individual crop requirements determine when irrigation is needed. When it comes to putting on water, many growers rely on rainfall measurements and their experience, along with the feel of the soil and the appearance of the crop. Soil examination is useful if samples are from the crop's rooting zone, not the soil surface. Charts are available to help determine how the feel of the soil relates to water availability. Relying on crop appearance can be a big mistake: by the time visual symptoms of drought stress are obvious in the crop, at least some reduction in yield is likely. Furthermore, some wilting may occur at midday, even when adequate moisture is available.

Sensors can be used to monitor how much water is available in the soil. Because this can vary among fields, in a single field, and with soil depth, multiple sensors are needed to give an accurate picture of soil moisture (figure 11.8). *Tensiometers* are sensors that measure soil moisture, based on how much vacuum is created as soils dry. They are relatively inexpensive, but many are needed to get a good picture of water availability. Tensiometers must be refilled with water and have the vacuum restored if allowed to dry out. Electrical sensors of soil moisture, such as *gypsum blocks,* require a voltmeter costing several hundred dollars to read them. Blocks can be placed throughout an area and multiple readings taken with the same voltmeter to assess moisture levels in the field.

On-farm measurements of water are useful to irrigation scheduling. A rainfall gauge in combination with an evaporation pan provides an input/output estimate of soil water. By measuring how much water evaporates into the air each day, growers can estimate crop water use. Early in the season, most crops are small and use only 10–

15% of pan evaporation. During the second third of the growth, crops will use 40–50% of pan evaporation. When mature, crops use 60–85% of pan evaporation, depending on how full a canopy or crop load they have.

Fertigation

Fertigation is the application of nutrients through an irrigation system. Fertilizer injectors are used to introduce a concentrated fertilizer solution into

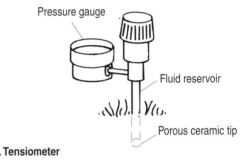

a. Tensiometer

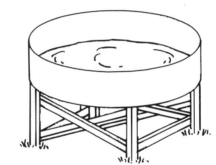

b. Evaporation pan

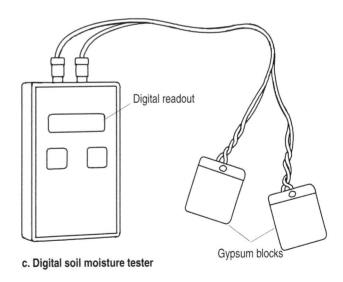

c. Digital soil moisture tester

Figure 11.8 Soil water measurement devices
Source (a. and b.): Adapted from *Trickle Irrigation in the Eastern United States,* NRAES–4

the supply pipe used for crop watering. Two basic types of fertilizer injectors are available: those that use a pump of some kind; and venturi types, which rely on the flow of water to create a pressure difference between the fertilizer container and the supply line (figure 11.9).

Fertigation should be based on soil tests or tissue tests and crop needs. In the field, lime, phosphate, micronutrients, and about a quarter of the N and K needs are usually applied during soil preparation. The remainder of the N and K can then be applied by injecting into the irrigation system on a regular basis, from daily to biweekly, depending on the system and the crop. Fertigation is effective only in conjunction with a well-run irrigation program. *Backflow protection devices* prevent nutrients and other injected materials from entering the clean water source and are required by law in some states.

Spraying

Spraying of materials is a common practice on vegetable farms to control weeds; to protect crops from insects or diseases; and to apply nutrients, growth regulators, or beneficial organisms. Growers should always follow current recommendations and label instructions when spraying any such materials. Extensive information is available through Cooperative Extension on the proper selection and application of pesticides for individual vegetable crops. Regional extension vegetable management guides are updated and published every year or two because pesticide information changes rather rapidly.

Whether conventional or organic, IPM or ecological, some form of spraying is usually done on vegetable farms. Synthetic pesticides are used on the majority of vegetable farms, although most growers are seeking ways to reduce application rates and utilize least-toxic materials. Most organic growers also apply organically permitted pesticides, such as botanical or microbial insecticides. In either case, effective application tools and techniques are important.

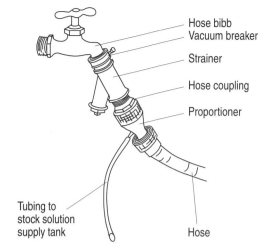

a. Temporary proportioner installation

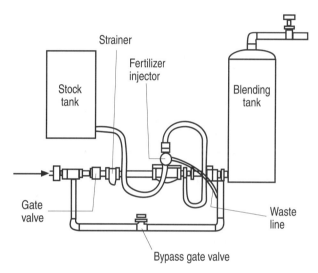

b. Water-operated pump injector

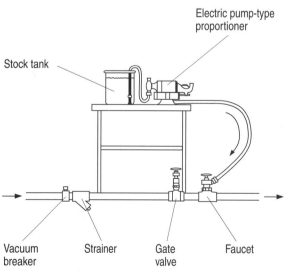

c. Pressure pump injector

Figure 11.9 Basic types of fertilizer injectors
Source: *Fertilizer and Manure Application Equipment,* NRAES–57

Spray Equipment

Spray equipment may be hand-held, carried by backpack, pushed on a cart, tractor-mounted, or tractor pulled. Spray pressure, nozzle type, dilution rate, and ground speed determine how much active ingredient is actually applied. Calibration of spray equipment to assure the proper rate of discharge is essential to achieving desired results and protecting against environmental contamination. Equipment should be selected for its effectiveness and efficiency in delivering the material to the desired target. However, versatility on a diversified operation may be of tantamount importance, so sprayers may be purchased because they can be used in a number of different situations. In such cases, it is especially important that after each use equipment be cleaned using recommended methods.

Good spray coverage of the canopy or the soil, depending on the situation, is necessary to achieve good results with most materials. Water-sensitive spray cards that change color when wetted are an inexpensive means of assessing the extent to which a spraying system delivers material uniformly and accurately. These can be clipped using clothespins to the target crops at different locations in the canopy to determine if a material is getting applied as desired.

Backpack Sprayers

Backpack sprayers usually hold about 4 gallons of liquid, dispersed through a hand-held wand (figure 11.10). Pressure is created by a small gasoline engine or by a manual piston or diaphragm-type pump that in some cases can be used while wearing the backpack. These sprayers are useful on small acreage, or on crops grown in small quantities that require special treatment.

Boom Sprayers

Boom sprayers of various widths have a rigid pipe with fixed nozzles that can be turned on or off to spray materials over the entire width of the boom, just over the rows, or between the rows (figure 11.11). *High-clearance boom* sprayers travel above a tall crop like sweet corn. High-clearance boom sprayers may be either self-propelled or trailed behind tractors that pull the base of the unit down the alleys. A high-clearance tractor with a

mounted boom sprayer can clear a crop of intermediate height, up to about 4 feet, with some bending of the plants.

Drop nozzles can be mounted on pipes attached perpendicular to the main boom. These travel between the crop rows, allowing materials to be sprayed from well below the top of the crop. In order to effectively spray the plant part that needs protecting, nozzles can be arranged in various fashions on the boom, and the drop pipes can be

a. Backpack sprayer

b. Powered backpack sprayer

Figure 11.10 Backpack sprayers
Source: *Strawberry Production Guide for the Northeast, Midwest, and Eastern Canada*, NRAES–88

angled; nozzles can be turned on and off as needed.

With a *wet boom* the spray is fed through hollow pipe to nozzles that are attached directly to the pipe (figure 11.11b). With a *dry boom* system, the spray is fed through hoses to nozzles that are attached to a framework made of pipe or angle iron (figure 11.11c). A dry boom system makes it easier to reconfigure the nozzle spacing to accommodate different row spacings or crop canopies by changing the lengths of tubing used.

Air-Blast Sprayers

Air-blast sprayers use a large fan to propel droplets of material into a crop from a distance (figure 11.12). They are pulled through an alley alongside blocks of a crop to be fogged or misted. Since they treat crops of many different row spacings and heights with little or no adjustment, they can be faster and more versatile than boom sprayers,

and more stable on uneven fields. However, they can't concentrate sprays on crop rows (versus unplanted areas) or on parts of plants needing protection, such as corn whorls or silks.

When relying on air-blast spraying, blocks of crops need to be kept narrow enough to assure spray penetration into the middle rows. The best use of air-blast sprayers is probably for disease control, rather than insecticide application, although they have the potential to blow inoculum through a crop (see "Sanitation to Reduce Inoculum," pages 158–159). Air-blasts are not used for herbicides because booms can better apply larger droplets lower to the ground, which minimizes drift.

Electrostatic Sprayers

Electrostatic sprayers apply electrically-charged spray droplets, greatly enhancing coverage and allowing reduced rates of pesticides to be applied. They are relatively expensive and not common in the field. Smaller units are more widely used in greenhouses.

Sprayer Components

The type of nozzle used in a sprayer affects the size of the droplets sprayed, spray pattern, spray angle, and amount of material applied. Tables in manufacturers' catalogs provide this information in detail. Three commonly used nozzle patterns are flat fan, hollow cone, and full cone. Nozzles wear with use, and this changes their output. They should be checked frequently.

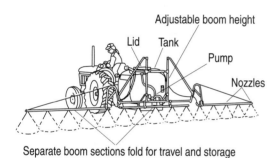

a. Tractor-mounted boom sprayer

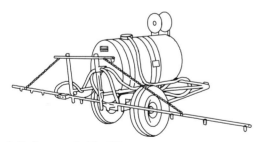

b. Trailer-mounted "wet" boom sprayer

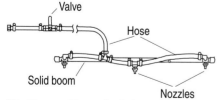

c. "Dry" boom with nozzles in hose

Figure 11.11 Boom sprayers

Source (a.): Adapted from Rear's Manufacturing Company; (b.): *Greenhouse Engineering,* NRAES–33

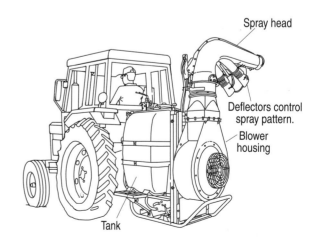

Figure 11.12 Air-blast sprayer

Source: Adapted from Maquinas Agricolas Jacto, S.A., Brazil

The sprayer tank should be large enough that it does not have to be refilled frequently, but buying a big tank that is rarely full is a waste of money. Stainless steel and fiberglass are durable and resist corrosion, but other tank materials are less expensive.

Strainers in the sprayer are necessary to keep rust, sand, and other particles from damaging the pump or clogging the nozzles. Sprayer pumps powered by tractor PTO include roller, centrifugal, diaphragm, and piston pumps. They operate most efficiently at different PTO speeds and have different pressure ranges, flow rates, and durabilities.

Drip Irrigation— A Grower Profile

Ted and Molly Bartlett
Silver Creek Farm, Hiram, Ohio
The Bartletts' farm is about 75 acres. Fifteen acres are in organic vegetables, certified by the Ohio Ecological Food and Farm Association (OEFFA). Another fifteen or so are pasture for their sheep, and the rest are wooded. The soil is a clay loam, not particularly well drained. There is some drain tile, but water still puddles even three feet away from it. Ted and Molly Bartlett grow dozens of different vegetables and are looking into growing herbs such as ginseng. Their markets include a CSA of 110 families, a farm market, and a couple of wholesale accounts that take vegetables, berries, poultry, and lamb.

When the Bartletts started farming commercially twelve years ago, there was no irrigation on the farm. "I knew we needed to irrigate to get consistent yields," said Ted, "but I didn't want to use an overhead system because it requires a lot of pressure and expensive pumps, and it's hard work hauling pipe. Also, I don't like to get the tops of the plants wet. So what we did instead was to start setting up a drip irrigation system a little at a time. We built a pond, figuring we could irrigate from that if necessary, but our main goal for the pond was recreation and enhancing the farm's ecosystem. The problem with surface water is that expensive filtering is needed. We discovered that we had two very productive artesian wells that could supply 200 gallons per minute just about forever. I find that many of my farmer friends ignore their wells as a possible source of irrigation water.

"We bought the most expensive pump we could afford, figuring that the pump would set the limitations of what could irrigate. We started with a 1.5-horsepower submersible pump, which meant we could irrigate about 2 acres. It's really hard to nail the irrigation area down because you don't irrigate everything all at once; you pick a section and move through it.

"From the well we needed a very large pressure tank; then we laid water lines from that tank. The main lines are 3 inches in diameter: and we laid these below the frost line using a backhoe. The main line runs east and west, and four 2-inch lines tee off that going north and south every 400 feet, which is the length of our rows. We have three risers off each 2-inch line, spaced about 130 feet apart. These numbers depend, of course, on your own field sizes and management issues such as traffic patterns on the farm.

"Off the risers on the surface we use blue lay-flat line, and off that we use drip tape. Recently there was a big change in drip tape quality, with the thinner ones, 2- or 4-mil, being a lot stronger than they used to be. Our debate has always been whether we should spend more on stronger tape and save it or buy the thinner stuff and throw it away. This year we used 4-mil tape and bought a tape winder that runs off the PTO and three-point hitch. It worked beautifully, making it easy for us to wind up 80% of the tapes. We'll protect them

" . . . the return on investment is well worth it. It's a mistake to think of irrigation as just for drought insurance—it's also very important to keep the plants free of stress, especially when they are setting fruit, etc. It really helps control the quality of our product."

over the winter and that's one less cost we'll face next year. Of course, you're going to have breaks and splices and things like that, so I don't know how long they will last. We lay the tape under plastic, and in drought years rodent populations build up under the plastic, seeking a source of water; and they damage the lines, so that limits how long they'll last.

"We're trying to get away from plastic mulch, and we are doing more direct-seeding. However, we find that plastic is necessary for us to produce red peppers and early tomatoes and to get ripe melons in August. These are items our customers want, and the hassle of using plastic is worth the extra money in our pocket. The challenge when not using plastic has been to cultivate without damaging the drip tape. I use a Farmall Cub with basket weeders belly-mounted. I had the center basket tines modified from a rectangular shape into a V-shape that rides over the drip line. The worst it does is push the tape deeper down into the soil, which is a probably a good thing. If your soil is fluffy enough, you could probably get away with the straight baskets without doing any damage, especially now that the plastics used in the tapes are stronger."

"Although I've used tensiometers and gypsum blocks to assess soil moisture, I also rely a lot on my experience and pay a great deal of attention to what's happening in the field to determine when to irrigate. I squeeze the lay-flat lines, feel the soil a lot, and watch the plants. After a few years irrigating and observing this way, you can tell what's going on."

"I'm not particular about drip-hole spacing, whether it's 6- or 9- or 12-inch; I go for the most plastic thickness for the best price. Probably 4-mil, or 6- at the most, will be good for a couple of years. As far as cost, I did do some tracking a couple of years ago, and the return on investment is well worth it. It's a mistake to think of irrigation as just for drought insurance—it's also very important to keep the plants free of stress, especially when they are setting fruit, etc. It really helps control the quality of our product. How much that additional quality is worth is hard to measure, but I can't imagine raising vegetables without being able to control the water."

Chapter 12

Harvest and Postharvest Handling

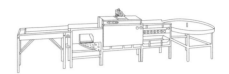

Harvesting in a timely, efficient, and careful manner is essential to making the most of all the effort and inputs that go into getting a vegetable crop to maturity. Most crops are harvested based on size and/or physiological maturity. Vegetables are alive, and their metabolic and ripening processes generally continue after harvest. The majority of crops will have better quality and shelf life if picked slightly immature. The more promptly a crop will be presented and sold to the final consumer, the closer to "dead ripe" it can be picked.

Harvesting Equipment

Harvesting equipment is needed to get the crop out of the ground and remove it from the field in the best condition possible. Marketable yield may be reduced by improper harvest tools or techniques, limiting what can be sold to the customer.

Harvest tools are those used for cutting or picking, carrying, and cooling produce prior to cleaning, sorting, and packing for sale. A variety of mechanized harvesters are available, but due to their cost, only the simplest or most necessary are found on small-scale vegetable farms. These include bed-lifters (or "undercutters") for undercutting root crops and potato diggers for lifting tubers out of the ground onto the soil surface (figure 12.1). With enough acreage, the purchase of costly harvesters for corn, beans, carrots, and other crops can be justified because of the savings in labor.

When produce is cut for harvest, as with lettuce or pumpkins, knives or other hand tools should be kept sharp and clean. Occasional disinfection by dipping in a dilute bleach solution is advisable.

a. One-row potato harvester

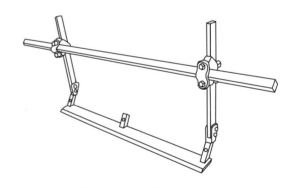

b. Under-cutter blade makes pulling up root crops easier

c. one-row corn harvester

Figure 12.1 Some vegetable harvest equipment
Source (c.): Adapted from Pixall Limited Partnership

Sustainable Vegetable Production from Start-Up to Market

Produce should be handled as gently as possible to avoid bruising, so careful placement into harvest bins, boxes, or baskets is important.

Once produce is harvested, promptly removing heat and keeping the produce cool thereafter are essential to prolonging shelf life. It is important to place harvested produce in the shade whenever possible until it can be cooled by artificial means. Sometimes harvested produce is brought to a packing shed for cleaning, cooling, sorting, and packing. In other situations produce is harvested into a vehicle equipped with a shade covering, water basins, and boxes to allow for field-packing. Teams of workers cut, wash if necessary, and pack produce in the field; then the boxes, pallets, or bins are moved back to the packing shed for cooling and cold storage. Harvest conveyors may be used to carry the crops from the rows to the field truck, allowing workers to cut in multiple rows at once without walking back and forth to the truck (figure 12.2).

Postharvest Handling

After harvest, crops are handled in the *packing shed*. This can be a simple structure with a minimum of services and only basic protection from the elements—a roof and a source of clean water. Generally, more elaborate facilities are used if significant quantities of vegetables are to be handled. The four basic functions of packing sheds are

1. Dumping—getting the crop safely out of the harvest container
2. Cleaning—washing with cool or cold water and/or brushing in some cases
3. Sorting—throwing out unmarketable product and separating marketable product into groups
4. Packing—placing sorted product into containers for storing, shipping, or marketing

Although the harvest process itself can cause reductions in crop quality and marketable quantity, it is often during postharvest handling where marketable yield or shelf life is reduced. *Impact injury* can occur when crops are thrown into harvest containers, dumped into bigger containers, and dropped onto packing lines. When crops are piled too deep in containers, containers are overfilled then stacked, or containers are too weak to

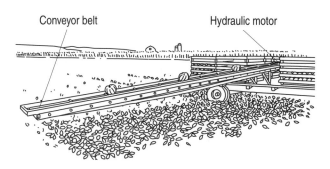

PTO drives a flat, moving belt that carries cut produce from field to wagon pulled behind tractor.

Figure 12.2 Vegetable conveyor, or harvest-aid belt

bear the weight of stacking, then *compression injury* occurs. Vegetables rubbing against each other, the belts or walls of a packing line, or the sides of a container can cause *abrasion injury*.

Decay caused by microorganisms is a serious postharvest problem that may be initiated during postharvest handling but expressed at a later date when crops are in storage, on the shelf, or in the consumer's home. Cuts, bruises, scrapes, and soft tissue associated with overmaturity all encourage invasion by decay organisms that are otherwise excluded by the crop's natural protection. Excessive moisture on stored crops also promotes decay. Cooling of perishable produce is the major defense against decay, as it slows crop metabolism and microbial activity.

Postharvest Cooling

Cooling crops begins with removal of field heat. This should be done in the field or as soon as possible after harvest in the packing shed. Hydrocooling is a fast means of removing field heat by drenching produce for 5–10 minutes in clean, cold water. Dirty water can cause disease problems, and certain crops can be damaged by hydrocooling and should be cooled by refrigeration instead. Crops not amenable to hydrocooling (since it may reduce their storage life) include cabbage, eggplant, parsnip, pepper, potato, squashes, sweet potato, and tomato. Unless vacuum cooling is available, prompt refrigeration or "room cooling" is the method used to remove field heat from these crops after packing. In this case, proper arrangement of boxes, bins, or bags in the cooler is critical to allow cold air to flow easily through the room and reach all of the containers to assure the most rapid cooling of produce possible.

Some crops are very susceptible to chilling injury, and care must be taken to keep the temperature of wash water and cold storage above 50°F. These include cucumber, eggplant, pumpkin, summer squash, and tomato.

Because optimal handling and storage conditions are different for each crop, it is essential for growers to find and follow recommendations specific to their crops (see Hardenburg, Watada, and Wang, *The Commercial Storage of Fruits, Vegetables, and Florist and Nursery Stocks,* 1986; or other references for this chapter, beginning on page 262). Producers should also monitor the accuracy of thermostats for their coolers and wash water. If in doubt of the exact temperature of your wash water or cooler, it is better to wash and store vegetables a few degrees warmer than recommended temperatures, rather than to risk chilling injury by subjecting them to temperatures any cooler than recommended.

Postharvest Washing

Washing prior to marketing is essential for many vegetables. A plentiful source of clean water for washing produce is needed in the packing shed. Wash water should be changed before it gets too soiled; otherwise crops may be inoculated with decay organisms, and a film of dirt may adhere to produce after washing. For crops that require thorough washing and are not easily bruised, such as many root crops, a barrel washer (figure 12.3) that tumbles them while spraying clean water is useful for removing soil. Chlorination of wash or rinse water is an option to control surface-borne decay organisms, although care must be taken to manage chlorine levels precisely. Chlorine dissipates and looses its effectiveness with the passage of time, the amount of material it is exposed to, and contact with contaminants such as organic matter in the wash water.

If possible, any heavily damaged produce that finds its way from the field to the packinghouse should be removed prior to dumping crops into a wash tank or running them through a wash line. Discarded produce should be placed in containers

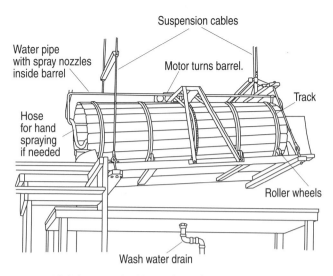

Figure 12.3 Suspended barrel washer

for easy and frequent removal from the packing area to avoid buildup of disease inoculum. Do not throw discards onto the floor or pile them where disease spores can easily disperse.

Packing Lines

Packing lines or sorting tables should be well lighted and provide for a good view of the entire surface of the produce being sorted (figure 12.4). Sorting by visual inspection requires workers to look at dozens, if not hundreds, of items per minute, so improper viewing conditions can result in employee stress and reduced efficiency. Of the many types of light sources available, SP-30 fluorescent lights are a good choice. Although relatively low-cost, SP-30 fluorescent lights offer superior performance compared to other fluorescent bulbs in terms of ability to assist people in seeing colors correctly and thus detecting defects on produce. Light fixtures need to be hung close enough to the sorting surface to provide at least 250 foot-candles of illumination. Darker produce or older workers may require twice that much light for good sorting. To minimize reflection, surfaces under the produce should not be glossy or light colored.

Mechanized packing lines should be designed to avoid vegetable bruising by minimizing height differences between pieces of equipment, reducing the velocity of vegetable movement, and cushioning areas of vegetable impact. The system should frequently be inspected for improper adjustment and loose parts and tested with a

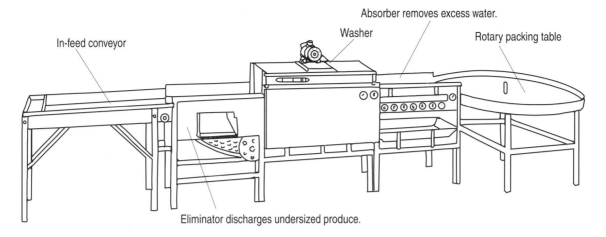

In-feed conveyor

Absorber removes excess water.

Washer

Rotary packing table

Eliminator discharges undersized produce.

Figure 12.4 Vegetable packing line
Source: Adapted from Tew Manufacturing Corp.

croquet ball to provide an audible indication of where vegetable impact may be excessive

Individuals doing the sorting should have as simple a function as possible so that the fewest possible decisions have to be made during sorting. In other words, pulling out culls and separating size grades should not be done by the same individual, at least not at the same time. Specific standards should be utilized for culls, various size and color grades, and container filling. These may be taken from USDA or specific market publications, or established by the grower/marketer. Quality-control checks should be performed to make sure standards are being followed. Consistency of product is required by wholesale buyers and is expected by most consumers. During packing, uniformity of color and size should be the goal.

Storage

Storage is the final postharvest consideration prior to transportation off the farm. The goal of storage is to delay changes in the crop that cause deterioration, such as decay, water loss, and loss of flavor components. Effective storage is accomplished primarily by lowering temperature and raising humidity, although modified atmosphere and fungicides are also used by larger operations.

Crops vary in their requirements for storage temperature and humidity. Separate walk-in coolers may be needed to optimize the shelf life of vegetables stored on the farm. Many vegetables

store well at a few degrees above freezing, while another large group will suffer from chilling injury at that temperature and must not be stored below 50°F to optimize quality. Sidebar 12.1 shows how a farm with two coolers might plan to store crops.

Sidebar 12.1 Sample Vegetable Storage on a Farm with Two Coolers

Cooler #1 (at 32° F)	Cooler #2 (at 50° F)
asparagus	beans, green
beets	cucumbers
carrots	eggplant
crucifers	peppers, sweet
lettuce	potatoes
muskmelons, ripe	pumpkins
onions	summer squash
parsley	tomatoes, firm ripe
parsnips	watermelons
peas, green	winter squash
radishes	
spinach	
sweet corn	
turnips	

Source: Adapted from Hardenburg, Watada, and Wang, 1986

Vegetable Yields

Vegetable yields vary widely and are hard to predict. As a result, the most useful yield data is generated by on-farm record keeping. However, table 12.1 provides some estimates that may be helpful to growers planning new crop enterprises. These figures are "average" yields. "Excellent" yields can be significantly higher when weather, pest management, fertility, and other factors are favorable; if unfavorable, yields can be much lower.

Harvest Management— A Grower Profile

Linda Hildebrand and Michael Docter
Food Bank Farm, Hadley, Massachusetts
Food Bank Farm is located on 60 acres of river bottom along the Connecticut River, with 40 acres in crops and cover crops. It is a unique organization that is a project of the Western Mass Food Bank. The farm is one of the largest CSAs in the country, with over 400 shareholders. In addition, half the produce raised on the farm is donated to the Food Bank, which provides food to agencies that serve people in need. The farm is financially self-sustaining. Income from shareholders pays for the entire operation of the farm, including the cost of the donated food. Roughly eighty different crops are grown. Organic practices are used; however, the farm is not certified since Linda Hildebrand and Michael Docter have a direct relationship with customers that know the farm well. (For specifics about the CSA management and production practices on this farm see references for this chapter, page 262.)

Together, Linda Hildebrand and Michael Docter manage the farm. Linda has farmed her whole life, having grown up on a truck farm in southeastern Massachusetts. Michael started the Food Bank Farm in 1989. Before that, he worked in community economic development in several large cities.

Because the farm is a CSA, the harvest systems have to meet the specific needs of the members,

Table 12.1 Average fresh market vegetable yields

| Vegetable | Average Yield in Pounds per Acre | | |
	New England	Michigan	United States
asparagus	2,900	2,000	2,700
beans, snap	5,100	8,000	4,800
broccoli	15,200	8,000	11,200
Brussels sprouts	—	10,000	17,000
cabbage	40,300	30,000	32,500
carrots	28,000	26,000	28,500
cauliflower	15,900	14,000	12,600
celery	50,000	60,000	61,800
cucumbers	14,500	20,000	16,300
eggplant	27,600	20,000	22,700
escarole/ endive	16,100	30,000	14,400
leeks	—	16,000	—
garlic	—	—	16,500
lettuce, head	21,000	40,000	32,000
lettuce, leaf	—	24,000	22,000
lettuce, romaine	—	36,000	27,800
muskmelons	15,200	16,000	18,600
onion, dry	31,000	40,000	38,900
parsnip	12,600	20,000	—
pea, snap	3,000	6,000	—
pepper, bell	14,400	20,000	22,300
potato, Irish	27,500	34,000	33,200
spinach	15,800	12,000	11,900
squash, summer	11,000	30,000	—
squash, winter	20,600	30,000	—
sweet corn	8,500	16,000	9,500
sweet potato	—	14,000	15,000
tomato	22,100	30,000	26,300
watermelon	11,000	20,000	19,200

Sources: Adapted from Ferro, 1998; Maynard and Hochmuth, 1997; and Zandstra and Price, 1988

Sustainable Vegetable Production from Start-Up to Market

namely, a steady supply of a wide range of produce. In 1997, a crew of five people (including Linda and Michael) harvested a total of 350,000 pounds of produce from the 40 acres, half of which was donated. Same-day, on-farm distribution eliminates the need for packaging, bunching, or refrigeration. "Harvesting efficiency is maximized by the well-organized growing and distribution systems we have developed," says Linda. "You have to think about harvest efficiency long before you actually get out there and harvest anything."

There are several issues Linda and Michael consider key to harvest management:

Field Layout. Heavy crops such as cabbage and melons are planted next to a road. Fields are divided into blocks based on harvest frequency. With crops that are harvested three times per week, such as peppers or eggplant, the blocks are set up to fill a single week's need. According to Linda, "A field is often divided into smaller blocks, each representing a single day's harvest. For instance, there are Monday, Wednesday, and Friday blocks for many crops." To enhance harvest efficiency, alleys are strategically placed where harvest buckets can be picked up with a minimum of hand-carrying.

"Planting crops in short blocks of multiple beds rather than single long rows reduces the distance someone has to travel while harvesting. It may take a little more planning while seeding, but it saves on movement while harvesting crops that are grown in small quantity. Crops that are grown in large quantity, such as brassicas, are planted two rows at a time so they can be harvested together. Corn is planted in four-row increments, so that three people can harvest efficiently. Two people just pick, while the third person picks a little but primarily moves buckets as the others pick and toss into a bucket. When all the buckets are filled they are dragged four rows out to the nearby road to be put on the truck. The 'road' is the previous week's corn that has been mowed. They can pick 40 bushels an hour this way."

Weed management. If fields are kept weed-free, there is no time spent hunting for the crop. The

Food Bank Farm employs a number of mechanical cultivation systems that are simple, effective, inexpensive, and well-suited to a diversified vegetable operation. For example, old Farmall Cubs with belly-mounted baskets or shovels are used in many crops, and a hand-held flame-weeder is used prior to emergence of some small-seeded crops to reduce in-row weed pressure.

Planting intervals. Consistent seeding and transplanting intervals are key to supplying sufficient quality and quantity of vegetables to meet market needs. Ongoing planting tends to result in some overproduction, but the Food Bank takes their surplus. With new plantings always coming on, they avoid recutting crops like greens, and as soon as quality or yield starts to deteriorate the crop can be plowed in. "If you spend too much time looking for the few good fruit left in the field, efficiency is reduced. Turning under crops before they go downhill also helps reduce disease pressure."

Corn is planted every time the previous planting reaches the spike stage, and three varieties with different maturity dates are always planted. Beans are planted again when the last planting "shoulders," or the young plants start to hook. Lettuce and greens are planted every week. Annual culinary herbs are planted every two weeks. Carrots and beets are planted every two to three weeks.

Proper equipment. "Harvest knives, especially lettuce knives with two edges, are used on a lot of crops, and these are kept sharp—there's a sharpener in the truck all the time. Clippers are used for eggplant and small paring knives for zucchini. White 5-gallon buckets are used to collect a lot of the crops, like tomatoes, pepper, eggplant, carrots, and beets. Two-bushel red harvest buckets with handles and round bottoms are used for heavier and bulkier crops like cabbage, broccoli, greens, and lettuce. These can be used like sleds, sliding them along the rows, and later as a sink; they go right into a washing area where they are filled up with water instead of transferring produce to a sink. This reduces handling and bruising."

Preharvest preparations. "The day before harvest, someone spends a few minutes throwing buckets into the field from the back of the pickup. Buckets are spaced at increments where they are likely to be needed for harvest the next day. The next morning there is no walking to get harvest containers. Having enough buckets is a key to efficiency. Before the crew arrives, the harvest manager has a harvest sheet prepared so everyone will know exactly what needs to be harvested that day."

Sequence of harvesting. Crops are harvested six days a week. On the three CSA pickup days, the goal is to provide the members with the highest quality food possible. The most perishable crops are harvested that morning. On the other three days, harvest is primarily for the food bank, and less-perishable crops such as beets and carrots are also picked for the CSA. Tomatoes are also harvested a day ahead so they can be sorted. Before the sun is up, the crew tries to have the corn, greens, and lettuce in the washing area. This reduces field heat, directly affecting shelf life and quality. Next, they will pick larger greens and broccoli while it's still fairly early and things are still cool. Summer squash, peppers, and eggplant are saved for the warmer part of the morning when the plants are completely dry. "We try to have everything organized so that everything is in by noon, since pickup starts at 2:00."

The crew starts in the newer section of the field and moves into the older sections only as needed. That maximizes the quality of harvested crops and minimizes the spread of disease.

Washing. "Removing field heat is the main reason we wash, because generally things aren't that dirty, except after a heavy rain." Some crops don't get washed—such as spinach, basil and summer squash—because they tend to hold better if they remain dry. "Good drainage after washing is critical. We put certain crops like greens into wicker baskets so the water drains away freely." Perishable produce is then covered with wet burlap and baskets are placed on the concrete floor of the barn to keep cool until ready for distribution. No refrigeration is used on the farm. Members pick up their produce at the farm on the same day it was picked.

Specific crop techniques. Carrot harvest begins with removing the tops. The crew goes through and pulls the tops off by hand. Then the tractor goes through with a bed lifter to loosen the carrots. To collect them, two people work side-by-side and fill 5-gallon buckets already in place. These get filled in about one minute each, every 4 to 6 feet of a double-row bed. The buckets don't move very far at all.

Lettuce is cut with a sharp knife. The use of upright varieties like Batavian, Romaine, and Oak-leaf types saves time and reduces the need for cleaning. Some crew members drag the 2-bushel harvest buckets along by putting a leg through the cord handle and dragging it down the row. It takes about two minutes to fill a bucket. Each crew member can harvest 360 pounds of leaf lettuce, or 36 bushels, in about half an hour, including getting it into the washing area. Linda and Michael do not let the lettuce get full size, but pick "adolescent" lettuce about 6 to 8 inches high.

Cukes and summer squash are picked every other day, with two people per row, so this reduces misses. On the Friday harvest they pick them smaller than usual so there are no great big ones by Monday. People wear socks on their arms to protect them from the spiny vines, and there's a lot less scratching that way. A new planting every three weeks makes picking easier by keeping yields up.

> *"The key part of crew management is that the two farm managers are an integral part of the crew: we set the pace, and we create the atmosphere. We try to be very organized. We work with apprentices who really want to be there and learn from the experience. Speed, efficiency, and quality are the focus; and the myriad of crops makes the work more interesting."*

Herbs are all treated like greens or lettuce— no bunching, just planted thick enough to be cut and put in bushel buckets. Peas are trellised, so tall-growing varieties are grown. The stake and weave system is used, as with tomatoes. Peas, beans, many of the herbs, such as basil, and Roma and cherry tomatoes, all of which are labor intensive, are not typically picked by the crew but instead are available for unlimited U-pick for shareholders, which they seem to enjoy. "In fact, the U-pick crops are a very significant part of the farm for CSA members," Linda says.

Several varieties of tomatoes with different maturity dates are planted, so they are coming in constantly from the second week of July through September. These are all trellised using the stake and weave system. A stake is driven in the ground every two plants and poly twine wrapped around the stakes every 8 or 10 inches in height. The fruits are picked into 5-gallon buckets that are filled only halfway to avoid bruising. Two rows at a time are picked, with each picker only doing the side facing the alley that he or she is in.

"The fastest picker starts in the middle of the block. When her bucket is full she hands it over into the next row. When the picker next to her reaches this bucket, he hands his and hers over to the row toward the outside of the block. Eventually all the buckets end up by the road, ready to be picked up."

On an average day, 5,000 pounds of produce is brought in by noon by five people working for seven hours each. That works out to nearly 145 pounds per hour per person.

Crew management. "The key part of crew management is that the two farm managers are an integral part of the crew: we set the pace, and we create the atmosphere. We try to be very organized. We work with apprentices who really want to be there and learn from the experience. Speed, efficiency, and quality are the focus; and the myriad of crops makes the work more interesting. The best part of all is a swim in the river after harvest."

Each crew person has done each job at least once, so they have an understanding of the whole process and can gain proficiency in one area. For example, one person directs washing and weighing and may do this three days a week. Linda and Michael try to develop routines, so the crew has a sense of what's next and can take initiative and develop job satisfaction. Linda is always trying to break down a task and analyze the various steps, so that precise instructions can be given. "Being aware of how I communicate is important so people understand what I'm telling them. We work closely with people; nobody works on their own. Even when someone knows what they are doing, I often go back and fine tune with some suggestions. We have a pretty good crew retention rate. We try to work with people who want to become farmers on their own. I think we are giving them a really good training and a good feel for farming. I'm not just directing people, hopefully I'm teaching, too. That's why I want people to take on some responsibility. We do have a good time, but being out there is about getting the job done."

Chapter 13

Season Extension

The vast majority of commercial growers in the Northeast use techniques to protect crops from cold temperatures in order to lengthen the period of time that fresh vegetables can be harvested and marketed. Such "season extension" is accomplished largely by modifying the crop's immediate environment using structures such as greenhouses, high tunnels, and cold frames; or materials such as plastic mulches and row covers. Plastic mulches and row covers raise daytime soil or air temperatures near the plant without providing the level of frost protection provided by protected structures (table 13.1).

Cultural Practices That Speed Crop Growth

Cultural practices that speed crop development are important to optimizing production in a short growing season without providing any season extension per se. Such practices include using raised beds, using transplants instead of direct-seeding, pre-sprouting vegetatively propagated crops such as potatoes, and pre-germination or priming of seeds. Also see chapter 10, "Seeds and Transplants," beginning on page 96.

Raised Beds
Raised beds can speed crop growth by improving drainage of the root zone and enhancing soil warming. By enhancing water drainage and increasing the soil surface area exposed to warm air, raised beds allow soils to be more readily warmed than they would be in flat fields early in the spring. This technique is more applicable to heavy soils than to sandy soils that tend to drain and warm up quickly in the spring.

Green-Sprouting and Seed Priming
Green-sprouting is a method used with Irish potatoes in an effort to get early, "new" potatoes that fetch a premium price. Green-sprouting is a process of promoting sprout formation in the greenhouse or hotbed prior to setting tubers in the ground. Seed priming uses the same approach by adding moisture to seeds so as to speed germination, usually prior to applying a seed coat. Priming is a special service offered by seed companies. It can enhance the performance of species such as parsley and carrots that germinate poorly in cold soils, and it may be used in conjunction with precision seeding methods in an effort to obtain uniform stands.

Table 13.1 Advantages and drawbacks of season extension tools

Tool	Advantages	Drawbacks
Double poly greenhouse, heated	Long growing season; has environmental controls	High initial expense; high utility cost to operate
Single poly high tunnel, unheated	Lower cost than greenhouse; extends growing season about one month	Minimal frost protection
Cold frames	Hardening-off transplants	Limited volume restricts uses
Solid row covers	Enhance early growth in field	Can overheat; require hoops
Floating row covers	Enhance growth in field; exclude insect pests	Must be removed for pollination; may tear in wind
Plastic mulches	Enhance early yield; easy to apply	Annual removal and disposal cost

Greenhouses

Greenhouses are the most effective—and expensive—form of microclimate modification, offering the potential for year-round plant production. For practical purposes, greenhouses are not often in production in midwinter, since heating costs are high and supplemental light is required for good growth of most crops. However, if low-cost heating fuel and electricity are available, the economics of winter greenhouse production for high-value crops may be worth investigating.

Closing down greenhouses for the winter offers several benefits. It allows time to review the previous year's production and plan for the upcoming year, and it facilitates pest control through complete removal of vegetation and subsequent exposure to extreme cold and, in some cases, heat. By sealing up a greenhouse during a sunny period and heating it up for several consecutive days or weeks, growers can kill overwintering insects in the greenhouse that will emerge and die of starvation or desiccation. Greenhouses kept in year-round operation tend to have more severe pest pressure than those that are "fallowed."

Currently, many vegetable growers utilize greenhouses for producing field transplants, bedding plants, ornamentals, or greenhouse vegetables. Although some growers produce field vegetables only from seed, this is increasingly rare in the Northeast. Transplant production is necessary to get a jump on the season and capture early markets and higher prices, while bedding plants are growing in popularity on vegetable farms as a way to increase early-season cash flow. As a source of earlier, premium-quality crops, greenhouse vegetable production is also on the rise.

Tomatoes make up the majority of greenhouse vegetable production due to the quality and yield of the crop, strong consumer demand, effective production methods, appropriate cultivars, and good utilization of greenhouse space because the crop can be grown upright. Some greenhouse cucumbers are also grown, but market demand is weaker. Lettuce, peppers, and greens are also greenhouse-grown; but they are more sensitive to high temperatures, and their low growth habit makes poor use of available greenhouse volume.

Scheduling Greenhouse Use

In northern areas, greenhouses are generally planted in February or March, although some growers start earlier, and others later, depending on location, markets, fuel costs, and growers' desire to take some time off in the winter. When it's quite cold outside, a single small greenhouse or a small section within a large greenhouse may be used as a germination house to minimize the energy consumed for heat and light.

In addition to scheduling greenhouse production to provide timely transplants for field setting, growers must consider their marketing plans in deciding when to start up the greenhouse. For example, growers who have roadside stands need to start production of bedding plants in time to assure that the stands are well-stocked for their opening date. Stands that open early in the season can also reap high prices for early greenhouse-grown crops when fresh local vegetables are scarce. In areas with large summer populations, peak demand for produce occurs later, and growers who sell to summer visitors through roadside stands may not find it profitable to start bedding plants as early as growers who sell primarily to permanent residents. Wholesale markets call for a consistent supply during as much of the year as possible, leading some growers to spend a lot on early-season or winter production in order to keep their markets satisfied.

Greenhouse Structures and Equipment

Greenhouse structures vary considerably. They may have wooden or metal frames; soil, gravel, or concrete floors; and a variety of heating and cooling systems. They may be attached to another structure such as a barn, or freestanding Quonset, gothic, gable roof, or gutter-connected structures (figure 13.1, page 132). Figure 13.2 (page 133) illustrates steel-tube greenhouse frame construction. A typical, fully equipped, market-garden vegetable greenhouse is a 24- to 32-foot-wide Quonset or gothic-shaped hoop structure with two layers of inflated clear plastic covering and solid end-walls. It may be any length, although 96 feet is common in order to accommodate 100-foot-wide rolls of plastic covering. In areas of heavy snowfall, a peaked roof (Gothic-style) structure is advisable to facilitate shedding of snow and slush. Larger greenhouse "ranges" of gutter-connected houses may cover several acres.

Greenhouses require permanent heating systems, usually natural gas, propane, oil, or wood-fired, with either forced-air or hot-water heat distribution systems. Ventilation systems are either mechanical fan driven or natural systems that depend on temperature differences between inside and outside or on wind. To minimize operating costs, natural systems are desirable, but their effective operation requires wind dependability. Electricity and water-supply systems are necessary. Optional features include horizontal airflow fans (for internal air movement), soil heating systems, temperature alarms, automated irrigation, thermal screens, mechanized materials-handling systems such as rolling benches or harvest carts, and computerized environmental control systems.

Effective management and maintenance of environmental control systems are essential to good crop performance in greenhouses. Temperature and soil moisture must be kept within desired ranges to optimize plant growth. Humidity must be kept low enough to prevent development of foliar diseases. Heating systems must be designed and operated to prevent accumulation of combustion by-products in the greenhouse that cause problems with plant growth or quality.

In addition to the growing structure, a headhouse attached to or near the greenhouse is needed for storing tools, seeds, fertilizers, pesticides, references, and records. The appropriate level of investment in a greenhouse is related to the potential profitability of a crop. *Greenhouse Engineering,* NRAES–33, by Aldrich and Bartok (listed in the references for this chapter, page 262) lists construction costs ranging from $1.50–$2.25 per square foot for simple poly-covered wood structures to $10.00–$13.00 per square foot for a glass greenhouse with a concrete foundation. To build a fully automated greenhouse can cost $20.00 per square foot.

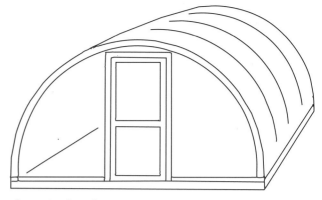

a. Quonset or hoop house

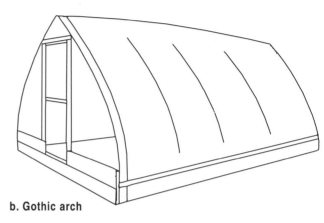

b. Gothic arch

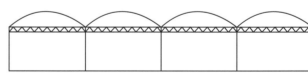

c. Gable roof

d. Gutter-connected greenhouses

Figure 13.1 Greenhouse structures

In addition to greenhouses, many growers use less-expensive high tunnels, cold frames, or row covers to meet the season-extension needs of their various crops and markets. A common practice is to have a small greenhouse for starting all seedlings, which is the first to be heated and perhaps lighted. Bedding plants and transplants are then moved from plug trays into larger-volume growing containers, and these are transferred to more greenhouses or high tunnels if the weather has

Sustainable Vegetable Production from Start-Up to Market

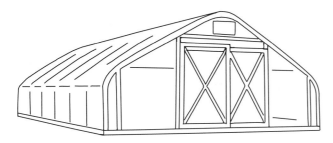

a. Exterior

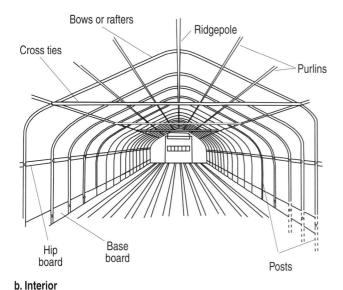

Bows or rafters

Cross ties

Ridgepole

Purlins

Hip board

Base board

Posts

b. Interior

Figure 13.2 Steel-tube greenhouse frame construction
Source: Adapted from Ledgewood Farm Greenhouse Frames

warmed sufficiently. Some may be transferred to cold frames for hardening-off before field setting. After starting seedlings, greenhouses or high tunnels may be planted to later-season, high-value vegetable or flower crops.

High Tunnels

High tunnels are simple, greenhouse-like structures that provide less control of environmental conditions than full greenhouses, at substantially less cost (figure 13.3, page 134). They are usually covered with a single layer of plastic and are ventilated only through roll-up sides. To protect against snow load damage to the structure, 2 x 4s can be placed under the peak; or the plastic covering can be removed each winter.

A typical high tunnel may not have a heating system. In colder areas prone to late freezes, or when growers start earlier in the season, a vented heating system is required. Unvented heating systems are not recommended because unvented combustion products, which tend to use up the oxygen in the growing area, can be harmful to the crop and potentially dangerous to humans.

Drip irrigation is usually used in high tunnels, and black plastic mulch or landscape fabric is often laid on the ground inside. The production system may be in-ground culture, or pots or trays may be placed on the ground or on benches.

High tunnel hoops are usually spaced 4 feet apart. Narrow widths of buildings, 14 feet or so, lend themselves well to natural ventilation systems using roll-up sides. Tunnels and greenhouses with vertical sides that go straight up before curving provide better side-to-side ventilation and allow for better use of growing space along the edges and reduce the need for crouching when working inside. For wider tunnels and greenhouses and for those located in areas where summer winds are not predictable, mechanical fan ventilation and shading may be required. High tunnels are commonly sold in units 48 or 96 feet long, but they can be of any length. The cost of a 14-by-96 unit with single poly, roll-up sides and including endwalls and doors, drip tape, and plastic mulch is about $2,000 to $3,000, depending on construction material and whether a heater is used, among other factors.

Tomato production is common in high tunnels. However, other vegetables, such as peppers, summer squash, greens, and cucumbers, as well as flowers, herbs, and strawberries, can be grown in tunnels, too. Upright crops benefit from staking or climbing on a trellis structure to enhance quality and make good use of space.

Cold Frames

Cold frames are used primarily to protect transplants from early spring freezes and to harden or hold transplants. They are low structures, usually no more than 2 or 3 feet in height (figure 13.4, page 135). They offer less protection against cold nights than bigger structures that enclose more soil and a greater volume of air. Supplemental heating, which can be provided by a deep layer of

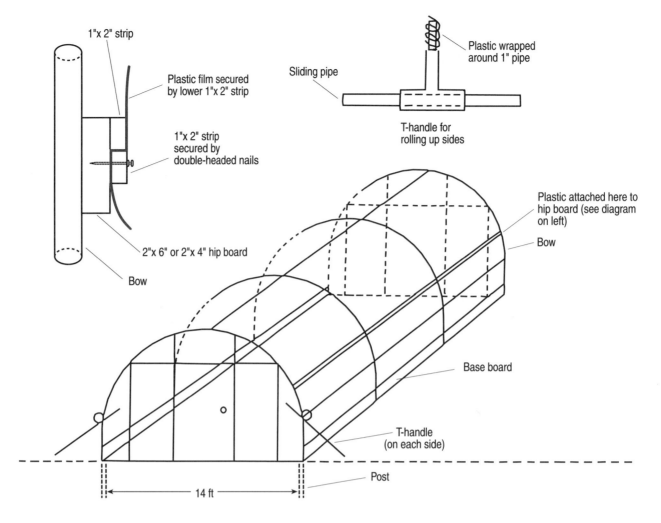

1"x 2" strip

**Plastic film secured
by lower 1"x 2" strip**

**1"x 2" strip
secured by
double-headed nails**

2"x 6" or 2"x 4" hip board

Bow

Sliding pipe

**Plastic wrapped
around 1" pipe**

**T-handle for
rolling up sides**

**Plastic attached here to
hip board (see diagram
on left)**

Bow

Base board

**T-handle
(on each side)**

Post

14 ft

Figure 13.3 High tunnel with roll-up sides
Source: Adapted from Wells, 1991; detail of hip board incorporates suggestions from William J. Roberts, Rutgers University.

fresh manure or by electricity, turns cold frames into cold frames into hotbeds, which were widely used in horticulture a century ago. Some contemporary farms with roadside markets find cold frames useful for displaying as well as hardening-off plants early in the season, once they no longer require greenhouse conditions. Cold frames can also be used at the end of the growing season to display harvested crops like pumpkins or potted mums and to protect them from cold temperatures at night.

Row Covers

Row covers are blanket-like sheets of material, which may be solid, slitted, or perforated plastic; or "breathable" spunbonded or woven polyester, polypropylene, or other synthetic materials (table 13.2). Row covers made of breathable, lightweight materials are often called floating row covers, since they can be laid directly on top of many crops without any supports. There are some

natural-material floating row covers, but these tend to be expensive.

Floating row covers are available in large sheets that can cover a wide section of field, or in rolls that are used to cover individual crop rows. Unlike the lighter-weight floating covers, plastic covers generally come only in rolls and require hoops or other supports to keep their weight off the crop. Plastic covers also need ventilation to avoid overheating the crop—by either slits, holes, or daily uncovering. Plastic covers are more likely to overheat on sunny, warm days, especially when used in combination with black plastic mulch.

Medium-thickness, woven or spunbonded row-cover materials are used primarily to enhance crop growth, and they may raise the daytime air temperature around plants by 10°F or more over ambient temperature. These row covers are very

Sustainable Vegetable Production from Start-Up to Market

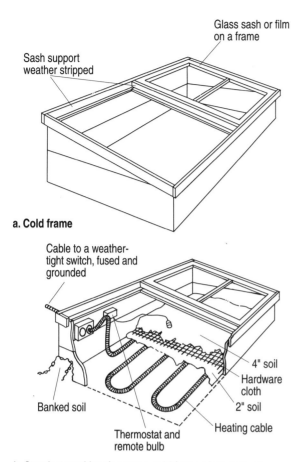

Glass sash or film on a frame

Sash support weather stripped

a. Cold frame

Cable to a weather-tight switch, fused and grounded

Banked soil

Thermostat and remote bulb

4" soil

Hardware cloth

2" soil

Heating cable

b. Supplemental heating turns cold frames into hotbeds.

Figure 13.4 Cold frames

effective for early- and late-season extension of cool-season crops such as lettuce, cole crops, and onions. They can also dramatically promote early-season growth of heat-loving crops such as melons.

The higher the temperature increase under a row cover, the faster a crop tends to grow; however, excessive heat can harm fruit production, especially with temperature-sensitive crops, such as melons and peppers. Thickness of material is an important consideration when selecting a floating row cover. Thicker materials are more durable and will stand up better to handling, strong winds, and reuse. Thicker covers also tend to hold in heat at night better than thin covers. Thinner row covers are less expensive, however, and are suited for exclusion of insects with less effect on growing temperatures. The thickest row covers are used primarily for frost protection.

Row covers allow light and water to pass through to varying degrees, although thicker materials reduce light penetration somewhat more. When covers flap in the wind, they can damage the growing points of crops like tomatoes and peppers, so support hoops are often placed over these crops. To keep covers in place, it is essential to secure any row cover firmly by covering all edges with soil or rocks. Careful handling of the covers during application and removal is necessary if

Table 13.2 Examples of row-cover attributes

Material and Method	Thickness or Weight	Dimensions (in feet)	Primary Use	Cost (per acre)
Solid polyethylene on row hoops	1.1 mil	6 x 1,000	Growth	$537
Slitted polyethylene on row hoops	1.1 mil	6 x 1,000	Growth	$566
Perforated polyethylene on row hoops	1.1 mil	6 x 1,000	Growth	$566
Spunbonded polyester on rows	0.6 ounces per square yard	5.6 x 2,550	Growth	$872
Floating spunbonded polyester	0.6 ounces per square yard	50 x 500	Growth	$1,085
Floating spunbonded polypropylene	1.25 ounces per square yard	15.5 x 300	Growth	$1,833
Floating spunbonded polypropylene	0.3 ounces per square yard	8.5 x 1,640	Insect control	$936
Floating spunbonded polypropylene	1.76 ounces per square yard	21.3 x 820	Frost control	$1,618

Source: Adapted from Wells, 1996

they are to be reused, as is storage that protects them from mice, degradation by sunlight, and other damage. Special equipment is available to assist with rolling up covers after a season's use.

Plastic Mulches

Plastic mulches raise soil temperature, promoting root and crop growth and thus enhancing earliness. Clear plastic is the warmest, but it does not suppress weed growth. Black plastic suppresses weeds effectively, avoiding the need to apply herbicides under the plastic. Black plastic mulch is not as warm as clear, however, and heats soil even less if it is not laid flat and tight. Recent research suggests that red plastic mulch may be very effective at promoting growth of crops such as tomato.

Selective wavelength mulches such as IRT (infrared transmitting) are intermediate in both their weed-suppression ability and the degree to which they warm the soil. While selective wavelength mulches are more expensive than black or clear plastic, some growers find they are worth the expense for high-value, heat-loving crops, such as melons.

Plastic mulch layers (figure 13.5) are necessary equipment for laying plastic straight, flat, and fast. Pan-type units have a press pan that smooths and levels the soil before laying the plastic on flat ground. Frame-type units can place plastic over wire hoops for tunnels, or on top of raised beds. Raised-bed mulch layers gather soil, form the raised bed, then apply the plastic in one pass. See figure 9.10, page 93, for a more expensive bed shaper that can also lay drip tape under the mulch.

Plastic mulches must be removed from the field and disposed of annually. Plastic mulch lifters (figure 13.6) can be used to assist with mulch removal. Incomplete removal of mulch can create a mess of plastic pieces on your land and perhaps your neighbor's. Given the labor involved and the cost of disposal, *photodegradable mulches* have some appeal. They break down slowly over the growing season, ideally leaving only plastic edges that were buried under soil and other small pieces of plastic. The degradable mulch formulation,

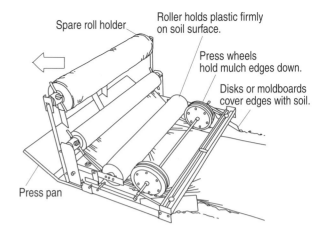

a. Press-pan type lays mulch on flat ground.

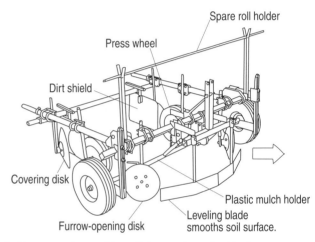

b. Frame type lays mulch on flat ground or raised beds or over wire hoops.

Figure 13.5 Plastic mulch layers
Source: Adapted from Mechanical Transplanter Co.

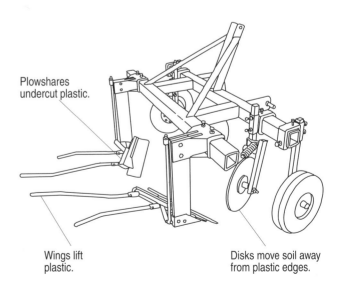

Figure 13.6 Plastic mulch lifter
Source: Adapted from Rain-Flo Irrigation

environmental conditions, and extent of canopy cover influence how quickly a photodegradable mulch breaks down; and that breakdown may be faster or slower than desired.

Emergency Frost Protection

Emergency frost protection refers to short-term methods for protecting crops in the field against a night of freezing or chilling temperatures. Heavy-weight row covers, or "freeze blankets," can be used, as can individual containers, such as inverted buckets or other containers, placed over plants. Such covers must be removed during the day, which requires a lot of labor in large plantings.

Sprinkler irrigating with low rates of water during a frosty night can protect plants from injury. This technique is widespread with strawberries in order to protect early flowers from late frosts. It can be used on vegetables in early spring or late fall as well. Irrigation can be applied over row covers, although these may need to be removed soon after to promote drying of foliage. Normally, irrigation is started when the temperature at crop level drops to 34°F, but if the dew point is below freezing, irrigation should commence at higher temperatures to avoid damaging plants.

Sprinkler irrigation for frost protection requires a reliable irrigation system and low-rate frost nozzles (about 0.15 inches per hour) to avoid drowning the plants. It works best in the case of frost on calm, clear nights when heat is lost from the earth's surface. It does not work well when a convectional freeze is caused by cold front passing through with high winds and a dew point below freezing.

Improper management of irrigation for frost protection can severely damage crops, since evaporative cooling can occur. Once the water is started, it should not be stopped until all ice is gone. If wind speed is over 10 mph, the irrigation pipes should be moved in closer, from 60- to 40-foot centers, to assure even distribution; and double the volume of water applied. If you cannot be sure of an adequate, evenly distributed volume of water, the risks of sprinkler irrigation for frost protection may outweigh the benefit.

Optimizing Investment in Greenhouses— A Grower Profile

Ed Person
Ledgewood Farm
Moultonborough, New Hampshire
The farm has been in Ed Person's family since 1947. There are 22 acres of fields and sixteen greenhouses and high tunnels containing various vegetables and flowers. The farm has soils of many types, divided roughly in thirds among light-textured soils that warm up earlier, loamy soils, and heavy soils that hold moisture well throughout the season. Almost all the crops are marketed through two roadside stands, with a little wholesaling that has been diminishing in recent years. Ed is planning to eliminate all wholesaling soon in order to free up some more land for a better cover crop rotation. "It's not worth that extra ten or twelve thousand dollars gross to tie up so much land that could be in soil-improving crops."

"Our season-extension structures include six 14 by 96 unheated tunnels for vegetables, a 14 by 48 cut-flower tunnel, three 21 by 96 and two 28 by 60 greenhouses for bedding plants, and four 19 by 96 greenhouses for tomato production. All these structures—and I'm really short on space this year! We started with season extension in the late 60s, using slitted row covers, and that didn't work so well since we had trouble keeping them down; so we made some 14-foot-wide by 3-foot-high 'pens' as we called them. We started growing every warm-season crop in these that you can think of. We had a couple of old glass houses growing tomatoes and bedding plants, too, and as the farm matured, so to speak, the number and volume of protected crops kept growing. Our growing season is geared to a summer tourist market—from June 20 to Labor Day basically, so we have to have heated greenhouses of tomatoes. Now I have four of them and only one high tunnel of tomatoes since these come in later. In other high tunnels we still grow our summer squash, zucchini, cucumbers, 'Jingle Bell' mini peppers, cut flowers, and even strawberries. A lot of other people also grow mixed greens in tunnels."

"You have to be sure the crop is valuable enough to justify the square footage cost of a structure, and the list is endless where that is true for high tunnels on our farm, except for eggplant and melons.

"Your markets determine what structure to build. If you have a market that doesn't start until mid-July and ends in mid-September, you're foolish to do anything but a high tunnel. Greenhouse structures are also defined by how many months you are going to use them to supply your market. If you start planting the first of April and shut down in November, then a simple unit heater and a small exhaust fan are sufficient; you don't need a real high-tech, expensive structure. If you are going to start growing in mid-February, then it is advisable to spend the money necessary to get the environmental control you'll need."

"In 1987 I bought a greenhouse, and it fell down the next year and was too expensive to replace, so I bought a pipe bender instead and made my own structure. Then a friend wanted a structure, too, and then another; and since then it's turned into a separate business that is actually more valuable than the farming is. It works out well because it's busy from October to Thanksgiving, then in the spring it's done by the first of May. So with the vegetable production, the only month that is really hectic is April, when it's busy on all fronts: field work, greenhouse growing, and sales of structures, but that only lasts for four to five weeks; then it slows up."

"Sometimes it's worth investing in expensive technology, and you wonder how you ever did without an item. In most cases I look for least cost for the value. For example, I buy the least expensive greenhouse exhaust fan I can find, which costs about $300, versus $700 for a name brand one. And even though it costs about $20 or $30 more per year to operate because it's less efficient, it keeps $400 more in my pocket to operate with. On the other hand, I've gone to trough benches

for irrigating all my bedding plants. These allow water to flow through them in a continuous fashion. They cost a lot—between $2 and $3 per square foot, or about $3,000 in an average-size house, but it is saving us $1,000 to $1,500 per year per greenhouse in labor for watering the plants. Now that labor can do something more productive than just watch the water come out of a hose. So the payback is in two years—even less if you consider that a rudimentary bench of wood and wire costs about $1 per square foot. But the biggest thing about this technology is the quality of the crop, because they get perfectly watered. The soil knows how much it needs to take up, and the pots dry from the top down, so that helps with pest control since the surface is not moist all the time. The whole root system is evenly watered, and the roots fill the pots and are drawn down to the bottom as they follow the drainage pattern of the water.

"Your markets determine what structure to build. If you have a market that doesn't start until mid-July and ends in mid-September, you're foolish to do anything but a high tunnel."

"Another example where it's worth investing in expensive equipment is a good thermostat: if a cheaper one is off by a few degrees, that can waste a lot of fuel. Buying a better grade plastic for your greenhouse covering is also worthwhile—an infrared versus a regular three-year plastic improves light diffusion and heat retention. Spending some extra money to accommodate future expansion is important. A lot of people are buying larger high tunnels, 17- or 19-foot-wide instead of 14-footers, because the extra size and air volume allow for putting in a permanent heater down the road and make it easier to circulate the heat as well as to ventilate. So if you are going to use this thing for twenty years, and you are looking at spending $1,600 versus $1,000, it may seem like a lot more up front, but it is well worth it over time. I'm not afraid to spend money as long as it is not going to waste."

Chapter 14

Integrated Pest Management

Integrated pest management (IPM) is an information-intensive approach to pest control. Ideally, IPM considers and applies a broad range of strategies to optimize management of pests. The goal of IPM is to effectively protect crops by combining biological, cultural, physical, and chemical tools in a way that minimizes economic, health, and environmental risks. The driving force behind IPM is the desire to reduce pesticide applications while maximizing profitability. However, in some cases IPM may increase pesticide applications. For example, a selective material (with fewer nontarget impacts) may be sprayed more often than a broad-spectrum pesticide in order to be effective.

Reasons for Practicing IPM

Organic as well as conventional growers practice IPM for many reasons, including the following:
1. Improve the cost-effectiveness of pest control.
2. Enhance the ability of natural biological control to occur.
3. Alleviate public concern about agricultural practices.
4. Minimize pesticide residues on crops.
5. Avoid development of pesticide-resistant pests.
6. Reduce applicator and farm worker exposure to pesticides.

Principles of IPM and ICM

IPM is a flexible management approach that accommodates personal preferences in terms of the types of materials and strategies used. IPM programs have the following fundamental principles in common:
1. Utilize nonchemical practices that minimize or prevent pest pressure.
2. Systematically monitor pest populations and/or environmental conditions.
3. Use pesticides only when a pest population and/or environmental parameter exceeds an economic threshold.

Initially, IPM focused primarily on insect management, rather than management of diseases, weeds, or wildlife. However, many IPM practices, such as pest monitoring, environmental monitoring, and pest prevention through crop rotation and sanitation also apply to other categories of pests; and formal IPM programs are increasingly being developed for non-insect pests. Further, management of crop nutrition, soil conditions, and irrigation can have a dramatic influence on crop health and susceptibility to damage by pests. Therefore, IPM is evolving into ICM, *Integrated Crop Management,* a holistic approach to crop management that considers the entire pest complex of a crop as well as non-pest factors that affect crop performance.

This chapter provides an overview of integrated pest management. For additional information, see the chapters on insect management (beginning on page 149), disease management (beginning on page 157), weed management (beginning on page 161), and wildlife management (beginning on page 173).

Cultural Practices for Vegetable IPM

Cultural practices are techniques other than pesticide applications that help to prevent or minimize pest outbreaks. Crop rotation and sanitation are cultural practices fundamental to IPM because they can significantly reduce insect, disease, and weed problems in many crops. Sidebar 14.1 lists key cultural practices for vegetable IPM and their purposes. Cultural practices for insect management include use of row covers, vacuuming, companion planting, trapping-out, and reflective mulches (see "Cultural Practices for Insect Management," pages 150–153). Disease-control cultural practices include arranging plantings to promote air movement and leaf drying, forming raised beds to enhance soil drainage, avoiding working in crops when leaves are wet, using hot-water seed treatment, and planting resistant varieties (see "Cultural Practices for Disease Management," pages 159–160). Composting of manure, mowing alleys and roadways, using mulches, and practicing cultivation are examples of weed-control cultural practices (see "Cultural Practices for Weed Control," pages 162–164).

Pest Identification and Monitoring

Pest identification and monitoring are two related steps at the core of IPM. Knowing that a pest has appeared, and knowing exactly what it is are essential to implementing effective controls. It is easiest to monitor for pests when they can be seen. However, some pests are not visible to the naked eye. In the case of diseases, nematodes, and sometimes mites, identification is usually based on crop symptoms or lab analysis of affected plant parts. Other pests are rarely caught in the act. Nocturnal or transitory pests must often be identified by the damage they leave behind. Once the pest, symptoms of its presence, or the damage it causes are noticed, accurate identification can be accomplished with the aid of books, university and private labs, consultants, and other growers. It's worth taking the time to do the necessary detective work, because without knowing what

Sidebar 14.1 Key Cultural Practices for Vegetable IPM	
Cultural Practice	**Purpose**
Crop rotation	Frequently alter the habitat, type, and timing of food supply available to pests
Sanitation	Remove habitat and inoculum by destroying crop residues, using clean seed and transplants, controlling weeds
Timely tillage and cultivation	Bury pests, reduce overwintering sites, uproot weeds
Crop and variety selection	Grow plants that can resist or tolerate expected pests
Crop timing	Plant or harvest to avoid known peaks in pest pressure
Crop health	Optimize fertility and irrigation to enhance crop's ability to cope with pests
Crop diversification	Plant several crops and/or several varieties to spread risk
Modify crop environment	Suppress specific pest using mulches, row covers, raised beds, and other techniques

you're up against it's not possible to make good management decisions. Similarly, going back to the fields after taking action and assessing subsequent pest populations and crop damage is the only way to determine if the treatment was effective, and if other control measures are required.

Once identified, an understanding of the pest is important to developing effective management strategies. Where does the pest comes from; what promotes its abundance; and at what stage it is most vulnerable to control?

Crop Scouting

Crop scouting means walking through the field—not just around it—and systematically sampling individual plants for the presence of pests or pest damage. *Sampling of plants* to determine the

Sustainable Vegetable Production from Start-Up to Market

presence or absence of pests may be through simple visual inspection, aided by the use of a hand lens to see small pests, such as mites; or a sweep net may be used to catch mobile, camouflaged pests such as leafhopper; or pests such as tarnished plant bug can be shaken from crop foliage onto a white plate. It is important to sample for pests in a manner that is representative of the whole field.

Sampling should cover several areas of each field, not just one corner, and must include enough plants to get an accurate representation of what's happening in the whole crop. However, some pests, such as Colorado potato beetle and cucumber beetle, do concentrate along field edges early in the season and should be scouted for accordingly. A commonly recommended sampling procedure is to walk a "W" pattern through the field and stop at five to ten locations and examine ten plants at each stop (figure 14.1). By counting and recording how many plants have a particular pest problem, an estimate can be made of percent crop infestation, percent crop damage, or average number of insects or lesions per leaf or per plant. This kind of numerical evaluation and record keeping is critical to IPM.

Crop Monitoring

Crop monitoring includes scouting as well as the use of devices that trap insects or measure environmental conditions and predict disease severity. A variety of insect traps can be used to provide a relative measure of pest abundance. They include blacklight traps to attract night-flying pests, and color-based sticky or pan traps to attract insects that are active during the day, such as flea beetles, aphids, and cabbage root maggot fly. Moth pests can be monitored using *pheromone traps* baited with mating "scents" that attract adult males.

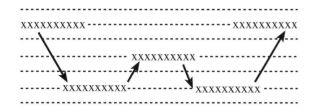

Figure 14.1 Using a "W" pattern to sample fifty plants in a field

Figure 14.2, page 142, shows a wing trap, water pan trap, delta trap, funnel trap, and Heliothis trap, all of which can be fitted with lures that attract specific insect pests. In some cases a pesticide strip is included inside the trap to kill the insects once they enter. Sticky card traps, available in several colors, and light traps attract insects visually. Sometimes traps will attract and catch non-pest species, so it is critical to be able to identify the species you are trying to monitor and distinguish it from non-pest species.

Weeds and diseases can be monitored, too, although not with traps, of course. Having made a weed map that shows the location and relative abundance of various weed species in the field can be helpful when making subsequent herbicide or cultivation choices or deciding which crops to grow in a field. Scouting the field for weeds is particularly useful to detect the arrival of a noxious weed that warrants intensive hand weeding of a small area to prevent it from spreading. Disease scouting that catches the first sign of symptoms can make fungicide applications more effective, since they are primarily intended to protect healthy tissue.

Computer models, such as TOM-CAST for early blight in tomatoes, are being increasingly used to predict disease severity and recommend optimal timing of fungicide applications based on such factors as temperature, rainfall, leaf wetness, and humidity. In some states, cooperative extension maintains weather stations and supplies growers with computer-generated disease management information. Satellite-based environmental data for specific locations is also available from private sources.

Pesticide Use and IPM

Pesticide use is part of IPM. Whether to use a pesticide, which one is most appropriate, and how and when to apply it is a complicated set of choices that requires timely observation of the crop and consideration of pest pressure, research results, and weather data. Experience and good record-keeping can help a lot, too. The extent to which pesticides are needed for the production of a marketable crop varies among crops and growing conditions. The extent to which growers

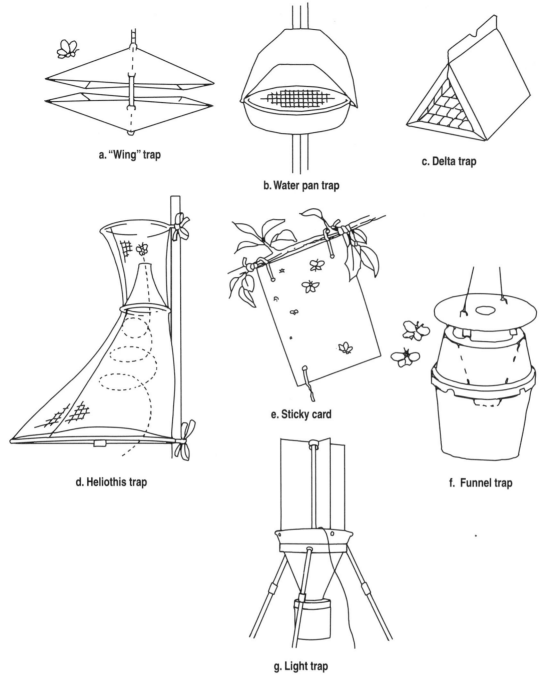

a. "Wing" trap

b. Water pan trap

c. Delta trap

d. Heliothis trap

e. Sticky card

f. Funnel trap

g. Light trap

Figure 14.2 Insect monitoring traps

Source (a., b., c., d., f., and g.): Adapted from Weinzierl, Henn, Randell, Nixon, and Gray. *Insect Attractants and Traps,* 1990

pursue non-pesticide controls varies also. The less a grower is willing or able to use pesticides, the more critical it is that cultural practices be optimized to prevent serious pest problems. However, cultural practices such as crop rotation, sanitation, stress avoidance, and resistant-variety selection make sense for any grower.

Much research goes into developing a pesticide and assessing which crops, pests, and environ-

mental conditions it is suited for. The results of such research are the basis for instructions on the pesticide label, which must be followed to obtain the best pest control and to be in compliance with the law.

For many pest/crop combinations, research has determined the level of pest pressure that causes a loss in crop yield or value, called the *economic injury level*; and the level of pest pressure that justifies pesticide use, called the *action threshold*. The idea is to avoid taking unnecessary action, but to take necessary action in time to avoid economic loss. An action threshold is usually based on certain assumptions about efficacy of the pesticide to be used. Using a less-effective material may call for a lower threshold, for example. Consult published cooperative extension pest management recommendations for more information.

In a number of crops, specific IPM practices have been worked out by research and extension personnel to optimize the use of pesticides. In the Northeast, scouting procedures and action thresholds have been published for many major crops such as sweet corn, cole crops, onions, potatoes, and tomatoes. Less extensive information is available for minor crops, but it is still worth monitoring, identifying pests, and assessing pest populations in minor crops.

While cultural practices for controlling pests are often similar across a region, individual states may differ in their recommended insect pest thresholds as a result of different climatic conditions or scouting procedures. As important as published action thresholds and recommendations for various pests and crops are, sometimes growers will have to make adjustments based on local conditions when making a pest management decision. Determining the best course of action requires data from field observations and experience collected over previous growing seasons. For example, knowing that you sprayed (or didn't spray) when 10% of plants were infested with a certain pest, and that you did (or didn't) get a satisfactory crop, will help hone your control strategies in the future, regardless of whether the "official" threshold is 5% or 15% infestation. Beyond that, observations of the impact of various actions on beneficial insect levels and subsequent pest populations can be of value in setting thresholds.

Extension vegetable management guides do an excellent job of explaining and keeping up with the conventional pesticide option available to growers for different pests and crops. Accordingly, this book does not include recommendations regarding pesticides for control of specific vegetable pests. Obtaining a current copy of pest management recommendations for your location is necessary because pesticide recommendations change from year to year and region to region as research reveals new information or pesticide labels change.

Types of Pesticides

Pesticide classification can be based on the type of organisms the pesticide kills. The pesticides commonly used in agriculture are insecticides, herbicides, and fungicides. Pesticides can also be classified by the range of species they affect. *Broad-spectrum* means they kill a wide variety of pests. *Selective* pesticides affect a narrow set of species. Another way of classifying pesticides is whether they are *contact* or *non-contact* materials. In other words, do they have to be applied directly to the pest—on the insect or the weed—or not? If a pesticide applicator license is required to apply a certain pesticide, it is called a *restricted use* pesticide. Otherwise the pesticide is for *general use*.

Pesticide Names

Individual pesticides have several different names. The chemical name indicates the pesticide's chemical composition, and the brand name is what a company calls their product. The formulation of a pesticide can be liquid, granules, or wettable powder. The same pesticide may be sold under several different brand names, sometimes in different formulations or concentrations. A chemical class of pesticide includes materials that have a similar chemical structure and thus similar modes of action and target pests. Table 14.1, page 144, lists some pesticides commonly used in vegetable production and their characteristics.

Pesticide Toxicity

Pesticide toxicity is assessed in several ways, and every pesticide has a "signal word" on the label that indicates its relative overall toxicity. "Danger" refers to the most toxic group, followed (in decreasing order of toxicity) by "Warning" and then "Caution." The Median Lethal Dose, or LD_{50} value of a pesticide (the amount needed in milligrams per kilogram of body weight to kill half the population of test animals), indicates the acute

Table 14.1 Some pesticides commonly used in vegetable production

Material	Chemical Class	LD$_{50}$ Oral [1]	LD$_{50}$ Dermal [2]	REI (hours) [3]	Animal Toxicity [4] Bee	Bird	Fish
Insecticides							
azadirachtin [5]	botanical	5,000+	2,000+	12	?	?	?
Bacillus thuringiensis [5]	biological	harmless	harmless	4	N	N	N
diazinon	organophosphate	300–400	2,020	12–24	H	H	H
carbaryl	carbamate	246–283	850	12	H	S	M
chlorpyrifos	organophosphate	92–270	2,000	12–24	H	H	H
endosulfan	organochlorine	23–160	359	48	M	H	H
imidicloprid	chloronicotinyl	450	5,000+	12	H	M	M
insecticidal soap [5]	salt of fatty acid	16,900	harmless	12	N	N	N
malathion	organophosphate	5,500	2,000+	12	H	M	H
permethrin	pyrethroid	430–4,000	2,000+	24	H	N	H
rotenone [5]	botanical	132–1,500	?	12–48	N	S	H
Miticides							
dicofol	chlorinated hydrocarbon	570–595	1,000–1,230	12	N	M	H
sulfur [5]	inorganic element	5,000+	5,000+	12–48	N	N	N
Fungicides							
benomyl	carbamate	10,000+	10,000+	24	N	M	M
captan	dicarboximide	9,000	?	96	N	S	H
chlorothalonil	benzonitrile	10,000+	10,000+	48	N	?	H
copper hydroxide [5]	copper compound	1,000	?	12–48	?	?	M
iprodione	carboximide	4,400+	2,000+	12	N	?	M
metalaxyl	acylalamine	669	3,100+	12	N	?	N
Herbicides							
glyphosate	glycine	4,300	7,940	24	N	?	N
linuron	substituted urea	4,000	?	24	N	?	M
metolachlor	acetanilide	2,780	10,000+	12	N	S	M
metribuzin	triazine	1,100–2,300	20,000+	12	N	?	M
sethoxydim	cyclohexenone	2,676–3,125	5,000+	12–24	S	S	M
trifluralin	dinitroaniline	10,000+	?	12–24	N	N	M

[1] LD$_{50}$ Oral is the dosage of a chemical (in milligrams per kilogram of body weight) expected to kill 50% of a test animal population when ingested.

[2] LD$_{50}$ Dermal is the dosage of a chemical (in milligrams per kilogram of body weight) expected to kill 50% of a test animal population when applied to the skin.

[3] REI (Re-Entry Interval) specifies how much time (in hours) must pass before people can legally reenter an area treated with a pesticide.

[4] N = nontoxic; S = slightly toxic; M = moderately toxic; H = highly toxic

[5] Historically allowed by organic certification standards.

Always consult the pesticide label before use. No endorsement or discrimination is intended.

Source: Adapted from Orzolek et al., 1998; *Pesticide Compendia*, 1984; and Meister, ed., 1999

toxicity of a pesticide, as a result of ingestion or contact with the skin. The lower the LD_{50} value, the more toxic the pesticide. Other measures of pesticide toxicity include the relative risk to birds, fish, and bees; carcinogenicity; and capacity to cause neurological injury.

Requirements for Pesticide Use

Pesticide labels are the legal documents which govern pesticide use. Besides following instructions about application equipment, rates, and frequency, growers must adhere to the personal protection requirements describing equipment that must be worn during application. The *restricted-entry interval* (REI) on the label is the length of time that farm workers must wait before going into a field after the pesticide is applied. *Days to harvest* (DTH) is the length of time that must pass before a crop can be harvested after the pesticide is applied. DTH may differ for the same pesticide if it is used on different crops.

"Organic" Pesticides

"Organic" pesticides as described here are those that have been historically allowed by organic farm certification standards. That category excludes most, but not all, "synthetic" pesticides. Until federal organic standards are implemented, including a national list of allowed materials, individual state certification programs are responsible for deciding which pesticides can be used. Some growers choose to follow organic production practices, whether their farms are certified or not, in an attempt to minimize risks and communicate a message to consumers.

Although some materials allowed by organic standards do in fact pose health and environmental threats, in general they are low in toxicity and environmental persistence. Some pesticides such as Bt *(Bacillus thuringiensis)* that are allowed by organic certification standards are very cost-effective and are used by many "conventional" and "IPM" growers as well as organic growers. Others, such as pyrethrum, have limited effectiveness or require repeated applications in certain situations; and they are more costly than their synthetic counterparts. When organic pesticides are to be used, the choices include botanicals, microbials, minerals, and some synthetics.

With all pesticides, read the label carefully to be sure the pesticide is appropriate for the crop and pest in question, and to learn the most effective means of application. Regardless of your farming philosophy or whether you use organic pesticides, all pesticides must be applied in a timely fashion to achieve control of the pest in question. Just throwing some material at the crop now and again is usually a waste of time and money.

Botanical Pesticides

Botanicals are plant-derived materials such as neem, pyrethrum, rotenone, ryannia, and sabadilla. Nicotine products, although natural, are not permitted organically due to their very high mammalian toxicity. Botanicals are generally short-lived in the environment, as they are broken down rapidly in the presence of light and air; thus they do not provide pest control for very long— perhaps a day or several days.

Botanicals, with the possible exception of neem, are broad-spectrum, and they may kill beneficial insects, as well as targeted pests. They tend to be moderately toxic to people and wildlife; many are irritating to mucous membranes. Pesticides made from extracts of neem tree seeds have azadirachtin as the active ingredient, which works like a growth regulator, inhibiting development of immature stages of many insects, and deterring feeding by adults. Neem oil also has fungicidal properties.

Microbial Pesticides

Microbial pesticides, formulated from microorganisms or their by-products, tend to have advantages over the botanicals in that they are safer to use and more selective in what they kill, so beneficials are not harmed. Bt, or *Bacillus thuringiensis,* is the most widely used type of microbial insecticide. Bt products contain a toxin made by a bacterium. Bt has expanded organic pest control effectiveness for insects such as Colorado potato beetle, the cabbageworm complex, and corn borer.

The major types of Bt are the *kurstake* strain for caterpillar pests and the *San Diego* or *tenebrionis* strain for potato beetle larvae. The *azawai* strain is similar to the *kurstake* strain and also controls caterpillar pests. The *israeliensis* strain controls mosquito and fungus gnat larvae. For Bt to be effective, you must use the right strain for the pest and apply it when susceptible larvae are present and actively feeding (a function of such factors as temperature and time). Because Bt must be ingested by the pest, thorough coverage of foliage is essential. Use spray water with a pH between 4 and 7 for best results. Bt and other biologicals often lose their effectiveness in one to several days because of photodegradation or other environmental factors.

Entomo-pathogenic fungi are those that infect and kill insects. Many of these are naturally occurring, and some are, or will soon be, available in commercial insecticides. They include species of *Aschersonia, Beauveria, Entomophora, Metarhizium*, and *Verticillium*.

At this writing there are several commercial products that contain live spores of *Beauvaria bassiana* and are labeled for use on vegetable crops. These *myco-insecticides* work best when applied at the onset of an infestation by soft-bodied insects such as whiteflies, aphids, or thrips. It takes a week or more after spraying to see evidence of control. The spores of the fungus will germinate once they come in direct contact with the insect pest; then the fungus must penetrate the cuticle and infect the body cavity to kill the pest.

Some nematodes, or microscopic roundworms, are plant pests, while others, such as those in the families *Steinernematidae* and *Heterorhabditidae*, are beneficial because they are parasites of certain plant pests. Beneficial nematodes may be present naturally in the soil but usually not at sufficient levels to provide meaningful pest control. Although commercially available, beneficial nematodes are very vulnerable to drying out. When applied under suitable conditions, as through a drip irrigation system to soils that are kept moist, they have potential to control some soil-dwelling insect pests.

Other microbials are available to suppress plant pathogenic fungi. These are usually applied as seed or seedling treatments or in-row soil drenches to optimize their establishment in the crop plant root zone. They may contain species of *Bacillus, Gliocladium, Streptomyces, Trichoderma*, and other beneficial fungi. Initially, such products were labeled to control root-rot organisms that cause damping off and similar problems in greenhouse crops, often ornamentals; but subsequently some have been labeled for vegetables and field use.

Mineral Pesticides

Insecticidal soaps (fatty acids of potassium salts) work by clogging the breathing pores of soft-bodied insects like aphids or thrips. Proper application to assure contact with the insect pest is necessary for control. Insecticidal soaps cause injury to some crops and are harmful to some beneficial insects. Herbicidal soap formulations are intended to cause burning of plant foliage; they are nonselective and will burn most crop foliage, too.

Horticultural and other dormant oils smother scale and other insects. Vegetable-based oils may also be effective in some cases. Various oils in combination with Bt properly applied to sweet corn silks can prevent corn earworm infestations.

Sulfur and copper compounds are the primary fungicides and bactericides used by organic growers to prevent vegetable diseases in the field. There are many formulations to choose from, including Bordeaux mixture, tri-basic copper, copper hydroxide, copper sulfate, elemental sulfur, calcium polysulfide (lime sulfur), and copper/zinc formulations. For many foliar diseases, sulfur and copper compounds are not as effective as synthetic fungicides. They can cause injury to crops if applied in hot, sunny weather. Potassium bicarbonate fungicides are just coming on the market at this writing, and they show promise for control of many foliar diseases, such as powdery mildew.

IPM—
A Grower Profile

Jim Quarella
Bellview Farms, Inc.
Landisville, New Jersey

Jim Quarella grows 150 acres of vegetables in a highly agricultural area of southern New Jersey. The soils are sandy, and most fields are double-cropped. The farm specializes in Oriental vegetables, but also produces some leeks, summer squash, and watermelon. Jim is a member of the Landisville Produce Cooperative, which has been in existence for over eighty years. He has been president of the co-op for the past eight years. It is a service-oriented marketing co-op, providing cooling facilities, an ice plant, and sales management for more than 100 members. Annual gross sales through the co-op are about $6 million, primarily to chain stores and local brokers.

"A few year ago we started an IPM program for the co-op members who wanted a scouting service. The co-op hired scouts to come and check the farms. Our farmers worked with cooperative extension to train these people in how to scout effectively, and what pests to look for in the member's specialty crops. The cost to participating growers was $2 per acre per week, and scouting was done three times per week. What's unique about our specialty vegetables is that there are no established action thresholds. Therefore, the program is designed to provide information about which pests are present and at what populations, but the decision of when and what to spray is left up to the grower.

"Only about ten growers took advantage of the program. I don't think many of them realize that spending a couple of dollars an acre on scouting can save them a lot of money down the road. The participating growers are pleased with the program, but recently the co-op turned the scouting over to a private ag consulting firm, in part because it is difficult to keep finding and training scouts. The timing of our crops makes it hard to use college students; our season runs from April to October, so students are in school for a month or two on either end. Even though you can train just about anyone to scout crops, the turnover is a challenge to keeping the program going.

"We started with some seed money, and because the co-op is nonprofit, the scouting cost was quite low. Since we turned the scouting over to the consultant firm, the cost has risen to a little over $3 per acre, and fields are only scouted twice a week, but we don't have to deal with recruiting and training scouts.

"Now, I'm evolving back to doing my own scouting. I feel that the grower has to spend time in the fields; I need to be there, looking at my crops more often. With the diversity of crops that I raise, it is really hard for a scout to be trained to know all the crops and all the pests and what to look for. I also feel that you have to be out there at least three times a week; it's hard to coordinate when the scouts are going to be there and when to spray. When you know that a weather "window" is going to open up that will allow you to spray, you need to scout ahead of time to see if some action needs to be taken."

"In a way, you can say that I always used IPM because I always used spray materials judiciously, and I never liked spraying on a schedule without first looking at the crops. That approach causes pesticide resistance and doesn't address all the environmental concerns that there are now. Even though we get too busy and often delegate responsibilities, at this point I feel it's important for me to get closer to my crops and make pest scouting

> *"Growing is not done out of a book, and scouting can't be done from the pickup truck. The best pest management decisions get made when I personally examine my crops on a regular basis. It helps that I constantly get feedback from my crew, even though they are not specifically trained in IPM. If they see some leaves with holes in them, or if they spot some insects, good or bad, they let me know right away."*

even more of a priority. You can run a farm out of an office, but that's not the direction I want to go in. Growing is not done out of a book, and scouting can't be done from the pickup truck. The best pest management decisions get made when I personally examine my crops on a regular basis. It helps that I constantly get feedback from my crew, even though they are not specifically trained in IPM. If they see some leaves with holes in them, or if they spot some insects, good or bad, they let me know right away."

"Starting a cooperative IPM program would probably be easier if there was less diversity in the crops that are grown in an area. In most large growing areas there are consulting firms that can be hired to do the scouting. If growers want to start their own program, they need to identify a group of growers with the same concerns, figure out the economics of what they're going to pay for scouting per acre, then hire a scout. One good scout can cover a lot of acres."

"IPM should be done on the farm, either by the operator or by someone else coming in. You definitely need to know what's out there and the condition of your plants, and then react to that. Just writing down a spray schedule and following it is too costly to the grower, and it's not an environmentally sound practice."

Chapter 15
Insect Management

Insects belong to a group of animals called *arthropods,* which also includes mites, spiders, centipedes, and millipedes. The majority of this group have a beneficial or neutral influence on vegetable cropping systems, but the relatively few species that feed on vegetables can cause serious problems. Insect management involves both the control of pest species and the conservation of beneficial species.

Insect Classification

Insect classification can be based on insects' life cycles, scientific groupings, common names, food preferences, or mouthpart types, or the types of damage insects do (see table 15.1). Understanding these classifications can help growers identify and address pest problems in the field.

Life cycles of all insects include an egg and an adult stage. In some species, the juveniles, or nymphs, look a lot like the adults, except they are smaller and may lack fully developed wings (aphids, leafhoppers, plant bugs and thrips, for

example). In other species, the juvenile forms, or larvae, do not look at all like the adults until they go through a complete *metamorphosis* (beetles, moths, flies and wasps, for example).

Major groupings of insects are called *orders,* which include many related species. The six orders that contain most of the common vegetable insect pests are listed in table 15.1, but some pests are in other orders, such as Deraptera (earwigs) and Orthoptera (grasshoppers).

Insect Pest Damage

Insect pests may feed on foliage, fruit, roots, stems, bulbs, or seeds by chewing, piercing and sucking, or rasping. This leads to either *direct* damage to the marketable portion of the crop (such as damage caused by corn earworm in corn and flea beetle in greens), or *indirect* damage to a nonmarketable portion that results in reduced yield or quality (such as damage caused by cabbage root maggot and asparagus beetle). In some cases, insects cause damage by spreading, or

Table 15.1 Classification of major vegetable crop insect pests

Order	Common Name	Pest Stage	Feeds on	Mouthparts	Primary Damage
Lepidoptera	moths, butterflies	larvae	foliage	chew	defoliation
Coleoptera	beetles, weevils	larvae, adults	foliage, roots, fruit	chew	defoliation
Heteroptera	plant bugs, stink bugs	nymphs, adults	foliage, fruit	piercing, sucking	fruit distortion
Homoptera	aphids, leafhoppers	nymphs, adults	foliage	piercing, sucking	leaf, fruit damage; spread virus
Thysanoptera	thrips	nymphs, adults	foliage	piercing	leaf, fruit damage; spread virus
Diptera	flies	larvae	roots, bulbs, stems	rasping	tunneling; seed/seedling loss

vectoring, disease-causing pathogens such as viruses (aphids and cucumber mosaic virus; western flower thrips and tomato spotted wilt virus); or bacteria (cucumber beetle and bacterial wilt; corn flea beetles and Stewart's wilt). In other cases, insect injury to crop tissue creates wounds and allows pathogens to enter the plant (thrips and botrytis on onion; corn borer and bacterial soft rot on pepper).

Cultural Practices for Insect Management

Cultural practices for insect management are essential to an integrated pest management approach that maximizes profits and avoids unnecessary pesticide use. They include the following cultural practices:

- Crop rotation to a non-host crop
- Sanitation by removing residues, cleaning greenhouses, controlling weeds
- Barriers to pests, such as row covers, green house screens, mulches, trenches
- Tillage to kill pests or remove their habitat or food source
- Vacuuming pests off plants
- Selection of plant varieties that tolerate insect feeding
- Timing of planting to avoid peak pest populations
- Companion planting to deter pest colonization of main crop
- Trap cropping to concentrate pests in a small area of the field
- Overhead irrigation to drown or dislodge pests
- Flaming of exposed insects on flame-tolerant crops
- Conservation of natural enemies of pests by appropriate pesticide selection and habitat maintenance.

Crop Rotation for Insect Management

Crop rotation is an important strategy for avoiding or slowing colonization of crops by pests that overwinter on or near the farm. (Also see chapter 7, "Crop Rotation," beginning on page 69.) It is not effective for control of insects that overwinter far from the crop and immigrate to fields each year from other regions via high winds or storm fronts (such as corn earworm, leafhoppers, some aphids, and diamondback moth). The use of barriers such as row covers, trenches, or mulches can be an effective tool for keeping these pests off crops and can exclude many other pests that have overwintered nearby. For pests that overwinter in the soil where a crop was grown, crop rotation is a prerequisite to the effective use of barriers.

Sanitation for Insect Management

Sanitation is critical to reducing pest pressure from insects, such as European corn borer, that seek out crop residues for overwintering. Another aspect of sanitation is timely elimination of alternate hosts on which pests can build up. For example, legume cover crops and many weeds can host tarnished plant bug. In this example, poorly timed elimination of host plants by mowing late in the season may actually drive the pest into adjacent crops. In greenhouses, removal of all vegetation after crop harvest, followed by freezing or heating, will minimize survival of insect pests.

Barriers for Insect Management

Row covers, mulches, and trenches are examples of barriers used to exclude insect pests from crops.

Row Covers

Row covers made of spunbonded or woven synthetic fabrics are often used for crop growth enhancement but can also be used as barriers to exclude insect pests. Keys to success include selection of an appropriate row cover material, timely placement over the crop, and complete sealing of the cover by burying the edges with soil. It is also essential to rotate crops to prevent infestation by soil-dwelling pests from underneath the covers. See table 15.2 for combinations of crops and insect pests that may be managed using floating row covers.

With cool-season crops, such as crucifers, or crops such as peppers in which fruit-set is sensitive to

Table 15.2 Insect pest/crop combinations that may be managed using floating row covers

Pest	Crops
Aphids (virus vectors)	Cucurbits, peppers
"Cabbage worms"	Crucifers
Cabbage root maggot	Crucifers
Colorado potato beetle	Solanaceous crops
Cucumber beetles	Cucurbits
European corn borer	Sweet corn
Flea beetle	Crucifers, leafy greens, solanaceous crops
Leaf miners	Beets, chard, spinach
Leafhoppers	Beans, lettuce, potato

high temperature, timely removal of the covers may be critical to avoid overheating. The use of lightweight row covers (approximately 0.3-0.6 oz per square yard) can minimize heating of the crop environment and reduce the cost of using row covers as well. However, heavier row covers are less likely to tear and thus easier to reuse, compensating for their higher cost. Some growers who use row cover over crucifers for all or most of the season claim that direct-seeded crops do better than transplants because they are better able to adapt to heat conditions under the cover.

Row covers can be placed over transplants even before they are set out in the field. Another way to use row covers is to cover bare seedbeds prior to planting. This may reduce infestation of soil-dwelling pests such as onion root maggots and seed corn maggots that emerge from eggs laid in the soil by adult flies. This may be particularly helpful for soils high in decaying organic matter, which attracts these flies.

To assure good fruit-set with insect-pollinated crops like cucurbits, row covers should be removed as soon as flowers appear. Although row covers allow air, water, and light to pass through, they do reduce air movement and leaf drying and therefore may promote the development of foliar disease.

Mulches

Mulches can be used to manage insects in several ways. Plastic mulches that speed early-season crop growth can enhance the ability of a crop to cope with insect feeding. For management of aphids on peppers or leafy greens, light-colored or reflective aluminum foil mulches may deter the pest from landing on the plants. This works better when plants are small and most of the mulch is exposed, before it is covered by the plant canopy. The use of straw mulch can reduce early-season Colorado potato beetle feeding in some cases, perhaps because it impedes their travel to the crop or slows soil warming and beetle emergence.

Trenching

Trenching is a barrier technique for intercepting adult Colorado potato beetles that have overwintered near field edges and must walk to the crop after emergence because they cannot fly for several days. A 12-inch deep, "V" or "U"-shaped trench is formed along the edges of the field and then lined with black plastic. Once the beetles walk into the trench, they cannot crawl out as long as there is some dust on the plastic and the walls of the trench are steep. They starve or desiccate in a few days.

Tillage and Insect Management

Tillage can control soil-dwelling insect pests by burying or crushing them, exposing them to harsh weather conditions, or destroying their food or habitat. For example, early tillage to control weeds or cover crops, combined with delaying planting two to three weeks, can starve black cutworms that attack corn, beans, tomatoes, and other crops. Prompt and thorough incorporation of cabbage residues can limit available overwintering habitat for cabbage maggot. Deep spring plowing is recommended to control overwintering leaf miner pupae that threaten spinach, Swiss chard, and other greens.

Vacuuming
for Insect Management

Vacuums for control of insect pests are available for use in the field either as push-type units or tractor-mounted units that cover single or multiple rows. Vacuuming is not widely used to control insects, and excitement about this technique seems to have diminished as problems with its application were encountered. For example, nonselective killing of insects included beneficials. With highly mobile insect pests, it can be difficult to vacuum them up before they fly away or drop to the ground ahead of the approaching vacuum. Frequent trips through the field to keep up with pests that need vacuuming is time consuming and can result in soil compaction.

Target pests for vacuuming might include aphids, tarnished plant bug, cucumber beetles, flea beetles, leafhoppers, or even Colorado potato beetle adults. In the greenhouse, hand-held vacuums have been used to control "hot-spots" of whiteflies on tomatoes until biological controls take effect.

Selection of Plant Varieties
for Insect Management

Variety selection can minimize pest problems by limiting host attractiveness or susceptibility to a pest. Varieties may differ in their susceptibility to some types of insect damage, although such differences are not as common as with disease susceptibility. Potato and bean varieties vary in their susceptibility to hopper burn caused by potato leafhopper; and some growers report differences in Colorado potato beetle preference among potato varieties. Selection of cabbage varieties that are tolerant to onion thrips is one of the most effective strategies for preventing damage. Sweet corn growers often report that some varieties are more prone to corn earworm infestation.

Timing Plantings
for Insect Management

Timing plantings to avoid peaks in pest pressure is another way to limit pest injury. For example, if cabbage maggot is a problem, crucifer planting can be delayed until after the first flight of egg-laying adults. On the other hand, imported cabbageworm damage tends to be reduced by early planting. Late planting of potato can avoid early-season colonization by Colorado potato beetle. Early planting of pumpkins can reduce potential losses from virus infection, since aphids may not arrive to spread viruses until mid-season. Pumpkin plants that have set fruit will suffer less yield loss from virus infections than will younger plants. In general, sequential plantings of crops can spread the risk when the arrival of pests is sporadic.

Companion Planting
for Insect Management

Companion planting refers to the concept that pests can be managed by planting certain plants next to each other. However, recommendations abound that have no scientific basis. There is evidence that mixtures of plants make it more difficult for specialized insects to locate their preferred host plants, so diversification in general may be helpful to minimizing pest problems. Since plants influence each other as well as pests, however, it is important that the relative competitiveness of neighboring plants be considered. A drawback to companion planting is that it can compromise the effective separation of crop families that is the basis for most meaningful crop rotations.

Trap Cropping
for Insect Management

Using trap crops is a form of companion planting. So that the effect of crop rotation is not compromised, crops in the same family are usually utilized as trap crops. This technique utilizes pest preferences to concentrate pest populations in certain areas, which can facilitate mechanical or chemical control or reduce pressure on the primary crop. For example, Colorado potato beetle prefers eggplant and potato to tomato, so immigration of overwintering adults into tomatoes can be delayed by planting a row of eggplant or potatoes along field edges three or four weeks before tomatoes are transplanted. Another example is "trapping" of flea beetles on single rows of a crop preferred by the beetles, such as mustard greens, which are planted in between blocks of a crop such as kale in order to protect it. Trap cropping can make it easier to apply an insecticide or to vacuum, since the pest is concentrated in a relatively small area of the field. Timing can be used to create a trap crop as well. For example, an early planting or transplanting of a row of cucurbits along the field edge can concentrate cucumber beetles before the main crop has emerged.

Under-Sowing and Insect Management

Under-sowing is another type of mixed planting that refers to planting a cover crop between rows of a cash crop (also see "Inter-Seeded Cover Crops," pages 79–80). That allows the cover to establish well before winter so it can protect against erosion even though vegetables may be harvested late in the growing season. Annual ryegrass, red or white clover, oats, or rye make good under-sown crops in vegetables, depending on the timing of sowing and crop development (see chapter 8, "Cover Crops and Green Manures," beginning on page 78). Under-sowings do not complicate rotational plans too much, since the legume and grass families include few vegetable crops but most of the cover crop species. Although aimed at soil stewardship more than pest control, this type of relay cropping may reduce pest pressure by confusing insects that specialize in a certain crop (for example, diamondback moth in cabbage) or by providing habitat for natural enemies of pests. On the other hand, in some cases under-sowing may improve habitat for pests, such as slugs in a succulent clover or tarnished plant bugs on legumes. Interplanting crops may also promote plant disease by reducing air movement and leaf drying.

Overhead Irrigation and Insect Management

Overhead irrigation, simple as it sounds, can reduce pest pressure from pests. Onion thrips may be drowned in the leaf whorl or dislodged from plants by heavy application of water. Diamondback moth eggs and larvae may be dislodged from plants and adult egg-laying disrupted by irrigation. Two-spotted spider mites, which favor dry, dusty conditions, can be deterred by timely irrigation in dry seasons.

Flaming for Pest Management

Flaming is a technique aimed at overwintering Colorado potato beetle adults. Propane burners are used to quickly pass a flame over young potato plants when beetles are on the top of them. This kills or injures the beetles, preventing further feeding and egg-laying, but does little harm to the crop when the plants are less than 4 inches tall.

See table 15.3, page 154, for a summary of common insects pests in the Northeast and nonchemical controls.

Biological Control of Insect Pests

Biological control refers to the use of living organisms to control pests. The term is commonly associated with insect pest control by predators, parasites, and pathogens. These may be indigenous to the farm ecosystem, or purchased and introduced. See table 15.4, pages 155–156, for a summary of natural enemies of vegetable insect pests.

The use of commercially reared biocontrols has been largely limited to greenhouses, where high-value crops and an enclosed environment make the purchase of biological controls cost-effective. The many successes in these situations offer promise for more widespread field-scale releases of biological control organisms in the future, perhaps as the cost of organisms decreases and our understanding of how to manage them improves. Meanwhile, universities and private industry provide a growing body of information about the utilization of predators and parasites.

Table 15.3 Common insect pests of vegetables in the Northeast and their nonchemical control

Insect Pest	Primary Hosts	Scout for	Damage	Cultural Controls	Biocontrols
aphids	many vegetables	nymphs, adults	spread virus, sooty mold	reflective mulches, floating row cover	ladybugs, *Aphidius spp.*
root maggots	crucifers, onions	eggs by stems, wilting plants	feed on roots, seedlings wilt	delay spring planting, floating row covers	beneficial nematodes?
cucumber beetle	cucurbits	adults on seedlings	defoliation	plant early trap crop, floating row cover	—
"cabbage worms"	crucifers	larvae on leaves	defoliation	floating row cover	parasitic wasp
Colorado potato beetle	solanaceous	larvae, adults, eggs on leaf undersides	defoliation	floating row cover, trench trap early adults, plant early trap crop, flame emerging adults, delay spring planting	twelve-spot ladybug (eats eggs), Tachinid fly
cutworms	many vegetables	larvae at night	plants or stems cut off	early spring tillage, good weed control	—
European corn borer	sweet corn	adult in trap, larvae	leaf, stalk, ear	floating row cover, plow in stalks	parasitic wasp
flea beetles	solanaceous, cruciferous	adults	shot holes in leaves	transplants cope better, floating row cover, trap on sticky reel, destroy weeds in field edges	—
leafhoppers	potato, bean	nymphs, adults	leaf distortion, low yield	tolerant varieties, floating row cover	—
leaf miners	beet, spinach	damage	leaf "mines"	floating row cover	—
mites	bean, tomato	leaf undersides	leaf "bronzing"	avoid drought	predatory mites
tarnished plant bug	many vegetables	adults, nymphs	fruit distortion, leaf lesions	avoid legume sods, control weed hosts	parasitic wasp
thrips	onions, cabbage	adults, nymphs	leaf lesions	remove cull piles, overhead irrigation	—

Source: Adapted from Foster and Flood, 1995; and Hoffmann and Frodsham, 1993

Conservation of Natural Enemies

Conservation of natural enemies is currently an important and realistic approach for field-scale use of biological controls. Many predators, parasites, and pathogens dwell in vegetable fields and provide some degree of natural control of insect pests (table 15.4). By encouraging their popula-tions, natural pest control can be enhanced. Avoiding the use of broad-spectrum insecticides, whether synthetic or natural in origin, conserves native enemies of vegetable insect pests.

Table 15.4 Natural enemies of vegetable insect pests

Name	Primarily Attacks	Main Crop Hosts	Commercially Reared?	Conservation
Predators [1]				
lady beetles	aphids, mites, eggs of corn borer, Colorado potato beetle (CPB)	asparagus, corn, lettuce, crucifers, solanaceae, and most others, late spring to early fall	*Hippodamia convergens* (but native species may be more effective)	provide pollen sources, high humidity, avoid early season aphid sprays
ground beetles	eggs and larvae: CPB, root maggots, cabbage "worms"	crucifers, onion, potato, many others	no	avoid insecticides or fumigation; hedgerows encourage overwintering
rove beetles	root maggot eggs, larvae, pupae	crucifers, onions, turnips	no	rocks, compost piles, hedgerows, and corn tassels and silks may all provide habitat
soldier beetles	soil insects and larvae, aphids	crucifers, cucurbits, sweet corn	no	provide pollen, nectar sources
flower beetles	aphids, insect eggs and larvae, flea beetles	potato, onion, others	no	—
stink bugs	insect eggs, caterpillars, beetle larvae	potato, crucifers, and others	*Podisus maculiventris,* pheromone lure available	allow to overwinter beneath leaf litter and other debris
flower bugs	insect eggs, thrips, mites, small caterpillars, aphids	corn, potato, others, greenhouse crops	*Orius insidiosus, Orius tristcolor*	provide spring/ summer flowering shrubs, weeds; diversity
big-eyed bugs	mites, insect eggs, larvae; aphids, thrips, leafhoppers	corn, bean, potato	no	provide pollen, nectar sources; avoid systemic insecticide
damsel bugs	small insect eggs, larvae, and adults; aphids, mites	many	no	alfalfa and low growing grasses provide shelter
assassin bugs	insect eggs, small larvae, aphids	many	no	—
lacewings	aphids, insect eggs, small larvae	corn, solanaceae, crucifers, legumes	*Chrysoptera carnea, Chrysptera rufilabris*	nectar and aphid honeydew attract; hairy plants deter
hover flies	aphids, small caterpillars	most	no	pollen and nectar, especially umbels
aphid midges	aphids	crucifers, others, greenhouse crops	*Aphidoletes aphidimyza*	prefer shelter, high humidity; moist soil for pupation
robber flies	generalist adults; larvae eat soil insects	most	no	—
predatory mites	spider mites, thrips, fungus gnats	greenhouse crops, some field vegetables	*Phytoseiulus* species, *Amblyseius* species, others	avoid most sprays
spiders	mites, aphids, small and large insects (including beneficials)	many crops	no	mulching

(continued on next page)

(continued from previous page)

Name	Primarily Attacks	Main Crop Hosts	Commercially Reared?	Conservation
Parasitoids [2]				
Aphidiid wasps	aphids	any susceptible crop in field or greenhouse	*Aphidius matricariae, Diaeretiella rapae, Lysiphlebus testaceipes*	spread leaves with parasitzed aphid "mummies"
Braconid wasps	moth, beetle, fly larvae, moth eggs	many	*Cotesia* species, *Microplitis plutellae, Dacnusa sibirica*	avoid insecticides
Ichnuemonid wasps	moth, beetle, fly larvae and pupae	corn, crucifers, many others	*Diadegma insularis*	avoid insecticides
Trichogramma wasps	moth eggs	corn, crucifers, tomato, and others	*Trichogramma* species	buy correct species for target pest; avoid insecticides
Tachinid flies	caterpillars, fly and beetle larvae	corn, crucifers, potato, cucurbits, others	no	—
beneficial nematodes	beetle larvae, maggots, cutworms, weevils	many possible	*Steinernema* species, *Heterohabditis, bacteriophora*	need protection from light, drying out, heat and cold
Pathogens [3]				
Bacillus thuringiensis	caterpillar, beetle, or gnat larvae	crucifers, solanacaea, others	several subspecies	buy correct subspecies for target pest
beneficial fungi	many pests	many crops	*Beauveria bassiana, Metarhizium* species, *Verticillium lecanii*	formulations and labeled uses are increasing

[1]Predators are animals that attack and feed on other animals. During their life cycles predators normally kill several individuals.
[2] Parasitoids are animals that at some time during their life cycles feed in or on another organism (host).
[3] Pathogens are disease-causing organisms.

Source: Adapted from Hoffmann and Frodsham, 1993

Sustainable Vegetable Production from Start-Up to Market

Chapter 16

Disease Management

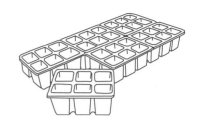

Healthy plants are necessary for profitable vegetable production. Diseases can be detrimental to plant vigor, reducing total yield; or detrimental to product quality, limiting marketable yield and shelf life. The key to effective disease management is prevention rather than treatment of disease. Once signs of disease are present, proper identification is essential to determining the appropriate response to follow to minimize further spread, and to decide which pesticides, if any, are appropriate for protecting healthy crop tissue. In some cases, it may be too late to take either cultural or chemical action to prevent crop loss.

Identifying Plant Diseases

Identifying plant diseases can be a challenge. While common diseases are clearly described and pictured in many publications (see the references, pages 264–265), unusual expressions of the disease, occurrence of two or more diseases together, or occurrence of uncommon diseases may be difficult to identify. In addition, abiotic, or noninfectious, disorders often cause symptoms similar to those that result from infection by plant pathogens. (Abiotic injury to plants can result from a wide range of stresses, including excess heat or cold injury, too much or too little moisture, air pollutants including ozone and sulfur dioxide, nutrient deficiencies or toxicities, mechanical or herbicide injury, soil compaction, and lightning burn.)

Disease identification is an investigative process based on close examination of plants and review of field history, soil conditions, plant nutrition, and environmental factors. When trying to narrow the possible causes of a crop problem, it is often

helpful to examine symptoms with a hand lens; dig up some plant roots; review soil test results; look for patterns of symptoms in the field; compare the performance of similar cultivars, crops, or fields; and talk to neighboring growers. Professional examination of plant samples by a diagnostic laboratory is available in most states at low cost. This resource should be utilized after ruling out as many non-disease causes of the problem as possible and consulting with a local extension agent, if available.

Managing Plant Diseases

Management strategies for plant diseases address one of the three conditions required for pathogens to cause problems in a crop: susceptible host plants, the presence of inoculum, or environmental conditions that allow disease development.
1. A susceptible host plant—Avoid with resistant and tolerant cultivars or by crop rotation.
2. The presence of inoculum—Reduce through sanitation.
3. Environmental conditions that allow disease development—Limit with cultural practices.

Disease Resistance and Tolerance

Disease resistance (reduced susceptibility) or *disease tolerance* (ability to yield well in the presence of the pathogen) are desirable characteristics in a cultivar. Selecting cultivars that have such characteristics is an inexpensive, effective means of disease management, assuming that such cultivars are also desirable in terms of production and marketing.

Table 16.1 (page 158) lists some common diseases for which resistant or tolerant cultivars are available. In crops where many diseases are listed, resistance or tolerance in a single cultivar is usually to just one or several of the diseases but not all. Therefore, cultivar choices need to be made based on prioritization of potential disease problems. Pathogen populations can change over time, so a previously resistant cultivar may become susceptible to a disease after a few years, or a few decades.

Unfortunately, resistance or tolerance to many common diseases is not available. However, dramatic differences among cultivars in their degree of susceptibility may still exist, and these differences are often visible in the field toward the end of the growing season. Since these distinctions are not described in seed catalogs, it is imperative that growers observe and record such extremes in cultivar performance in terms of disease.

Sanitation to Reduce Inoculum

Sanitation is the cornerstone of inoculum reduction. Farming does not take place under sterile conditions, so diseases or their propagules, such as spores, are always present to some degree in the field, on tools, and in the greenhouse. However, preventing the buildup of inoculum can sometimes avoid a disease epidemic even with a susceptible host and favorable environmental conditions for development of the disease.

Sanitation includes an array of cultural practices, starting with the use of clean seed, free from

Table 16.1 Vegetable crops and diseases for which resistant/tolerant varieties are available

Vegetable Crop	Diseases for Which Resistant/Tolerant Varieties Are Available*
Asparagus	fusarium, rust
Beans	anthracnose, bacterial blight, bean common mosaic virus (NY15, BV-1), downy mildew, halo blight, powdery mildew, sclerotinia, bean rust, bacterial brown spot
Beets	cercospora leaf spot
Broccoli	black rot, bacterial leaf spot, downy mildew
Cabbage	black rot, black speck, fusarium yellows
Carrots	alternaria, bacterial blight
Cauliflower	black rot, downy mildew
Celery	fusarium wilt, yellows
Cucumber	angular leaf spot, anthracnose, bacterial wilt, cucumber mosaic virus, downy mildew, powdery mildew, scab, target leaf spot, watermelon mosaic virus (races 1,2), zucchini yellows mosaic virus
Eggplant	cucumber mosaic virus, tobacco mosaic virus
Lettuce	bottom rot, brown rib, corky root rot, lettuce mosaic virus
Melons	anthracnose (races 1,2), crown blight, downy mildew, fusarium wilt (races 0,1,2), powdery mildew (races 1,2), watermelon mosaic virus (races 1,2)
Onions	botrytis, fusarium basal rot, pink root
Peas	bean leaf-roll virus, bean yellows mosaic virus, common wilt, enation mosaic virus, pea streak virus, powdery mildew
Peppers	bacterial spot (races 1,2,3), potato virus Y, tobacco mosaic virus (races 0,1,2)
Potatoes	early blight, fusarium dry rot, late blight, net necrosis, potato leaf roll virus, potato viruses A, X, Y, potato etch virus, verticillium, scab
Pumpkin	black rot, powdery mildew
Spinach	downy mildew (races 1,2,3,4), cucumber mosaic virus, white rust
Tomato	alternaria stem canker, bacterial speck, early blight, fusarium crown rot, fusarium wilt (races 1,2) gray leaf spot, late blight, root knot nematodes, tobacco mosaic virus, verticillium wilt (races 1,2)
Watermelon	fusarium wilt, anthracnose

*Based on descriptions in commercial vegetable seed catalogs

disease. Depending on the crops and pathogen concerns, this may mean using seed that is hot-water-treated (tomatoes), fungicide-treated (sweet corn), disease-tested certified (potatoes), or western-grown (beans).

Transplant production should be in clean, sterilized containers and growing structures, using soilless mix. If other media such as compost or soil-based mixes are used, care must be taken to avoid damping-off and other seedling diseases by providing optimal seedling growing conditions and using fungicides, either synthetic or biological. For transplant production it is critical to have good air movement and temperature control. Using benches or other means of keeping flats up off the ground avoids contact with soilborne pathogens.

Removal of isolated infected plants during the growing season to reduce the spread of disease is called *roguing*. Prompt removal or incorporation of infected crops and crop residues can prevent sporulation and spread of infectious agents. Plowing, disking, or rototilling fields immediately after harvest speeds the decomposition of plant tissues when compared to leaving them on the soil surface. In general, by the end of the season crops are more prone to disease since plant tissues are old and readily invaded by pathogens. Incorporation soon after harvest avoids further buildup of disease and also leaves as much time as possible for breakdown of diseased tissues before the soil gets too cold. This is of particular importance for control of diseases that overwinter in undecomposed tissue.

Power-washing tillage and other field equipment before moving it from fields with a known disease problem to other fields is a practice that is underutilized in the fight against plant disease. With some diseases, working fields when crop leaves are wet or handling infected plants without washing hands before moving to other fields encourages the spread of disease. Soilborne diseases can sometimes be transferred on clothing or boots. Air-blast sprayers may play a role in spreading air-borne diseases, especially bacterial pathogens.

Reducing or excluding insect vectors of plant diseases is another means of minimizing inoculum levels. For virus diseases, many of which are spread by insects, control strategies include spraying insecticides, using physical barriers such as row covers, or laying reflective mulch in an attempt to make it hard for pests like aphids to locate a crop like peppers. Screening of greenhouse openings can prevent entry of some insect vectors, provided the screen mesh size is smaller than the insect. Weeds and other non-crop plants may provide reservoirs of disease that can spread to nearby crops on wind, in water, or via insect vector. Maintenance of a mowed sod area around crop production fields and greenhouses and control of weeds in fields and alleyways address this problem.

Crop rotation can also be thought of as a form of sanitation, whereby tissues and propagules of diseases that attack a certain group of crops are allowed to decompose for a long time so that the field is "clean" for the next planting of a susceptible host. On vegetable farms with rigorous, consistent crop rotations, disease pressure can be kept to a minimum. Conversely, farms that rarely rotate crops usually have high disease pressure and consequently require a lot of pesticides to protect their crops. For management of some diseases, such as downy mildew on spinach or early blight on tomatoes, rotation may deviate from the approach of bunching families of crops together. Rather, successive plantings and related crops may be separated by substantial distances in order to minimize the movement of inoculum from early to later plantings.

Cultural Practices for Disease Management

Cultural practices can be used to modify the growing environment of a crop in order to prevent the conditions that favor disease. Such practices are essential to minimizing diseases without relying on pesticides. Some general practices such as optimizing soil fertility and rotating crops can reduce a wide range of disease problems, but most cultural practices have an effect on a particular class of diseases (table 16.2, page 160).

Table 16.2 Cultural practices for the prevention of vegetable disease

Practice	Conditions Affected	Diseases Prevented
Staking, pruning Wide-row spacing	Increase air movement and leaf drying	Many foliar diseases
Timely irrigation Drip vs. sprinkler irrigation	Minimize leaf wetness period	Many foliar diseases
Windbreaks Boom vs. air-blast sprayers	Limit spread of airborne spores	Many foliar diseases
Plastic or straw mulches Do not work in fields with wet foliage	Prevent soil splashing onto foliage, fruit Reduce spread of inoculum	Many foliar diseases
Raised beds Chisel plow or subsoiling	Improve water drainage	Many root and crown rots
Careful cultivation	Promote healthy root growth	Many root and crown rots
Floating row covers Reflective mulches	Reduce aphid (vector) feeding	Many viruses
Good weed control on farm	Reduce source of inoculum	Many viruses
Gentle harvest methods	Avoid cuts, bruises	Postharvest diseases
Rapid cooling at harvest Store at cool temperatures	Slow microbial activity	Postharvest diseases
Optimize NPK fertility	Reduce stress, avoid rank growth	Diseases in general
Rotate crops religiously Incorporate crop residues	Reduce inoculum buildup	Diseases in general
Wash equipment frequently	Reduce spread of inoculum	Diseases in general

Fungicides to Control Vegetable Crop Diseases

Fungicides and to some extent bactericides are the pesticides used to control vegetable diseases. They need to be used in a manner that effectively protects crops throughout the "critical disease period," or they should not be used at all. In other words, applying these materials in a haphazard fashion, i.e., spraying something every once in a while, is almost always an unnecessary use of pesticide as well as a waste of time and money. Consult the current edition of your regional extension vegetable management guide for advice on disease-control materials and the timing of their application.

For crops prone to root diseases, treatments may have to be applied to the root zone shortly before planting, during planting, or shortly after planting. For seed rots or seedling diseases, treatments are often applied directly to the seed. Once these diseases are in progress, subsequent pesticide applications will often be ineffective.

Many vegetable diseases are of the foliage and fruit, and these above ground, later-season infections require that tissue be protected long enough for an unblemished product to be harvested. If pesticides are going to be used for disease control, they must be used as long as weather and crop conditions are conducive to infection. They must also be applied at or before the first sign of disease, and reapplied on a regular (usually weekly) basis in order to keep growing tissue protected from infection. Application methods that assure good coverage of all foliage are essential. This requires an appropriate sprayer, nozzles, spray adjuvant (such as spreader-sticker, if called for), and calm weather that minimizes pesticide drift.

Weather-based software models for predicting disease development and thus the need for fungicide application are now available. These models help growers to optimize the timing of fungicide applications, sometimes reducing pesticide use without the risk of increased disease and reduced yield. Examples include "Tom-Cast" for tomatoes, "Wisdom" for potatoes, "Blight-Cast" for onions, and "Melcast" for cantaloupes.

Chapter 17

Weed Management

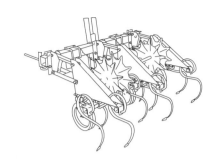

Weeds are plants that grow where they are not wanted. Many vegetable growers consider weeds their primary pest problem. Weeds cause crop losses due to competition for light, water, nutrients, and space. They are consistently present every year; they're not host-specific; they may encourage insect and disease problems; and when poorly managed they lead to a dramatic decline in production as well as to increased weed pressure in subsequent years. Weeds can also increase the cost of harvesting by getting in the way and slowing the process down.

Classification of Weeds

Classification of weeds is based on their life cycle and growth habit. *Summer annuals* live for a year or less, germinating in the spring, setting seed, and dying in the fall. *Winter annuals* germinate in the fall, overwinter, then produce seed and die the following spring or summer. *Biennials* live for two growing seasons, usually forming a rosette that overwinters in the first year, and then setting seed and dying in the second season. *Perennial* weeds live for more than two years, persisting by the formation of seed or vegetative structures such as persistent roots, rhizomes (underground stems), stolons (runners), and daughter plants.

Broadleaf weed seedlings have two seed leaves, or cotyledons, that appear before the true leaves form. Broadleaf weeds can be identified by the shape of their true leaves and the pattern in which the leaves are attached to the stem. *Grass seedlings* do not have cotyledons. Grass weeds can be identified by differences in the structures where the leaf blade attaches to the stem, such as the

collar, ligule, and *auricle*. Flower characteristics and the presence of hairs, waxiness, or odor are other features used to identify weeds. Proper and timely identification is a key to planning effective weed control measures.

Weed Control Techniques

Integration of weed control techniques is the way to achieve effective weed control. On vegetable farms, herbicides are widely used because they reduce labor costs for weed control. The use of herbicides is thoroughly described in extension publications. Product label warnings and instructions should always be followed carefully. With judicious use, herbicides can be part of a sustainable cropping system. However, alternatives to herbicides are needed because of environmental concerns, the development of herbicide-resistant weeds, and the cost of new product development.

Weed control techniques include both strategies aimed at preventing weeds from germinating and those aimed at suppression once weeds are present. Techniques aimed at weed prevention include the following:

- Rotate among crops with different tillage practices.
- Compost animal manures to kill weed seeds.
- Clean farm implements before traveling between fields.
- Control weeds in hedgerows, alleys, and ditches.
- Mow or cultivate weeds before they set seed.

Techniques for suppressing weed growth include the following.

- Mulch with plastics or organic residues.
- Grow smother crops or intercrops.
- Hand-hoe.
- Use tractor cultivation.
- Use chemical control.
- Flame-weed.

Short-Term Weed Control

Short-term weed control is essential to production and profitability in a single year because it avoids reductions in crop yields. The *critical weed-free period* is the time during the life of a cash crop that weeds must be controlled in order to avoid significant yield loss.

In theory, the critical period starts a few weeks after a crop emerges and ends several weeks before crop harvest. This will vary depending on the competitiveness of the crop and weeds in question. For example, if broadleaf weeds such as redroot pigweed and common lamb's-quarters are allowed to grow only during the first two weeks and the last month of a sweet corn season, but eradicated in the interim, sweet corn yields should not be seriously affected. With a less-competitive crop, such as direct-seeded onions, or with less-competitive weeds, such as chickweed and purslane, the critical period would be different.

Critical weed-free periods *per se* are not particularly practical as the basis for weed control strategies. For one thing, they are not documented for many of the weed/crop/climate combinations that growers deal with. Another consideration is that shallow tillage cultivation tools are most effective on small weeds, which are not yet competitive. Shallow tillage is often targeted at weeds that have recently emerged, or may even be in the "white thread" stage, where they have germinated but not emerged from the soil. If the weather is right and labor is available for cultivation, it would be unwise to delay simply because the weeds are not yet competitive. Delay may result in missing the opportunity to use a fast, shallow tillage tool early. At a later date, a slower or more aggressive tool will be needed that may cost more to use and may bring more weed seeds up to the soil surface.

Long-Term Weed Control

Long-term weed control has to do with management of the soil *weed seed bank*. That is an ongoing battle to minimize the number of viable weed seeds or other propagules in a field. To deplete the soil weed seed bank, the grower needs to keep weeds from going to seed or building up their stored energy reserves, even though they may not threaten crops with competition. Drawing down the soil's weed seed bank takes consistent management over many years, but the rewards can be dramatic in terms of reducing weed pressure and lessening time spent on weed control. Partial efforts at weed seed bank management are probably not worth the time. Many growers may simply control weeds as necessary to get acceptable yields each year but not bother with weeds that grow after harvest, in hedgerows, or in fallow fields. In fact, some growers actually use weeds as natural cover crops. Whether this is advisable has a lot to do with the particular weed species on the farm, the competitiveness of crops to be grown, and the alternatives, in terms of cultivation tools, skills, and labor available, and cost.

Drawing a *weed map* that shows the location of weed species and their relative abundance in different fields is a useful tool for monitoring the progress, or lack of it, in long-term weed control on a farm. It can also help with planning the next year's weed control program.

Cultural Practices for Weed Control

Cultural practices that help prevent and suppress weeds during the growing season are important to successful vegetable production and essential for growers using little or no herbicide. Without these practices, the need for cultivation will be excessive, eating into time and profits and destroying soil structure and organic matter. Preventive practices—such as cover crops in rotation, smother-cropping, stale seedbeds, and clean fallowing—begin well before planting a crop. Other practices are aimed at suppressing weeds that directly interfere with a crop. These include mulching, intercropping, mowing, and concentrating resources (water and nutrients) near the crop.

Crop Rotation
for Weed Prevention

Crop rotation subjects weeds to an ever-changing habitat, thereby reducing the proliferation of species that prefer certain conditions. (Also see chapter 7, "Crop Rotation," beginning on page 69.) Just as herbicides should be rotated in a field to discourage the development of resistance, so too should cultivation regimes in a given field be changed regularly, and rotation helps accomplish this. While weeds do not develop resistance to cultivation, those that survive a particular cultivation regime may proliferate if the regime is not altered.

Rotation strategies for weed control include planting row versus sod crops, frequently versus rarely cultivated crops, deep- versus shallow-tillage crops, and early- versus late-season crops, as well as rotating fallow versus cash-cropped periods. Growers that use herbicides on just a few crops may rotate fields with high weed pressure to those crops as a cleanup strategy, assuming that there are labeled herbicides that are effective on the problem weed species present.

Smother Cropping
for Weed Suppression

Smother cropping is cover cropping with competitive species in an attempt to starve weeds of light, nutrients, moisture, and space (also see "Smother Crops," page 79). This approach is useful in fields that have such high weed pressure that they warrant being taken out of production. Smothering weakens perennial weeds by depleting their carbohydrate reserves and reduces annual weed pressure by preventing large numbers of fast-growing weeds from maturing and setting seed, although the soil weed seed bank may still be large.

Fast-growing, high biomass species are generally used as smother crops, because establishing smother crops before weeds is essential. Vigorous, warm-season cover crops such as buckwheat, Japanese millet, and sorghum-Sudan grass are good summer smother crops as they grow well in hot conditions. However, they should not be planted until soils are thoroughly warm. Cool-season crops such as rye, oats, field pea, and ryegrass are candidates for smother cropping in the early spring and fall.

Besides suppressing weeds, smother crops also add organic matter to the soil, protect against erosion and compaction, and, in the case of crops like buckwheat, provide bee forage. High seeding rates, adequate moisture and fertility, and good soil-seed contact by drilling or otherwise covering seed are important to establishing a thick smother crop.

Stale Seedbed Technique
for Weed Control

The stale seedbed technique takes advantage of the fact that most weeds have small seeds that germinate from the top inch or two of the soil, usually within a couple of weeks of preparing soil for planting. By letting these weeds germinate and then killing them without disturbing the soil and bringing up new weed seeds, subsequent weed pressure can be greatly reduced. In some cases, growers using stale seedbeds actually encourage weed germination with irrigation or row covers to overcome dry or cool conditions that slow weed growth. Weeds can be killed with flaming, nonselective herbicides, or extremely shallow scraping, after which it is critical to minimize soil movement when planting or transplanting. Early-season stale seedbeds are often ineffective, as most broadleaf weeds germinate in warm soils.

Composting Manure
for Weed Control

Composting manure is helpful for reducing the number of weed seeds added to the soil, as well as stabilizing nutrients. Hot composting, where temperatures reach approximately 140°F, can kill many weed seeds. Maintaining the proper C: N ratio, moisture, and aeration and turning piles inside-out several times is important to ensure that most or all of the compost does indeed get hot (also see chapter 6, "On-farm Composting," beginning on page 63). Turning also keeps weeds that sprout on the pile surface from going to seed.

Mulching for Weed Suppression

Mulching the soil provides a physical barrier to weed growth. Organic residues such as straw or leaves can suppress weeds for many weeks if put on thick enough, but they also keep soil temperatures cooler, which may slow the growth of warm-season crops. Black plastic mulch placed in close contact with a smooth seedbed to ensure effective convective heat transfer will warm the soil for crops and block light from weeds. The planting hole may require hand-weeding with slow-growing crops. Clear plastic mulches warm the soil to a greater extent than black plastic, but allow light to penetrate, thereby encouraging weed growth. Clear plastic therefore requires herbicide application prior to laying. However, under conditions of strong sunlight, solarization can be used to kill weeds under clear plastic by leaving the plastic in place for several weeks prior to making holes in it and planting a crop.

Selective wavelength mulches, such as Infra-Red Transmitting (IRT) are intermediate between black and clear plastic in their transmittance of photosynthetically active light and their ability to warm the soil. This can be an advantage for growers that want to avoid the use of herbicides but get the most soil warming possible for heat-loving, high-value crops, such as melons.

The edges of plastic pose a special challenge because weeds often grow well there but the plastic is easily ripped by close cultivation. To avoid hand-weeding, some growers have developed innovative cultivation tools to deal with this unique zone. These tools usually undercut then replace the plastic, or cultivate extremely close to, but not on top of, the plastic. Both approaches require straight runs of plastic with uniformly buried edges.

Intercropping for Weed Suppression

Intercropping is growing two or more crops simultaneously in close proximity and includes planting cover crops between cash crop rows, or inter-seeding (also known as under-sowing). Used primarily to improve soil, inter-seeding can prevent soil erosion, reduce wind injury, and improve travel through the field, as well as suppressing weeds. The trick in inter-cropping is to avoid competition with the cash crop. (Also see "Inter-Seeded Cover Crops," page 79.)

Mowing for Weed Suppression

Mowing vegetation between the rows of a cash crop can control weeds (or certain intercrops) by reducing competition for light, water, and nutrients and limiting the ability of weeds to photosynthesize and set viable seed. Mowing also enhances the environment for harvesting and pick-your-own sales. In most cases, between-row mowing is only practical on a small scale, or where rows are wide enough to accommodate tractor-pulled mowers. Side-discharge mowers may be used to manage mulch strips between rows, but they have the potential to do damage to crops by blowing debris on them.

Careful Placement of Resources

Careful placement of resources such as water and nutrients can be used to favor crops over weeds. By banding and side-dressing fertilizer, and in some cases by using drip irrigation, growers can deny weeds nutrients or water needed for good growth. A word of caution is that many plants send roots laterally to obtain resources, so locating water and fertilizer only in the row may be useful in limiting between-row weed pressure only if the rows are far apart.

Crop Establishment Techniques for Weed Control

Crop establishment techniques that encourage the rapid early growth of vegetables and discourage rapid early growth of weeds are critical to minimizing weed control costs. Production from transplants, compared to direct-seeding, gives crops an obvious jump over weeds. Carefully placed starter fertilizer feeds crops, not weeds. Timing the planting of crops to available soil moisture promotes their rapid establishment.

Cultivation Equipment for Weed Control

Cultivation equipment is used to kill weeds, although in some cases it may also be used for tillage to prepare ground for planting, incorporate fertilizers, or improve soil conditions and water infiltration (see chapter 9, "Tillage Equipment and Field Preparation," beginning on page 87).

Cultivation tools designed specifically for weed control vary in aggressiveness and are usually suited to killing weeds either before the crop emerges ("pre-emergence") or after it emerges ("post-emergence"). Tools designed for use after crop emergence provide either *between-row* weed control or *in-row* weed control, or in some cases, both. Cultivation implements may be designed to dislodge, cut, or bury plants. Matching the tool to the weeds, crops, and soil conditions is key. Juggling the uncertainties of weather and other management demands on the farm is the challenge to using a cultivation tool at the right time. For contact information for suppliers of weed-control equipment, see appendix C, beginning on page 244.

Equipment for Pre-Emergence Cultivation

Pre-emergence cultivation often involves shallow tillage of the soil with rotavators, various harrows, or field cultivators. If performed repeatedly, this approach is called a "clean fallow," which can occur before or in between plantings. The objective is to kill annual weeds, reduce the soil weed seed bank, and remove perennial weed growth.

Disk harrows (see figure 9.7, page 92) are often used for clean fallowing, but they may not be the best choice with a perennial weed problem like quack grass, since rhizomes tend to be chopped up and spread throughout a field. *Field cultivators* (see figure 9.8, page 92), equipped with rows of *C-tines* or *S-tines* and sweeps or shovels with lifting action, can be used to dig up and lift quack grass rhizomes to the surface of the soil, where they will dry out and die in hot, dry weather. A variety of field cultivators are on the market.

Equipment for Blind Cultivation

Blind cultivation relies on tools that work the entire surface of the soil "over the top" of a recently seeded or in some cases a recently emerged crop. The technique combines in-row and between-row cultivation, to control small weeds as well as those that have not yet visibly emerged, in the so-called white-thread stage of growth. This timing disturbs and dries out weeds before they get well established alongside the crop. Such fast, shallow cultivation works best on weeds that have been up for a week or less, and those in the white thread stage. Large-seeded crops sown deeply are able to tolerate such cultivation, while very small annual weeds cannot.

Flex-tine weeders, or "tine weeders," (figure 17.1, page 166) can be used for blind cultivation on a number of vegetable crops. They work well on a variety of soil textures and can even handle soil with small rocks. The weight of these units may be borne by the numerous thin metal tines that, when pulled at fast speed, vibrate in the soil and dislodge weeds, or by gauge wheels attached to the frame. Gauge wheels help control tine depth and avoid gouging soil on uneven fields. With some units, the three-point hitch can be used to adjust downward pressure on the tines. The width of tine weeders ranges from narrow, bed-covering sizes to very large units useful in large fields. Lely tine weeders have three rows of 6 mm (or 7 mm) tines with individual tine tension adjusters with working widths of 2.25 to 6 meters. Einböck tine weeders have 6.5 mm (to 8 mm) tines in widths of 1.5 to 15 meters or more.

A more aggressive blind cultivator is the *rotary hoe* (figure 17.2, page 166), which consists of many thin spider wheels, each with 16 or 18 "spoons" (tips) that dislodge very small weeds after planting the crop. Some models are drawn by three-point hitch and some are drawn by a simple hitch. The spider wheels move independently and bear the weight of the unit, although gauge wheels are available on larger units. Rotary hoes come in widths of 6 feet and up. They are most often used for weed control in corn and beans and for breaking up the surface of crusted soils. Rocks will jam in the wheels, keeping them from turning prop-

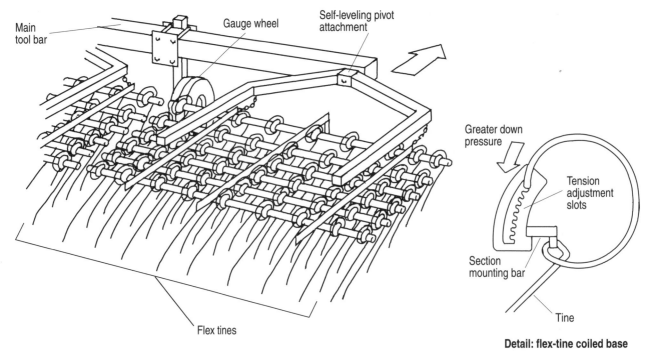

Figure 17.1 Flex-tine weeder
Source: Adapted from an illustration by John Gist in *Steel in the Field: A Farmer's Guide to Weed Management Tools*

erly. Plastic mulch pieces in the field will also collect on wheels and require removal. Dull spoons reduce the effectiveness of rotary hoeing.

Equipment for Post-Emergence Cultivation

Post-emergence cultivation is performed after crops are up. The size of the crop influences the timing for using various post-emergence cultivation tools. Less-aggressive tools designed only for control of between-row weeds are used when crops are small, or on delicate crops. Tools that bury weeds in the crop row by throwing soil over them can be used once sturdy crops are well established.

Tractors for Post-Emergence Cultivation

High-clearance tractors facilitate mechanical weed control for many vegetable crops (figure 17.3). These tractors can be used to cultivate long into the growing season since crops up to several feet tall pass unharmed under the tractor. In addition, tools can be "belly-mounted" underneath these tractors and in view of the operator, increasing precision of cultivation in terms of how close to the crop weeds can be killed.

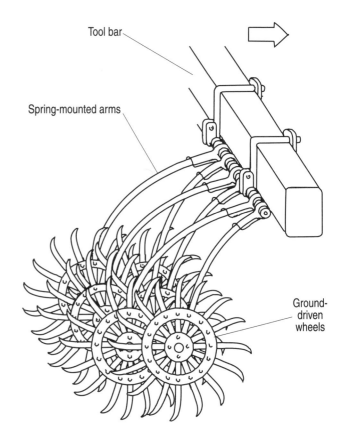

Figure 17.2 Rotary hoe

Source: Adapted from an illustration by John Gist in *Steel in the Field: A Farmer's Guide to Weed Management Tools*

Sustainable Vegetable Production from Start-Up to Market

Offset tractors assist with close cultivation of crops because the driver's seat is off to the side of the tractor body, enhancing vision of the row. The operator can look directly down on the crop rows as they pass under the steering wheel and tractor seat. Manufacturing of this type of tractor has declined in recent years, so used models are in great demand. While often available at low cost, used models may lack modern safety equipment, such as Roll-Over Protective Structures.

Cultivating tractors (figure 17.4) are small, low to the ground, easy to guide, and used only for precision cultivation of young or low-growing crops. Cultivating tractors are designed to allow the operator an unobstructed view of crops that are being cultivated. The Allis Chalmers "G" tractor, no longer made, is the classic of this type. Other brands, Hyspan, Saukville, and Friday, all somewhat like the G, are currently available.

Other Equipment for Post-Emergence Cultivation

Basket weeders (figure 17.5) are metal cages that roll on top of and scuff the soil surface without moving soil sideways into the crop rows. This action makes them ideal for use in crops like lettuce that have to be kept free of soil. Buddingh basket weeders are custom built for two- to eight-row beds. Angled baskets are available to work the sides of raised beds. Basket widths range from 2 to 14 inches, depending on the space between rows. For wider widths, and for inner-row widths that change as crops grow, overlapping baskets are available that "telescope," or expand in and out to adjust for the width.

Commonly used at rather fast speeds of 4 to 8 mph, basket weeders are best used with straight rows and by an experienced operator in order to avoid crop damage. The front row of baskets turn at ground speed, while a chain drives the rear row of baskets a little bit faster; so these kick up soil and dislodge weeds that survive the first baskets. This tool is usually belly-mounted to assist with close cultivation. The baskets handle some small stones but work best in fine soils free of clods and residues.

Caution: To help protect yourself and those who work with you, use a tractor with a certified Roll-Over Protective Structure (ROPS).

Figure 17.3 High-clearance Farmall tractor with front-mounted engine and belly-mounted cultivators

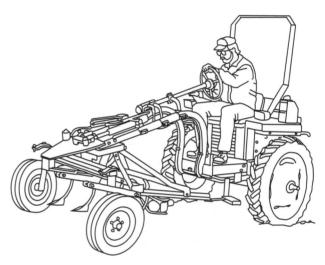

Figure 17.4 Rear-drive cultivating tractor
Source: Adapted from the Saukville® Tractor Corporation

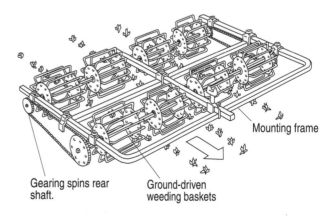

Mounting frame

Gearing spins rear shaft.

Ground-driven weeding baskets

Figure 17.5 Basket weeder
Source: Adapted from an illustration by John Gist in *Steel in the Field: A Farmer's Guide to Weed Management Tools*

Finger weeders (figure 17.6) cultivate around the stems of crop plants that are sturdy enough to handle some contact. Rubber-coated metal fingers provide some in-row weeding. These are connected to a lower set of metal fingers that work deeper in the ground and drive the unit at ground speed. These units are used at slow speed since they are in such close proximity to the plants. They require belly-mounting and are ideal for a G-type tractor. Wet clayey soils can stick to the fingers and require frequent removal.

Brush weeders (figure 17.7) are European tools for close cultivation in narrow rows. Brush weeders are expensive and not very common here. Shields protect plants from bristle wheels that rotate independently between the rows, "sweeping" weeds out of the soil. An operator sits behind the rotating wheels and steers the unit to assure precision.

Sweeps, shovels, and knives (figure 17.8) are metal tools that attach to the cultivation shanks (vertical pieces of metal that attach to a horizontal tool bar—see figure 9.9, page 93). Depending on their shape and orientation, these tools move soil in different ways as they are pulled between crop rows. People are not consistent in how they name these tools, so there can be some confusion. The shanks can be clamped to different places on the tool bars to achieve an arrangement that provides the desired in-row coverage and extent of soil movement. Tractor mounted-tool bars can be rear-mounted, belly-mounted (underneath a high-clearance tractor), or in some cases front-mounted.

Sweeps are wing-shaped and come in various sizes. They are used to dig up large weeds between crop rows while throwing soil into the row. Big sweeps, or duckfeet, are often used behind the tractor to cultivate the wheel tracks. Half-sweeps have a wing on just one side, so the wingless side can cut closer to crops or plastic edges.

Shovels are narrower than sweeps, throw less soil, and sometimes have two points that are reversible. Knives are like angled shovels that are used to cut more horizontally and closer to a crop than shovels.

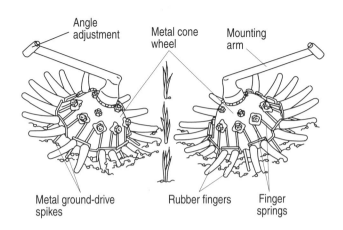

Figure 17.6 Finger weeder

Source: Adapted from an illustration by John Gist in *Steel in the Field: A Farmer's Guide to Weed Management Tools*

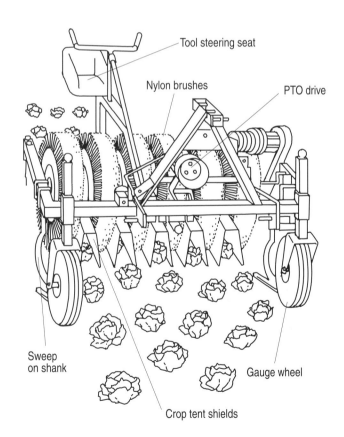

Figure 17.7 Brush weeder

Source: Adapted from an illustration by John Gist in *Steel in the Field: A Farmer's Guide to Weed Management Tools*

Sustainable Vegetable Production from Start-Up to Market

General purpose or row-crop cultivator sweeps can uproot weeds and move soil aside into the crop row.

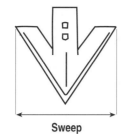

Sweep

Half-sweeps, left or right-sided, can work up close to the crop row or plastic mulch edge.

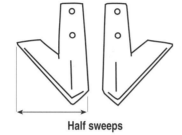

Half sweeps

Duckfoot sweeps are used to loosen soil and remove weeds from tractor wheel tracks.

Duckfoot sweep

Double-pointed shovels are used to uproot weeds without moving as much soil as sweeps. They can be reversed.

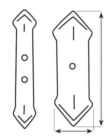

Double-pointed shovels

Crescent hoes are used to cultivate the side shoulders of raised beds.

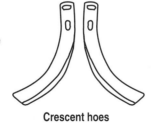

Crescent hoes

Side knives can reach under the row canopy, working close to the base of the plants and hilling slightly if mounted at an angle.

Side knives

Figure 17.8 Sweeps, shovels, hoes, and knives

Wiggle-hoes have shanks with half sweeps attached that can be hand-steered around plants in a row by an operator seated on the back of the tractor-pulled unit. Close cultivation is possible, but extra labor is required for the operator. Slow tractor speed and wide crop spacing must be used to allow shanks to be moved in and out of the row.

Row-crop cultivators (figure 17.9) consist of tool bars on a tractor-pulled frame with various shanks and cultivation implements attached so as to leave space for the crop rows to pass. These are much like field cultivators (see figure 9.8, page 92) except for the spacing of the shanks and the absence of implements, such as rolling baskets or cultipackers, that completely cover the soil. Shields of various types may be mounted on either side of the crop rows to protect them from soil and rock movement during cultivation.

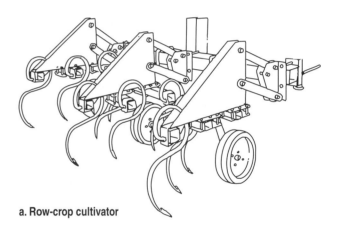

a. Row-crop cultivator

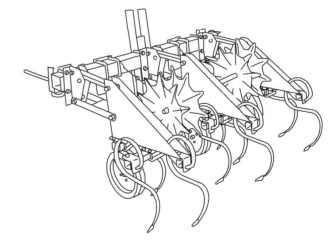

b. Shielded row-crop cultivator

Figure 17.9 Row-crop cultivators

Spyders™, torsion weeders, and spring-hoes (figure 17.10) are used alone or in combination for close between-row cultivation. The Spyder™ is a wheel of staggered curved teeth that is ground-driven on a ball-bearing hub. A pair of 12-inch Spyders™ can be angled at 45 degrees toward or away from the row to either pull soil away or throw it back. Aggressive and rapid cultivation of a variety of row crops is possible, even on rather stony soils. Torsion weeders are square stock metal bars that can be mounted to follow the Spyders™, leveling the soil and flexing around the plants to clean up spots missed by the Spyders™. Spring-hoes are flat blades about 16 inches long that oscillate just below the soil surface and are a bit more aggressive than the torsion weeders. Spring-hoes or torsion weeders are usually used following a pair of Spyder™ wheels, but not alone.

Rolling cultivators consist of gangs of heavy slicer tines that aggressively dig up weeds and pulverize soil between rows (figure 17.11). Individual gang width ranges from 10 to 16 inches, depending on number of slicer tines. Mounted on a tool bar, units are available for one to twelve rows. Gangs may contain two to five rolling spiders that swivel as a unit to move soil into or away from the crop row, dislodging weeds as they go. Gangs can be angled to "hill up," or throw soil into the row. Used with fertilizer

attachments, rolling cultivators make side-dressing possible while cultivating. Rocks may jam in tines, and action may be unduly aggressive for sandy soils. Pairs of rolling cultivators can also be belly-mounted under a cultivating tractor.

Hilling disks (figure 17.12) are used to aggressively pull soil away from small crops or to throw soil into the rows of crops such as potatoes, leeks, sweet corn, and other crops that tolerate or benefit from being buried. Properly timed, this results in excellent in-row weed control.

Equipment for Flame Weeding

Flame weeding is the killing of weeds with intense, directed heat, usually with a propane-burning device. Usually, flame weeding is used to control small weeds using the stale seedbed method. This involves preparing the soil as if for planting, without actually planting a crop. Instead, weeds are allowed, even encouraged, to grow, and then killed with flame. (Instead of flaming, an herbicide or shallow cultivation may be used to kill weeds in the stale seedbed; also see "Stale Seedbed Technique for Weed Control," page 163). After planting the crop but before it emerges, another flaming may be applied to kill weeds that have emerged in the interim. With slow-to-germinate crops, this final flame weeding is often critical to success.

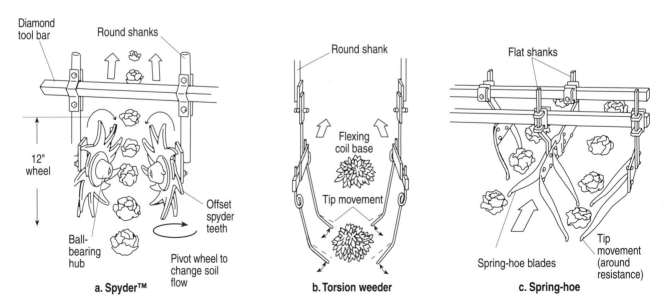

Figure 17.10 Spyders™, torsion weeders, and spring-hoes
Source: Adapted from illustrations by John Gist in *Steel in the Field: A Farmer's Guide to Weed Management Tools*

Because weeds tend to emerge in flushes stimulated by seedbed preparation, the initial emergence of weeds often represents a major portion of the weed pressure in a given field, provided subsequent tillage that brings new seeds to the surface is avoided. Like contact herbicides, flaming does not involve soil disturbance, so it is well-suited to stale seedbed preparation.

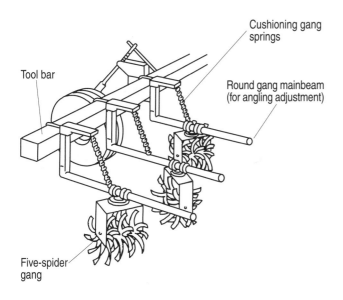

Figure 17.11 Rolling cultivators
Source: Adapted from an illustration by John Gist in *Steel in the Field: A Farmer's Guide to Weed Management Tools*

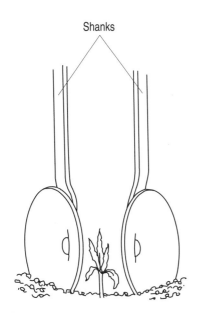

Disk hillers set to move soil away from row

Figure 17.12 Hilling disks
Source: Adapted from an illustration by John Gist in *Steel in the Field: A Farmer's Guide to Weed Management Tools*

Backpack or hand-held flamers are the simplest and least expensive tools for flame weeding (figure 17.13, page 172). A small canister is carried by hand or in a backpack, while a single burner at the end of a solid wand is aimed at the area to be flamed. The burner size, walking speed, and flame adjustment determine how much heat is applied to an area. This technique is getting popular for stale seedbed flaming in small plantings of crops that will later be close-cultivated between the rows. Examples are lettuce, radishes, spinach, herbs, and other crops that will not tolerate soil being thrown into the row.

Tractor-mounted flame weeders (figure 17.14, page 172) are used to flame large areas of the soil or large plantings of crops. Several different designs are in operation; some are commercially available, and others have been built by growers. Units that burn propane in the gas phase, as hand-held flamers do, may "freeze up" as ice forms in and on the lines when large quantities of gas pass through them. To minimize this, canisters of gas may be kept in a heated water-bath, which pre-warms the fuel. Other units are designed to burn gas in the liquid stage, which avoids freeze-up of the gas lines and can generate a lot more heat.

Flame weeder components include a tank (or several), valves, gas lines, regulators, pilot lights, and emergency shut-off components. Gas may flow directly from tanks to individual burners, or it may be distributed through a manifold first. Burners are specific for gas or liquid burning systems, and are available with different British thermal unit (BTU) ratings. Burners are usually arranged in a row so that the entire width of the bed, including wheel tracks, can be uniformly flamed. They may be fixed to the unit, or adjustable. Having individual shut-off valves for burners and the ability to change their position on the flamer and adjust their angle toward the ground allows for more flexibility in using the flamer.

Tractor speed when flaming should be just a few miles per hour. The larger the weeds or the heavier the dew, the slower tractor speed needs to be. Flaming does not have to burn the weeds. A short exposure to intense heat "blanches" the weeds, and they collapse and die within minutes

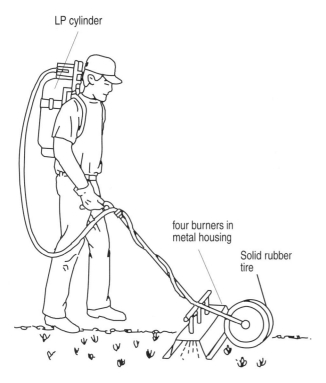

a. Wheeled manifold backpack flamer

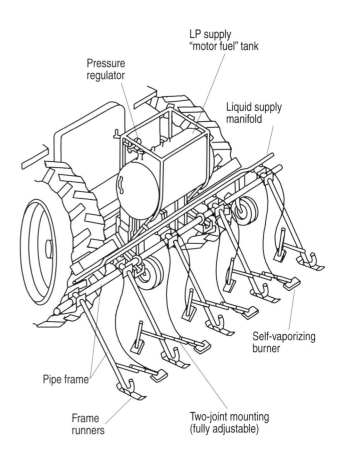

Figure 17.14 Tractor-mounted flame weeders
Source: Adapted from an illustration by John Gist in *Steel in the Field: A Farmer's Guide to Weed Management Tools*

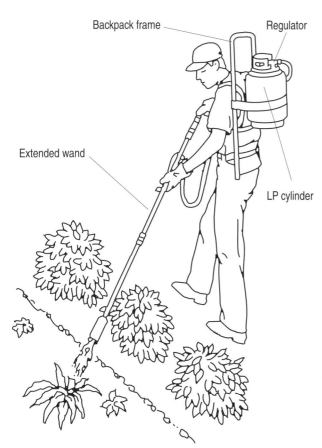

b. Wand-type backpack flamer

Figure 17.13 Backpack flame weeders
Source: Adapted from illustrations by John Gist in *Steel in the Field: A Farmer's Guide to Weed Management Tools*

or hours. Exceptions to this are grasses with below ground growing points and purslane, which can take the heat. These weeds require hotter temperatures or subsequent cultivation to control.

The propane containers used on tractor-mounted flamers must be "motor fuel" tanks intended for mobile use, unlike stationary propane canisters. Motor fuel tanks can be rather expensive. The design of the system and the selection of valves and controls should be done in consultation with a propane professional. All tractor mounts, canister straps, and lines should be carefully examined before each use of the flamer. Besides the potential for explosion, concerns when using flame weeders include liability insurance, regulations, and the possibility of starting fires in dry grass or hedgerows.

For contact information for suppliers of weed-control equipment, see appendix C, beginning on page 244.

Sustainable Vegetable Production from Start-Up to Market

Chapter 18

Wildlife Management

There are few things as frustrating in vegetable production as the loss of crops to wildlife, especially when the damage is at key stages—right after the crop has emerged or just days before harvest. To make matters worse, many plants may be partially damaged, rather than wholly consumed (as when a single bite is taken out of every head of lettuce down the row).

Wildlife damage is most frequently caused by deer, woodchucks, raccoons, rabbits, and birds. In remote areas, bear can be a problem; and in some settings, voles or other small rodents may bother vegetable crops, especially when mulches are used. Generally, physical exclusion by fencing or netting is the most effective means of reducing wildlife damage, and it may be the only practical solution under conditions of severe wildlife pressure. Exclusion systems incur the highest up-front costs, but these should be considered over the life of the system when compared to less costly, less effective short-term controls.

When they are legal and appropriate, habitat modification around fields; the use of repellents, trapping, and removal; and lethal controls such as shooting or poisoning are other options for wild-life control. Whenever possible, sport hunting during legal seasons should be encouraged near the farm to reduce the number of vertebrate pests near vegetable fields and the damage they can do. State laws vary, but in many cases they allow for control of animals when they are damaging crops, regardless of the legal hunting season dates. Check with your state wildlife agency to determine the regulations and reporting requirements before attempting to kill or trap any wildlife that is damaging your crops.

Common Wildlife Species That Damage Vegetable Crops

Although there is variation in wildlife pressure among vegetable farms even within a locality, crops in the Northeast are commonly damaged by wildlife as shown in table 18.1.

Controlling Damage by Deer
Fencing to Control Deer

Deer are most effectively controlled with 8- to 10-foot high *woven-wire fencing* (figure 18.1, page 174). Because such fencing is expensive, on the order of $6 to $8 per running foot, few growers can afford it on large fields. However, the 30- to 35-year life expectancy of a well-constructed fence makes its annual cost relatively low, especially if the value of crops protected and aggrava-

Table 18.1 Wildlife and the vegetable crops they frequently damage

Animal	Crops Damaged
Deer	Lettuce and other greens, crucifers, legumes, squash, pumpkins, sweet corn, and others
Woodchucks	Seedlings, crucifers, lettuce and other greens, legumes, and squash and pumpkin fruit
Raccoons	Mature sweet corn and melons
Rabbits	Spring seedlings, lettuce and other greens, carrots, parsnips, and beets
Birds	Corn seedlings and mature corn, tomatoes, and melons
Voles	Various seeds, seedlings, beets, potatoes, and other root crops

tion avoided are factored in. The use of galvanized high-tensile wire reduces the need for costly repair due to rust or to objects falling on the fence.

High-tensile electric fencing with a half-dozen or so smooth-wires, 4 to 6 feet high and either vertical (figure 18.2) or slanted (figure 18.3), is effective against moderate to high deer pressure. The cost is about $2 to $3.50 per linear foot to construct. Deer prefer to go through or under fences rather than over, so these fences are psychological as well as physical barriers. An optional "hot" wire 8–10 inches off the ground and supplied with a pulsed electric current further deters deer and teaches them to avoid fenced areas. Vegetation must be controlled below the hot wire. Slanted fence may be more effective, but it

is harder to construct and makes vegetation control more difficult than vertical fence.

Single or double-strand *poly-tape electrified fence* provides no physical barrier but acts as a psychological deterrent (figure 18.4). Single-wire electric fence baited with aluminum foil strips smeared with peanut butter can be effective on small fields (figure 18.5, page 176). These lure deer into contact with the wire so that they will get a shock, which trains them to stay away from the area. As with chemical repellents, effectiveness depends on the timing of installation and the level of deer pressure. Since deer establish feeding patterns, early use of repellents is critical to their effectiveness. When there are high populations or low alternative food sources, repellents are unlikely to be effective.

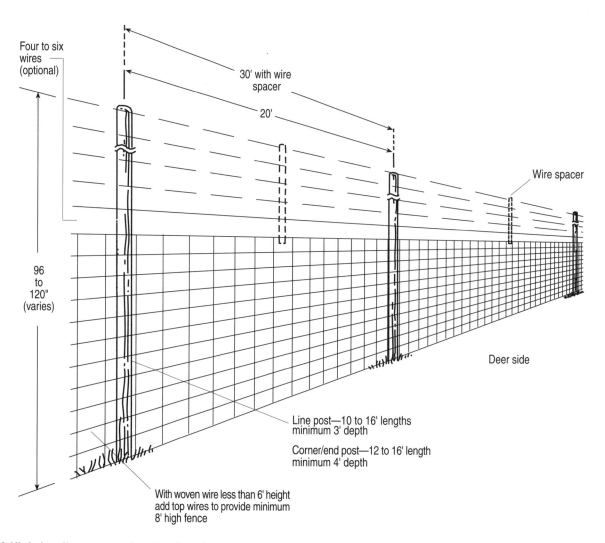

Figure 18.1 High-tensile woven-wire deer fencing

Source: Adapted from *High-Tensile Wire Fencing*, NRAES–11

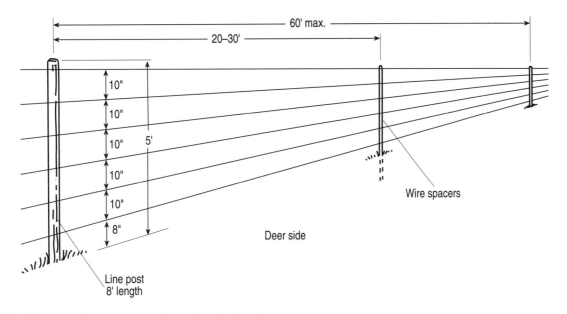

Figure 18.2 High-tensile six-wire vertical electric fencing
Source: Adapted from *High-Tensile Wire Fencing,* NRAES–11

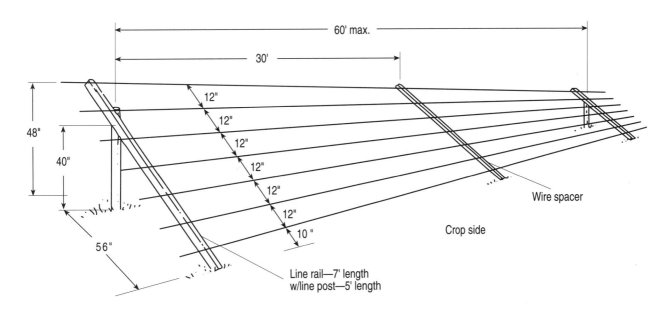

Figure 18.3 Slanted seven-wire high-tensile fencing
Source: Adapted from *High-Tensile Wire Fencing,* NRAES–11

Repellents to Control Deer

Repellents are based on odors or taste that deer find unpleasant. "Contact" repellents are applied directly to plants to be protected, and "area" repellents are applied near plants. Area repellents are usually less effective than contact repellents, but some materials cannot legally be applied directly to vegetable crops. Commercial formulations of ammonium soaps are among the few products registered for use on edible crops. Other products contain rotten eggs, capsaicin, or a fungicide that is distasteful to deer. Cloth strips

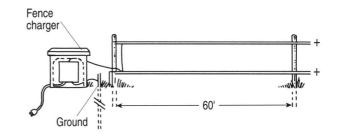

Figure 18.4 Poly-tape electrified fence (double-strand)
Source: Adapted from Hygnstrom, Timm, and Larson

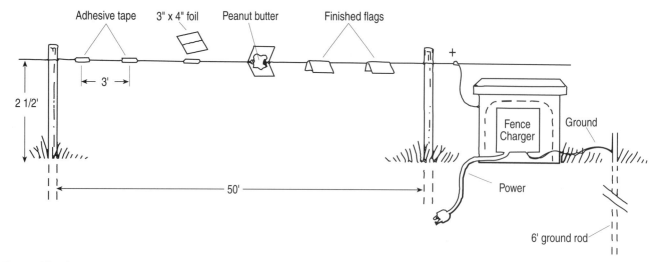

Figure 18.5 Single-wire electric fencing baited with peanut butter in foil flags
Source: Adapted from Hygnstrom, Timm, and Larson

attached to an electrical fence that are sprayed with these materials may increase the effectiveness of the fence. No material should be applied directly to a crop unless it is labeled for use on that crop. To get the best results, the label instructions should be followed in terms of application rates and intervals. Reapplication of materials may be necessary after a rain.

Many noncommercial materials have been used to deter deer, including deodorant soap bars, stockings filled with human hair, and garlic or hot pepper sprays. The effectiveness, and, in some cases, the legality of these items is questionable.

Fields on a farm often vary in deer pressure. Those with nearby cover such as woods with low brush or with nearby forage such as legume hay may have more problems. Removal of brush and mowing of forage can help, but growers often simply avoid planting the crops most palatable to deer in these fields.

Controlling Damage by Woodchucks

Woodchucks are an unprotected species in most states and are often controlled with lethal means, such as *fumigation* of burrows with gas cartridges or shooting. These tactics do provide short-term control, but studies show that burrows are rapidly reoccupied and populations may be largely unaffected over time by these methods.

Hardware cloth fence buried 1 foot deep and standing 3 feet high can reduce woodchuck damage. Adding a hot wire a few inches outside the fence and about 5 inches off the ground can help. Two hot wires added at 5-inch intervals to the bottom of deer fences can also be effective at deterring woodchucks.

Habitat modification can reduce the damage caused by woodchucks since they tend to live in burrows near fields, in hedgerows, and along stone walls and roads. Eliminating overgrown areas and brush piles, and frequent mowing may make an area less attractive to them.

Commercial repellents sold for control of other wildlife species have little effect on woodchucks and are not registered for use to control woodchucks.

Controlling Damage by Raccoons

Raccoons feed at night, and they prefer mature crops high in sugar, such as sweet corn and melons. They are intelligent animals, not easily deterred by frightening devices or repellents. Raccoons are excellent climbers, so a "hot" wire is needed if fencing is to be effective. Two-strand electric fencing can provide effective exclusion (figure 18.4, page 175). One wire should be 6 inches off the ground and the other wire 6 inches above that. In some cases, a single low wire may be sufficient. The fence should be put in place at least two weeks before the crop is attractive to raccoons. If the fence is left on continuously, it will also deter deer and woodchucks during the day.

Raccoons may be trapped and then removed or destroyed, depending on local game laws. Baits may include marshmallows on a wire landing in the back of the box trap. Peanut butter and jelly also works, as does a slightly open can of sardines. These baits may also attract other nontarget species.

There are no practical means of habitat modification to avoid raccoon damage, except to remove obvious sources of food and shelter that may be attracting them.

Controlling Damage by Rabbits

Rabbits (the eastern cottontail species) feed on a variety of vegetables, sometimes devouring succulent plants such as beans, carrots, parsnips, peas, or beets down to ground level. Corn, cucurbits, and solanaceous crops are not usually damaged by rabbits. Two-foot-high fencing can provide exclusion, as long as there are no small spaces for rabbits to squeeze through. Chicken wire alone is effective, or it can be affixed to the bottom of a taller, sturdier fence used to deter deer or other large animals. The fence must be tight to the ground, but not necessarily buried. Placing repellent materials on cloth along the fence may provide additional protection. Hinder is the only repellent that can be applied directly to plants among those products currently labeled for rabbits damaging vegetable crops.

Removal of nearby dense vegetation may reduce rabbit pressure by eliminating their habitat. This requires clearing brush and frequently mowing near fields. Piles of brush, stones, and other debris should be removed, as they provide good habitat for rabbits. Cats running loose can reduce the number of nesting young as well.

Controlling Damage by Birds

Birds can cause severe damage to vegetables, depending on the crop and its stage of growth as well as the species and abundance of birds in the area. Sweet corn can be particularly hard hit,

either when seedlings are pulled just after emergence or during maturation. Tomatoes and other soft fruits are sometimes damaged by bird pecking. While netting is far and away the most effective means of control, it is rarely applied over vegetable crops due to the high cost of materials and labor.

Visual scare devices, such as reflective tape, scare-eye balloons, and scarecrows can be effective over the short term, but only in some situations and with some species. In many cases the birds habituate, or get used to, the devices. Frequent moving of the devices and using them in combination with auditory deterrents such as noisemakers or shooting can improve their effectiveness. Visual deterrents need to be placed at close intervals for best results. Use at least six scare-eye balloons per acre, and one balloon every 10 or 15 yards may be necessary to get effective control in some cases. Strips of reflecting Mylar tape placed 3–7 yards apart can be effective in protecting small fields from bird damage. However, the tape frequently breaks in high winds and becomes entangled in the field.

Auditory scare devices include noisemakers and recordings of the distress calls of various bird species. Cannons, sirens, and bangers can be effective for short-term control by scaring birds, but by themselves do not usually affect the overall impact of birds on a crop over the long run. To get the best results, vary the sounds; move the devices around; use in conjunction with other methods such as distress calls or visual devices; and reinforce with real danger, such as shooting.

Federal law protects migratory and resident birds except for pigeons, house sparrows, starlings (or "blackbirds"), cowbirds, grackles, crows, and magpies committing or about to commit damage to agricultural crops. All state and local regulations must also be followed, so be sure to check with wildlife officials before killing or harassing birds.

Cultural practices to keep crows and blackbirds from pulling sweet corn seedlings include avoiding planting corn in fields with convenient perches such as power lines, planting deep to make pulling difficult, and scheduling multiple plantings to minimize damage to at least a few blocks. Reducing damage during harvest can be accomplished by selecting cultivars with good tip cover, controlling insects such as corn borer that may attract birds, and moving harvest up by a few days to limit the time that the crop is attractive and available to birds.

Controlling Damage by Voles

Voles are small rodents sometimes mistakenly referred to as field mice. Meadow voles tend to live on the ground surface and move about through pathways an inch or two wide in low-growing vegetation. Pine voles dwell underground, forming extensive tunnels that lead to small openings at the soil surface. Both species can be managed with rodenticide, but materials are labeled for use nearby, not within vegetable fields. Removal of ground cover in fields through clean cultivation can help with control of voles, especially meadow vole. Conversely, use of plastic or straw mulches may encourage vole problems.

Trapping can effectively reduce vole damage in smaller fields, up to 4 acres or so. Meadow voles are easily captured in either snap-back mousetraps or box traps baited with apple pieces. Trapping effectiveness will be increased by providing overhead cover (such as a roof shingle or slab of wood). Usually four consecutive days of trapping are needed to remove most voles from a field.

Wildlife Management— A Grower Profile

Brian Caldwell and Twinkle Griggs
Hemlock Grove Farm
West Danby, New York
Brian Caldwell and Twinkle Griggs have run a 110-acre diversified hill farm in West Danby, New York, for twenty years. Until recently, when Brian took a full-time job off the farm, the couple managed 4 acres of intensive mixed vegetable production, 2 acres of cover crops for rotation, 1 acre of orchard crops, and 15 acres of hay and pasture for their twenty-ewe flock of sheep. The remainder is in woods, and the farm is surrounded by woodland, including 7,000 acres of state forest. Their market is the Ithaca Farmers Market, with some wholesaling through the Finger Lakes Organic Co-op.

"Our farm is classic wildlife habitat. Unfortunately we have several small fields that are separated from each other due to the topography, so there is a lot of border area for wildlife incursion from within the farm as well as from outside—it's pretty much a worst-case scenario.

"Deer have been our main problem, followed by woodchucks. We cope with rabbits, rats, and mice, too. We don't grow much sweet corn, and no berries, so we never had much raccoon or bird damage. For five or six years we managed to control deer using three-strand electric sheep fence with surveyor flagging baited with peanut butter, and that really seemed to keep them out. A lot of our vegetable fields are bounded by pasture, so deer would have to get through two sets of fences, and that probably helped. What started happening was that in the fall they would knock the fence down and move into the vegetable fields. Over three to four years they were doing that more and more until the fences didn't work at all. Then we put up a seven-strand high-tensile fence, 6 feet tall, and that worked for only a few months. I've watched them just dive through the upper strands, which are about 15 inches apart. That was a major disappointment, since we have about 8 acres fenced. Our terrain is hilly, and it cost about $2,500; and I feel like I threw the money away.

> *"The catch is that once you wait until deer are accustomed to being in the field it is much more difficult to change their habit, yet nobody wants to spend the money on deer protection before they know they have a problem. Putting up fence in early spring, when there is a lot of alternative feed for deer, is probably a good idea since they won't be used to going in your fields."*

Sustainable Vegetable Production from Start-Up to Market

"The catch is that once you wait until deer are accustomed to being in the field it is much more difficult to change their habit, yet nobody wants to spend the money on deer protection before they know they have a problem. Putting up a fence in early spring, when there is a lot of alternative feed for deer, is probably a good idea since they won't be used to going in your fields. It seems to me that people that have slanted high-tensile fence get pretty good protection versus an upright fence of the same height. I've been advised by a wildlife specialist that slanted fence will work on up to 20 acres; bigger than that it makes sense to use an 8-foot-high woven wire upright fence.

"The smaller the area that you're enclosing, the more trapped the deer seem to feel, so the less fence you can get away with. We've enclosed small sections of carrots, probably ⅛ acre or less, with electric sheep fencing, only 33 inches high, and that still seems to help. On a really small scale, we used to place concrete reinforcing wire, the kind we used for tomato cages, directly over beds of greens to keep deer out, and that works, but it is expensive and labor intensive. Providing alternative feed on parts of the farm away from the vegetables has helped protect against deer damage. Buckwheat, alfalfa, and soybean are very attractive to deer.

"Woodchucks are much easier to deal with. If you have an active dog or two and you're not too big an operation, it is possible to keep the populations down within a quarter-mile or so of the house. When we lost our two dogs and just had a puppy for a year, the woodchucks increased dramatically; and that was quite a revelation. Besides the dogs, to deter woodchucks I've tried putting bird netting along the ground by field edges. It was a pain to use and didn't work that well, either. Grass grew up through it and I forgot it was there. So we switched to "Electronet" electric fencing. It looks like woven wire except it's made out of plastic with a few strands of metal in each wire. There are eight live wires and a neutral wire at the bottom, and it has built-in posts with metal spikes at the bottom. It costs less than 70 cents per foot; it's what a lot of sheep farmers use. We use the electric fence anyway for our sheep, so there are lots of hot wires around the farm to plug into for protecting the vegetable fields.

"We use the fence along edges of the fields where woodchucks are the worst problem, on crops they really like, such as brassicas. They'll bother squash, but not quite as severely. If we have problem areas we'll use the gas cartridges, or woodchuck bombs, which does kill them; but the burrows get repopulated, sometimes in a few weeks, especially in midsummer; so you have to check them all the time.

"Rats and mice have been a real problem, too, getting into buildings and stored crops. Thoroughly cleaning out the storage areas and putting mouse bait out regularly is a good way to keep populations from building up all summer long. All these rodent populations are really high in late fall and are bound to invade buildings. We use the vitamin-D baits since they are allowed organically in New York, but they are just not very attractive to the rodents, and probably not as effective as some other rodenticides. There are a number of different products available, and switching among them is a way to avoid development of resistance in the population. Sticky boards are disgusting, but they work, as do rattraps and mousetraps baited with peanut butter or cheese.

"Rabbits have been a minor problem, but it's not too hard to shoot them. The dogs seem to help keep the population down, too.

"It's the deer that have really caused major losses. If you have low numbers they're not a big problem—it's when the population density gets high that there is no way you can deal with it without huge expense. I feel that regulatory agencies should be much more supportive of farmers and try to manage the populations at lower levels. I also think they should look at more creative ways to help us out. Perhaps they could allow farms to have out-of-season hunting permits, allowing people to come on our land to reduce local deer populations to manageable levels. Maybe the hunting parties would pay us; we could have a niche market. One hunter that got a 160-pound deer on our farm told me, 'That organic broccoli feed is really great stuff.' "

Chapter 19

Grower Profiles and Enterprise Budgets for Vegetable Crops

Asparagus—
A Grower Profile

Bob and Jane Pomykala
Pomykala Farm, Grand Isle, Vermont
Pomykala Farm includes about 30 acres of mixed vegetables, sold roughly 75% wholesale and 25% retail, through the farm stand and farmers market. The soils contain a lot of clay and are quite heavy, and the growing season is relatively long for Vermont, due to their location next to Lake Champlain. Bob Pomykala grows 3.5 acres of asparagus. Most of his fields are fifteen years old and planted to Washington-type cultivars. These are gradually being rotated out of asparagus, and new plantings are being made of Jersey all-male hybrids in other fields.

"One thing that's essential for asparagus is well-drained soil because you have to get on the ground so early to harvest. I have always told people, if alfalfa will grow there, you're probably all set; if it won't, you're probably not going to be successful. Another important consideration is freezing of the tips from cold weather. As I've talked to other growers in Vermont, I realize this is a common problem in the rest of the state; but here we rarely get late spring frosts due to the lake and the slope of the field, so we have never had a freeze affect our asparagus."

Before former hayfields are brought into production for asparagus, the soils are tested, plowed, and fertilized, and mixed vegetables are grown for a season. This allows fertility to be built up and weeds to be worked on. In the planting year, soils are sampled and tested again, fertilized as needed for asparagus, perhaps with some extra P applied.

About 30 tons to the acre of aged dairy manure is spread. There is no need for lime on these soils, which have a natural pH of 7 or slightly higher. The manure is rotavated in; then furrows are formed using an old two-bottom plow with the first bottom set all the way up, the other bottom set all the way down. One pass is made up the row and then another back again to make a ditch about 6 inches deep. Row spacing is 67 inches apart, the width of the tractor tires.

Originally, Bob grew his own crowns by direct-seeding in early spring on some sandy land on a friend's farm. A year later, he dug these in late April and transplanted them immediately (within one day) into his field. Crowns were planted 14 inches apart using spacing sticks, bushel baskets, and lots of high school kids. Not much care was taken to spread out the roots at planting. Hand rakes were used to cover up the crowns with a couple inches of soil.

As the year progressed, furrows were filled in and the weeds were cultivated with a Farmall Cub using a homemade rake that pushed soil into the furrow a few inches each time without burying the little ferns. Cultivation was timed to the new flushes of weeds. Sweeps were used for between-row weed control. Later in the season, once ferns were taller and stronger, the rake was adjusted to throw some soil onto the base of the ferns to get in-row weed control. Three or four cultivations were necessary in the first year.

In subsequent years Bob used to use a rotavator to till the field, going over the top of the crowns very lightly. First he would dig up a few crowns and examine them for signs of bud swelling; and when that started, he would rotavate. The idea was to wait as long as possible to get the best weed control. He would burn the ferns in late fall, winter, or early spring to get them out of the way. Fires would be lit with newspaper, and with enough dry matter and a slight wind blowing away from the woods this worked well.

As the years went by, the crowns grew slowly toward the soil surface, as close as two inches. It became impossible to use the rotavator without chewing up crowns, so Bob changed his system. He now uses Lilliston rolling cultivators to control weeds during harvest.

Once the weed populations merit control, the Lilliston cultivators are used with the gangs of cultivators angled to take soil from the row middles and throw it onto the crop rows. This is done during the harvest period, after the day's harvest. This technique digs up weeds between the rows as well as burying weeds in the row. Asparagus spears continue to grow up through the soil added to the row. Putting a couple of inches of new, softer soil onto the row also helps with cutting shorter spears under the soil surface, which can be difficult in heavy soils. The Lilliston is used about once a week through the harvest season, or about five times a year.

Some weeds do escape, so two or three times during the season, after the field has been harvested, a brush hog goes through the fields, just above the raised beds, to cut down tall weeds. Then the Lilliston is used immediately afterwards to bury low weeds in the row. If there is a lot of quack grass, a contact herbicide may be applied in the spring just as the very first spears peek through. This has been necessary three times during the fifteen years since fields were planted. Bob has applied an herbicide for control of broadleaf weeds after harvest only twice in fifteen years, when annual weed pressure was getting severe in some spots. One year it rained after application, and this was very effective; the other time it was dry and results were poor.

The fields are fertilized once a year based on soil tests, using a synthetic fertilizer blend that matches the nutrient needs as closely as possible. Immediately after the last harvest, Bob spins this on, then harrows it in with light disks. He goes deep enough to smooth out the raised beds but not so deep as to injure the crowns. A wooden drag smooths the soil after the disks. Having a hydraulic cylinder on the disk allows for good depth control. Without it, it would not be possible to disk shallow enough to avoid severe crown injury.

"One thing that's essential for asparagus is well-drained soil because you have to get on the ground so early to harvest. I have always told people, if alfalfa will grow there, you're probably all set; if it won't, you're probably not going to be successful."

Asparagus beetle is not a big problem because a complete harvest is done every day or every other day. All spears that are big enough are harvested, and everything else is removed and discarded, including any spears that get too big, all volunteer seedlings, and wispy spears. By preventing any ferns at all from developing during harvest, Bob leaves nothing for the asparagus beetle to feed on. At the end of the harvest season, when the raised beds are knocked down, it takes the asparagus two weeks to regrow. This lack of food seems to starve the beetles, as few are present on the ferns later in the season. The only time Bob has had to control beetles was during crown production.

There is some rust disease, and probably some fusarium, but the fields are old, and the process is underway of rotating to new fields and to new varieties, such as Jersey Giant. The first planting of these was of transplants. Bob grew these from seed planted in May, and transplants were set out in August. They were 2 feet tall by October that year. In the future, he is considering buying crowns, because the seedlings take so much attention, especially on heavy soils in a wet or dry year when soil conditions are not good for transplanting or delicate cultivating.

Harvest of a new field begins in the second year after planting and goes for two weeks. A week is added to the harvest period each year, up to five weeks. This has been maintained for the last twelve years. Spears are cut using a square-edge knife, or snapped if they are high enough. Pickers try not to dig into the ground, especially early in the year when other spears can be injured. When there's not a lot of asparagus, picking is by hand. Plastic shellfish trays about 4 inches deep, a foot wide and 16 inches long are used to collect the spears. Trays are set out at equal intervals in the field, so that spears can be held until one hand is full and then deposited in a tray; and pickers can keep going up the row toward the next tray without retracing their steps.

When the asparagus harvest is heavy, a self-propelled Walker harvester, made in Georgia, is used. This unit is also suitable for harvesting cucumbers and similar crops. It is a three-wheel unit with a seat over each of three rows and a place to put a basket for each row. All three people harvesting must be either right- or left-handed, since they drive next to the rows on one side. A 7-horsepower engine drives a hydraulic pump that goes through a valve that controls how fast the unit travels.

As much as possible, spears are cut to a uniform length of 8 inches in the field. The ideal is to never have to trim them in the shed. Harvest trays or baskets are unloaded in the field and stacked upright into shallow trays filled with water. As they travel in the truck to the shed, most of the soil on butt ends of the spears washes off with the movement of the water. The shallow trays are refilled with water in the shed; the spears are lined up nice and straight, since when stored they will assume whatever contour they are placed in. Then the trays are placed on pallets and moved into the cooler. Obviously, they cannot be stacked, so they take up a lot of space; but there's not much else in the cooler at that time of year. Before delivery, spears are removed from the trays by hand, examined, dunked in fresh water to clean if necessary, and placed into 5-pound plastic bags.

About 1,500 pounds per acre has been the average yield from years five to fifteen. Bob feels he could get a better yield if he set up irrigation. Prices are stable over the season, and they have been going up every year. Retail ranges from $2 to $2.50 per pound and wholesale brings $1.60 to $1.75.

"Having a relatively small amount of a crop that is not very available locally is a good position to be in. You can stick to your price. Asparagus doesn't make a lot of money, but it's something early in the season. However, it does interfere with other early-season work."

"Besides the early-season cash flow, asparagus is important to our farm because people recognize us for it. Not a lot of other farms have a good supply of high-quality asparagus every year, so it is an integral part of our farm image."

Broccoli—
A Grower Profile

Skip Paul
Wishingstone Farm
Little Compton, Rhode Island

Skip Paul farms about 20 acres of heavy silt loam soils, along the coast of eastern Rhode Island. He sells many kinds of vegetables but is trying to cut back and specialize in fewer crops, buying in what else is needed for the farm stand. The farm is certified organic on 9 acres but is "conventional" on the rest. Skip does not try to do some crops organically any more, such as sweet corn, muskmelons, and pumpkin, where insect or disease pressure in his location is too great to make them profitable using organic methods.

At Wishingstone Farm, very little spring broccoli is grown, just enough for the stand. This is because the weather goes from cold to warm very quickly along the coast, and the plants just can't take it; they tend to bolt. Also, things are so busy early in the growing season that broccoli doesn't get the attention necessary to secure wholesale markets. In contrast, the fall broccoli grows beautifully in this climate. The buffering effect of the ocean provides a long growing season with cool, steady temperatures throughout September and October. Skip grows at least 3 or 4 acres of organic fall broccoli, plus an acre of purple cauliflower and green cabbage. The majority of this is wholesaled to local supermarkets.

The broccoli crop is preceded by a vetch/rye cover crop in fall that is knocked down when it gets really rank, usually in early June. First the cover crop is flail-mowed, then disked or skim-plowed (turning the soil over about 6 inches deep), and the fields are harrowed with a large steel bar to smooth the soil.

"Depending on soil test results, bagged organic fertilizer may be applied to the rows before planting. It's too expensive to spread organic fertilizer by broadcasting, so I place it in a 1-foot-wide strip right over the row. An old 5-foot-wide grass seeder was modified to do this by adding bigger wheels to raise it up and installing sheet metal dividers to regulate the width of fertilizer drop from 1 to 5 feet wide. The grass seeder is also used to drop fertilizer on 3-foot-wide beds for crops grown in that system. In a rainy season, foliar feeding with seaweed or fish emulsion assures high fertility."

"Transplants at the three-leaf stage are set out with a Holland transplanter, spaced 3 feet between rows, 18–20 inches between plants. The water tank applies a seaweed or fish emulsion starter solution to the plants. There isn't any overhead irrigation on the farm, so if the weather is dry in the days that follow, the transplanter may be pulled through the field again just to apply a shot of water to the plants. Starting with healthy transplants is key to a successful crop. In the past, we had problems with watering seedlings in the summer; and they often dried out and were stressed prior to setting. To avoid this, I built an ebb and flow watering system, using 2 x 6 boards to make a box that is lined with plastic and holds the transplants. A uniform application of water is given to the whole box this way."

"One thing I learned late is that everywhere I put cow manure as a young organic farmer I am paying the price for it now in terms of weed control. I never use it any more. In fields that were hay fields for a long time and I never applied manure, very little hand-weeding is necessary."

Strong transplants are key to using the Lely tine weeder soon after transplanting, otherwise it pops the plants out of the ground. If transplants are vigorous and set out roots quickly, they anchor well. The fall broccoli planting starts in early to mid-July, with plantings made every eight to ten days. Flaming is done on parts of field that are prepared but don't get planted early. A custom-made, tractor-mounted system with six liquid burners is used. It covers a 54-inch-wide swath. Usually one pass is all that is needed to keep weeds in check until planting. If the weather has been drier, sometimes the Lely will be used instead to scuff up the soil. In Skip's heavy soils, the Lely won't do the job if the soils are too moist.

After the plants go in, the Lely is used twice, usually five to eight days after setting, and again about the same time later. Timing depends on the weather and on how well the roots have taken. Then, cultivation switches to belly-mounted sweeps, usually just once to get anything that's deep-rooted that the Lely didn't get. After that, Lilliston rolling cultivators are used twice, until it's not possible to get in without damaging the crop. These are angled so as to hill-up the crop somewhat to bury in-row weeds. Some hand-weeding, and sometimes quite a bit, is usually necessary. "One thing I learned late is that every-where I put raw cow manure as a young organic farmer I am paying the price for it now in terms of weed control. I never use it any more, unless I can thoroughly compost it. In fields that were hay fields for a long time and I never applied manure, very little hand-weeding is necessary."

Insect control is pretty simple. Skip uses botanical pesticides on flea beetles early if control is needed. He feels that healthy transplants can put up with a fair amount of flea beetle feeding. Then the imported cabbageworm is controlled with Bt plus a spreader-sticker, applied every seven days while pressure is high. Skip watches adult butter-fly activity, as it is a bit hard to scout for the larvae since they can hide up under the dome. He has had no problems with cabbage maggot. Usually the crop is disease-free. In a really rainy season, copper fungicide will be applied to protect against head rot, which isn't a problem in normal seasons.

"I try to offer a little bit bigger head than Califor-nia, so the timing of harvest depends on visual criteria: I want the heads tight but large. That's a selling point in the stores. Next year, product identification tags with our farm name will be clipped to rubber bands on the broccoli. If you have a superior product it's important that the buying public know who you are."

Harvest starts in mid- to late-September generally. The crop is cut by hand and put in boxes. Once ten to fifteen boxes are filled, they are run up to

Sidebar 19.2 Enterprise Budget for Fall Broccoli (per acre)

Variable Costs
Labor and Machinery Costs

	Labor hrs	Machinery hrs
Sow rye/vetch in fall	.50	.25
Flail-mow rye/vetch	1	.75
Skim plow or disk	2	2
Disk and harrow	1	1
Apply fertilizer	.25	.25
Grow transplants	9	1
Set transplants	12	4
Flame weed, 1 x	.75	.75
Lely cultivate, 2 x	1	.75
Sweep cultivate, 1 x	1.5	1.25
Lilliston cultivate, 1 x	.75	.75
Foliar feed, 2 x	.50	.50
Hand weed	22	–
Spray flea beetles, 2 x	2	1
Spray cabbageworms, 4 x	4	2
Spray copper, 2 x	2	1.5
Harvest, 3 x	27	4.5
Flail-mow	.75	.75
Total Hours	88	23
	@ $10/hr	@ $20/hr
	= $880	+ $460

Total Labor and Machinery Costs
          = **$1,340**

Materials

Rye, vetch seed	$32
Broccoli seed	$20
Potting mix	$45
Bagged fertilizer	$230
Seaweed or fish fertilizer	$30
Insecticide and fungicide	$45
Boxes	$129
Ice	$149
Propane	$55
Total Materials Costs =	**$735**

Marketing Costs
(phone, accounting, shipping)
          = **$455**

Fixed Costs
(buildings, land, insurance, interest, office ex-penses, utilities, taxes, fees, permits)
          = **$255**

Total Costs   =   **$2,785**

Gross Returns
(average yield of 425 boxes per acre @ $14.50 per box)
          = **$6,163**

Net Returns   =   **$3,378**

the farm, packed in ice, and placed in the walk-in cooler. Orders are shipped three times a week directly to large supermarkets in the area and some wholesalers. Although the boxes are packed full of large heads cut to the standard length of 8–10 inches, the weight is a little lower than boxes from California, so some supermarkets complain. Skip thinks that perhaps his larger heads reduce the total weight of the box.

Depending on the variety, Skip and his staff will go through and harvest a planting two or three times; then in the late fall they will harvest the broccoli side shoots. This can fill up boxes pretty quickly, and there is a good market for side shoots at Chinese restaurants.

Wholesale organic broccoli prices tend to be about 35% over the price of nonorganic broccoli. Over the season the price tends to be pretty stable, usually climbing a little late in the season. The middle of September seems to be lowest point in prices. The lowest price Skip has ever taken was $9 per box; the highest was $28, when a hailstorm in Colorado destroyed the broccoli crop there, and there was very little organic broccoli on the market.

By the middle of October, most of the crop is finished, and the residue is flail-mowed. The soil will be lightly scuffed, and winter rye broadcast. In fields that are done in September, Skip prefers to sow oats, just because they're easier to deal with the following spring.

A goal of Skip's is to increase management effectiveness. "I would rather not be winging it the way I do—sometimes it's gotten me in trouble. I've gotten too big and lost some control, so I'll be trying to shrink the farm by 10 or 15 percent so I can do a better job of handling all the management tasks. It's virtually impossible to hire anybody capable as a vegetable farm manager, so downsizing is the only option for me to do a better job of management."

Carrots— A Grower Profile

Hank and Cecelia Bissell
Lewis Creek Farm, Starksboro, Vermont

Hank and Cecelia Bissell have a 145-acre farm with 50 acres of tillable river bottom soil. The couple produce 25 acres of vegetables and keep the other 25 acres in green manures. Hank feels that mix is a both a luxury and a liability. "Our management skills and markets seem appropriate to the 25 acres, but as a result we are carrying a lot of land that other people might have in production. On the other hand, I have the opportunity to grow all these cover crops, and I am a little obsessed with cover crops. Every time I do try and expand production, management isn't as good, and things don't look great. So I back off and things look great and profits are better. There's something about my management skills, and my desire to micromanage that has me 'trapped' at 25 acres. I'm not willing to spend all my time in the office, and maybe I don't have the skills to do that, whereas I know I can make money in the field."

Although all kinds of vegetables are grown on Lewis Creek Farm, there is an emphasis on a few families appropriate to the climate and markets. About a third to a half the vegetables are cole crops, and this poses a challenge to crop rotation, even with the green manures. Two acres of carrots are grown. In general, Hank tries for a six-year rotation among vegetable families, but it isn't strict. "Every time I make a rotation plan, in a year or two I tweak it here or there, so it gets changed around, due to wet fields or double-cropping." In one field, cole crops do come within two years of each other, but that's an exception.

Fields are all prepared by moldboard-plowing a cover crop in the spring. Before carrots, Hank tries to go particularly deep, 8 or 9 inches with his 12-inch bottoms. He likes to turn under an oat/vetch mix before carrots because it breaks down quickly compared to other sods, and he doesn't want much debris in the way. He tries to plow early in the season in order to allow a month or so until main planting, although a few small plantings will go in at the beginning of the growing season: early May and then mid-May. The main planting is around the first of June; and then there's another small planting in mid-June. The smaller, sequential plantings help keep supply steady to meet market demand, but the main season planting generally performs best.

For most crops, shallow rotavation follows plowing. With carrots, rototilling is as deep as the unit will go, about 8 inches. At the same time, a band of fertilizer is applied in rows 3 feet apart, using a homemade applicator. This is made from old fertilizer hoppers off a horse-drawn corn planter. The units are ground-driven and dribble out a band of material just in front of the rototiller. Another wheel with spikes behind the rototiller marks the fertilized rows at the same time. Most crops, including carrots, are planted on a 3-foot row spacing. A synthetic fertilizer blend is applied to provide the per-acre equivalent of 10 pounds N, 40 pounds phosphate, and 150 pounds potash, plus micronutrients. When the carrots are about 7 inches tall, 50 pounds per acre of actual N as urea is cultivated in, along with additional K if called for by soil test results.

Seedbed preparation is immediately before planting, to minimize any jump that weeds may get on the crop. Seeding is done with a two-row Stanhay precision seeder, using three lines per row at thirty-three pelleted seeds per foot. In theory, that puts eleven seeds per line, but fewer go in the center and more go on the outside. Hank says it's the overall density that matters anyway; and he suspects that a Planet Jr. seeder would work just as well.

"Seedbed preparation is everything—you can't change your soil conditions after you plant. A carrot sends down a thread of a root, and then the thread fills out. If anything gets in the way, you've got an imperfection in the carrot. I used to prepare the beds with an old field cultivator with tines only in the rows, set really deep, sort of like subsoiling. That worked really well, too, but I had to hill and roll the soil afterward to fix the trench it left, so the rototiller is simpler; plus it bands fertilizer, too."

"Usually we have enough soil moisture and rain around planting time; but if it is dry, I irrigate to get the crop going. When carrots are coming up through the soil it's most important to get water on them. We're on very good ground here, so I don't pay a whole lot of attention to irrigation under normal conditions."

"Seedbed preparation is everything—you can't change your soil conditions after you plant. A carrot sends down a thread of a root, and then the thread fills out. If anything gets in the way, you've got an imperfection in the carrot."

Weed control is really the most critical when the carrots are 3 inches or less. Hank used to use a pre-emergence herbicide but all the incorporation was a lot of fuss, and then the control wasn't that good. He followed that with a post-emergence herbicide applied at the full labeled rate once the carrots reached at least 3 inches in height. The post-emergence herbicide is applied in a band about 18 inches wide over the row. He's tried a 12-inch band but found it a little awkward; one swerve and you are off target. Having a trailer-sprayer reduces accuracy; if Hank had a tractor-mounted sprayer he feels that narrower bands would probably work.

Recently Hank has gone to earlier applications and reduced rates of post-emergence herbicide and eliminated the pre-emergence application entirely. As soon as there is one true leaf, he puts on a very light application, and then at the three-leaf stage he applies a bit more. This way, he uses less total material and gets better weed control. There is the possibility of minor injury to the carrots, but they grow out of it; and the herbicide does less damage to the crop than a heavy weed population will do. So far, Hank has not seen any herbicide injury at all with the carrot varieties he uses.

The first cultivation for weeds usually takes place two to three weeks after planting, using belly-mounted sweeps on a Farmall H. These are far enough from the plants that ground speed can be quite fast, and the sweeps really tear up the weeds, even if they have gotten large. Unlike crops for which cultivation is the only control, Hank doesn't bother to get really close to the carrots since the herbicide controls in-row weeds. In most seasons, he tries to cultivate every week from two weeks to six weeks after planting, then maybe two more times every other week, by which time the plants are pretty big; so the last cultivation may be delayed three more weeks. By the end of August, he may have cultivated seven times, but these are quick runs-through, taking about 1.5 hours to do the two acres.

"Carrots are the only crop on the farm that I use herbicides on," says Hank. "That's because weed control is so important when the carrots are less that 3 inches tall, and it takes them so long to get to that height, sometimes four or five weeks. Early plantings take up to two weeks just to germinate! Instead of herbicide, I've tried running the basket weeders over the crop as a blind cultivation, which works pretty well on spinach or corn. With carrots, however, blind cultivation resulted in a lot of split and misshaped roots at about an inch below ground. That's the depth that the baskets go down, so I'm pretty sure that they caused the damage. I've also tried a hand-held flamer, but found crabgrass control to be poor; and that is one of the big weed problems on the farm. For all the other crops, early weeding with baskets or finger weeders takes care of weeds early."

Last year, about a half an acre of carrots were grown organically as an experiment, since Hank is interested in reducing even his limited chemical inputs. These were hand-weeded early, starting two weeks after planting right as they came up, totally cleaning the field; then again a month later to clean up what was missed. The carrots received no synthetic fertilizer, just an organic blend to provide a low rate of N-P-K, 50-30-60 per acre. The hand-weeding did cost quite a bit more than the herbicide treatment. Overall, yields were good compared to his conventional crop. Disease losses to alternaria seemed to be much less in the organic block, and Hank feels it has something to do with the different nutrient levels.

For the first few years of carrot production, dis-

ease wasn't a factor. Then, alternaria became a serious problem. Now, Hank grows Bolero and Navajo, varieties that are tolerant to alternaria, and this has provided pretty good disease control in the past few years. However, this past year carrots were on a field where four or five years ago nonresistant carrots had been grown and had suffered great losses to disease. This year, the weather was wet, and alternaria was rather severe. If he hadn't used these varieties, he doesn't think he would have been able to get the carrots out of the ground. Still, yield was reduced significantly, especially in terms of size. In the future, Hank will monitor more closely for alternaria and think about applying a fungicide. "Alternaria really causes problems with early-season bunched carrots, because the tops look terrible. Later in the season, weak tops reduce the effectiveness of machine harvest. In terms of insect pests, once in a while carrot rust fly causes a little trouble, but there's not enough of it to warrant control at this point."

Bunch carrots are harvested by hand starting in early August, on a very small scale. The first of October is when mechanical harvesting starts. Hank uses an old carrot harvester that he bought sight-unseen from a farm in western New York through an ad in *American Vegetable Grower*. It had been used for baby beets, so Hank modified it a little bit so it could handle a good carrot yield without plugging up. It pulls the carrots by the tops and cuts the tops off, and then an elevator loads them into a wagon. It takes very little power to run and works well off the Farmall H, which is only about 30 horsepower. However, it is important to match the ground speed to the pickup head speed, otherwise the harvester rips off the carrot tops before pulling them up.

The harvest wagons are old manure spreaders with the beaters removed. The unloading chain unloads the carrots at the packinghouse, which is an old dairy barn. The carrots are dumped into the hayloft and gravity-fed down to the washer. "That's my favorite part of the operation—gravity: it works every time." Hank had the barrel washer made at a nearby machine shop. He made the grading line himself after a visit to Quebec to see how they worked on large carrot farms. The grader separates carrots by diameter as well as length. The small carrots are put into cellos, the large ones into 50-pound bulk bags. They are held in the cooler around 35°F, rather than right at freezing, since a lot of different crops are in there.

Sidebar 19.3 Enterprise Budget for Carrots (per acre)

Variable Costs
Labor and Machinery Costs

	Labor hrs	Machinery hrs
Plant vetch, oats	0.5	0.5
Moldboard plow	1	1
Deep rotavation (and band fertilizer)	1.5	1.5
Seed carrots	1.5	1.5
Irrigate 1 x	1.5	2
Band herbicide 2 x	1	1
Cultivate 7 x	10.5	10.5
Sidedress N	1	1
Hand harvest, bunches	48	0
Machine harvest	10	10
Wash and grade	44	0
Pack, store cellos	62	0
Pack, store bulk bags	36	0
Marketing costs	13	12
Total Hours	231.5	41
	@ $10/hr	@ $9/hr
	= $2,315	+ $369

Total labor and machinery costs
  =   **$2,684**

Materials

Rye, vetch seed	$30
Carrot seed	$200
Fertilizer	$98
Herbicide	$7
Miscellaneous supplies	$128
Cello bags	$310
Bulk bags	$178
Total Material Costs =	**$951**

Fixed Costs
(buildings, land, insurance, interest, office expenses, utilities, taxes, fees, permits)
  =   **$329**

Management Costs
  @ $500 per acre   =   **$500**

Total Costs   =   **$4,464**

Gross Returns
Bunch yield = 1,164 lb x $ 0.60   = $698
+ 50-pound cello yield = 157.50 x $8.50 = $1,339
+ 50-pound bulk yield = 445 x $7.50   = $3,338
  =   **$5,375**

Net Returns   =   **$911**

"One of the things that sells carrots is brightness. One way to get that is to wash them as soon as possible. If you can store them without the dirt drying on them at all, they will wash up quite bright, but that is pretty hard to do. Generally, I don't store them more than a couple of weeks since they sell so fast. Otherwise, I would probably wash them as needed during the winter."

Carrot harvest is usually done by early November, which is too late for sowing winter rye, so this crop is the only one on the farm that goes without a winter cover crop. Last year Hank tried to inter-seed rye between the rows to see if it would take despite the harvesting, which does not disturb the soil a whole lot. It didn't work out, however, so he just leaves the bare soil roughed up, without even disking, to minimize erosion. That's hard for Hank, as he is partial to cover cropping. "It's the only crop I do that with, so I console myself that way."

Hank carefully calculates costs for all his crops, enters the figures into his computer, and prints out work sheets for each crop. Because he records the time and material inputs for all activities associated with a crop, he knows that the bulk packs of carrots are far more profitable because of the reduced packaging and handling compared to cello packs. The cost to grow 50 pounds of carrots, until harvested, ranges from to $2 to $3. To put the carrots into cellos costs about $5 per 50 pounds; to put them into a 50-pound bulk bag costs about $1.

"Some of the most startling revelations about my business have come through the use of these cost work sheets. Even if the numbers are not exactly right, they allow me to see where I should be focusing my attention to reap the greatest and easiest return. An important feature I include in my calculations is management cost. I figure I spend a third to a half of my time with most crops making decisions, walking around, telling other people what to do, showing them how to do it, solving problems, and cogitating on a better way to do things. All this is a cost of doing business, and I don't want to be considering the time I spend managing my business as profit."

Eggplant— A Grower Profile

Gary Gemme and Dave Wojciechowski
Harvest Farm, Whately, Massachusetts

Gary Gemme and Dave Wojciechowski grow approximately 100 acres of vegetables for wholesale markets. They work on light-textured, river bottom soils. Typically they grow 5 acres of eggplant, and they maintain records of all fields for many years and use these to help plan rotations. Eggplant is a tough crop for rotation because they like to go at least five years out of solanaceous crops. So far, they have access to enough land to adhere to that. Planning rotations on the farm is a challenge because of the crop mix. They have about 50 acres of brassicas, which are in a three-year rotation, and about 20 acres of solanaceous crops, along with some Swiss chard, beets, and minor crops like basil. Soil-building cover crops like rye, sudax, and hairy vetch help fill out the rotation as well as maintain fertility. Sometimes, land will be sublet to neighbors to get a different crop into rotation.

Eggplant transplants are started in greenhouse about the last week of March or first week of April, in 72-cell 1020 flats using a soil-less mix. Currently, Epic and Classic are the varieties of choice, although most varieties of the classic "type" perform well. Plants are fed with a soluble fertilizer and hardened-off by drying out. When the weather has settled down, they get set out, usually by the end of May. They are often the last crop to be set out, after peppers.

Fields are prepared for planting by moldboard plowing, hopefully turning under a lush cover crop, although it doesn't always happen. Rather than disking, the soil is packed with a roller to prevent excessive drying. Then, Gary and Dave let the soil sit, allowing the cover crop to decay, while they wait for wet weather. Just before it arrives, beds are formed; based on soil tests, fertilizer is incorporated into beds at the same time. High N rates are used, as the crop seems to respond well to up to 200 pounds per acre under the plastic; more than that and there is a danger of burning the plants. If it doesn't rain, they irrigate, then immediately lay black plastic mulch. In many years, irrigation is necessary. Although it's a headache compared to letting rain do the work, the soil must be moist before the mulch is laid.

Plants are set out in double rows 15 or 16 inches apart, on plastic mulch spaced 6 feet apart on center, with trickle irrigation underneath. A water-wheel transplanter sets two rows at a time and applies a starter solution to "mud-in" the plants. Gary feels they have been crowding the plants and plans to reduce the population a bit. He thinks that by giving plants a little more room, they may produce a little bit longer. It's hard to keep the high population fed well all season long. Gary and Dave fertigate through the irrigation system; but doing it right without overfeeding or underfeeding specific nutrients is tricky. After plants are set out, overhead irrigation is applied if the winds blow. This prevents the sand from blasting the plants. The wind can also desiccate the plants, especially since the root systems are still small. Using overhead irrigation also buys some time to set up the trickle system pump, filters, and end plugs and to make sure it's all working.

Early in the season monitoring begins for the first generation of Colorado potato beetle (CPB). To reduce infestations, Gary and Dave try to locate the eggplant field as far away from current potato fields as possible and away from fields that were in potatoes last year. Nearby potatoes that will be harvested early can cause a really severe CPB problem. Thus, the eggplant rotation for CPB management is affected by what neighboring potato growers do.

"Scouts help us with insect monitoring. With CPB it's a question of when, rather than if, the beetles

> *"Once you push the numbers around you realize that there is very little in it unless we improve the price we sell for. Based on the budget for this crop with an average wholesale price of $8 per box, I figure the farmer actually works for about $8 an hour, and there is almost no net profit."*

Sidebar 19.4 Enterprise Budget for Eggplant (per acre)

Variable Costs
Labor and Machinery Costs

	Labor hrs	Machinery hrs
Moldboard plow	0.5	0.5
Roll fields	0.3	0.3
Form and fertilize beds	1	1
Lay plastic and drip tape	1.25	1.25
Set transplants	15	2.5
Set up overhead irrigation	1.5	0.5
Apply irrigation 3 x	2.25	9
Set up trickle system	4	–
Fertigation management	6	–
Cultivate 4 x	4	4
Scout for pests 12 x	4	–
Apply Bt 3 x	2	2
Apply adult CPB control 1 x	0.3	0.3
Apply aphid control 1 x	0.3	0.3
Apply disease control 2 x	0.6	0.6
Apply mite control 1 x	0.3	0.3
Harvesting and packing	150	30
Seed down winter cover crop	0.7	0.7
Total Hours	194	53.25
	@ $8/hr	@ $10/hr
	= $1,552	+ $533

Total Labor and Machinery Costs
= **$2,085**

Materials

Transplants @ .09	$864
Greenhouse utilities	$100
Fertilizers	$400
Plastic mulch	$300
Drip tape	$100
Pump, headers (10 years)	$500
Pesticides	$150
Boxes @ $1	$1,000
Storage utilities	$100
Miscellaneous supplies	$50
Total Materials Costs =	$3,564

Marketing Costs = **$1,200**

Total Variable Costs = **$6,849**

Fixed Costs
(buildings, land, insurance, interest, office expenses, utilities, taxes, fees, permits)
= **$1,097**

Total Costs = **$7,946**

Gross Returns
(1,000 boxes per acre x $8 average price)
= **$8,000**

Net Returns = **$54**

are coming," says Gary. "I prefer to allow the first generation of adults to feed and lay eggs. If CPB is seriously defoliating the crop, usually in one area of a field, then that block would be treated, just to knock down the hot spots. Spraying for adults is avoided because I figure they've survived because they are already resistant to some chemical or another. When hatch occurs, I'm 'Johnny-on-the spot' with Bt, which is the primary means of control by spraying. Depending on the year, that approach may go out the window; and I may have to spray adults, too, with a stronger material.

"Most years, I can do a reasonable job with the Bt, keeping pressure down to a dull roar. Having neighbors using a new at-planting systemic material has reduced pressure in our fields, too; but how long this material will be effective is uncertain. If need be, I'll spray CPB adults once or twice over the course of the season, if the larvae get by or if adults migrate in from an early-dug potato field in which CPB was not controlled. I will do what has to be done to protect the crops, but I prefer not to have to control the adults."

In August, Gary has to keep an eye open for aphids, which require close observation because of long days-to-harvest interval of ten to fourteen days for effective aphid-control materials. Often, Gary and Dave have to spray right behind harvest, then let the fruit ripen up until harvest can resume. In order to do things right, a map is kept of all the fields that were sprayed. The aphid honeydew can be a serious problem, completely ruining the fruit. Heavy aphid feeding can do severe damage to the plants, reducing yields; but control is not related to virus problems.

When the foliage fills in, Gary will apply a copper fungicide to protect against early blight if moist weather threatens. He tends to forgo the fungicide if it's dry, especially with trickle irrigation, which minimizes foliar disease pressure. However, trickle has exacerbated spider mite pressure with dry conditions; and he never had spider mites before going to trickle. After taking severe losses one year, he has had to spray for mites in recent years. He spot sprays particular areas of the field if he can get away with it, based on scouting information.

For spraying, a one-sided, 38-foot boom is used. Gary drives down the harvest lanes, never in the crop. Using hollow cone nozzles, 12 inches on center at 175 psi and 40 gallons per acre, gives excellent penetration and coverage of the materials he needs to apply.

Verticillium wilt has been controlled most years with site section and rotation, but in recent years it came in on wetter, low spots. Once it gets a foothold, it can spread rapidly. Where it occurs, yields may be reduced by 90%. When irrigating, Gary tries to keep puddling from occurring at the ends of the trickle lines, or at least set up the system to prevent puddling near the crop.

Weed control is primarily by cultivation. Although they would like to apply a pre-plant herbicide to some fields, they never seem to have the right weather. Sweeps, spring tines and Lillistons are mounted in different combinations on a Farmall 200. They use what is necessary to do the best job to get weeds where the last pass didn't. At some point, hand-weeding of the planting holes is required, and at the same time they clip the weeds along the edge of the plastic.

Around the third week in July, picking begins by hand. Pruning shears are used, with one person to a row. A conveyor harvest-aide carries fruit to the wagon, where it gets wiped with a rag and packed into newspaper-lined boxes. The newspaper keeps fruit from getting marked up by the box edges. The wagons go to the packing shed, and boxes are generally shipped out that night, or otherwise held at the proper temperature, which is not very cold.

Yields will routinely top 1,000 boxes an acre. Gary is confident that he could get much more than that with better nutrient and irrigation management and improved insect control. Keeping the plants healthy longer into the season is the challenge. He feels he still has a lot to learn about keeping fruit quality high. Some years the fruit turns pimply late in the season, and he doesn't know what causes that.

Prices range widely. Gary and Dave hope for $12 per box early, but by the time they are in full production, they hope the price will be at least $7 to $8. Sometimes the price gets down so low that they have to choose their markets carefully. It can go as low as $4 per box, and they try not to sell for that.

"Once you push the numbers around you realize that there is very little in it unless we improve the price we sell for," says Gary. "Based on the budget for this crop with an average wholesale price of $8 per box, I figure the farmer actually works for about $8 an hour, and there is almost no net profit. As the saying goes, if you own the land you farm, 'live poor, die rich.'"

"A grower either has to accept that the wholesale prices are volatile or to try to grow on a contract basis for a prearranged price," Dave says. "That's a much better system because you have a good idea of what you're going to make and can budget accordingly. We've recently started growing several of our crops on contract for local supermarkets."

Garlic— A Grower Profile

Grace Reynolds
Hillside Organic Farm
Brunswick, New York

Grace Reynolds cultivates 3 hillside acres in eastern New York, with 1 acre planted to garlic each year. She farms organically but feels no need to spend the money to get certified. Her soils are officially described as gravelly silt loams, but she finds them to be fine and heavy, requiring lots of organic matter to be productive. In recent years, she has grown garlic in a three-year rotation that starts with sweet clover frost-seeded in late winter. The clover stays on a whole season, then is turned under the following June. After a few weeks for decomposition, buckwheat is planted. This gets turned under six weeks later, and oats are planted in August. Garlic is then planted right into the oats in October. After garlic harvest, oats are again planted the following August. The rotation begins again when sweet clover is frost-seeded into the dead oats.

A couple of things have not worked out with that rotation. The sweet clover grows slowly the first season, so despite mowing it once to control tall weeds, low-growing chickweed is becoming more of a problem. Also, there are other crops that could contribute N more quickly to the rotation than sweet clover, as well as crops that could add more biomass to the soil than buckwheat.

So, the rotation plan is changing. Now after garlic harvest, a mixture of vetch and rye is planted. Grace has grown it before and found that it works well, getting thick and lush in the spring and suppressing weeds better than the dead oat cover. She mows the mixture in late May, then tills it under. To beat back the chickweed, she may till the soil several times before sowing sorghum-Sudan grass in June. This is planted to produce organic matter and suppress weeds, and is left on all season but mowed short a few times to suppress weeds and encourage the growth of multiple stems. Grace has tried mowing sorghum-Sudan grass very short and finds that it comes back OK. Since this cover crop takes up a lot of N, it makes sense to use it as a catch crop to help recycle the N released from the previous vetch cover crop.

The next spring the dead sorghum-Sudan grass is tilled in along with 50 cubic yards of horse manure and bedding. The soil may subsequently be cultivated while the weather is cool in an effort to control the chickweed, which tends to grow a lot in cool weather. Then buckwheat is sown in June; it is incorporated in August and oats are sown. Then the garlic is planted directly into the oats and the cycle begins again. Grace uses certified oat seed (at 3 bushels per acre) to avoid introducing weed seeds.

The fields are prepared for garlic planting in August, just prior to sowing oats. The soil is rototilled, incorporating limestone, bone meal, sulpo-mag, and kelp meal, using soil tests as guide to what nutrients are needed. Then the field is subsoiled down the middle of each bed with a single shank subsoiler. Disk-hillers are then mounted on the tool bar behind the tires to throw soil up onto the beds. Behind the disks follows a homemade V-shaped configuration of 2 x 4s that drags the soil and levels the beds.

Recently, Grace has added tines onto the leveler so that oat seed can be broadcast after bed formation and incorporated with another pass of the same equipment. The final result is a fall cover crop of oats in a field of raised beds about 4 to 6 inches high, 36 inches across on the top, 55 inches on center, and 225 feet long.

> *"My catalog mailing list has been developed by having people sign up at fairs and shows. I make an effort to change where I go each year, trying many different events . . . I'm lucky to have received a lot of free local publicity that I haven't looked for, such as articles in newspapers."*

Grace grows about ten different strains of garlic for sale. These are of three different "varieties" of garlic, although there is no official or uniform nomenclature for garlic, other than "topset" or "stiffneck" types, which produce a scape, or false flower stalk, and "softneck" types, which do not. Grace grows only topset types for sale. The three so-called varieties are Rocambole, which has pink or purple bulb wrappers and a curling scape that produces large bulbils on it, and which generally produces six to ten cloves per bulb. Porcelain has white wrappers and a tall, straight scape that may arch and curve but does not spiral. Porcelain garlic makes small bulbils, and the bulbs contain four to six cloves. Purple-stripe is her last variety, and it has the plant character of a Porcelain, and the bulb character of a Rocambole. All three types are very pungent in flavor.

All of the farm's "seed" stock is propagated on the farm, except for trial varieties or strains. Grace experiments with small patches of a dozen or so strains, although one year she trialed over a hundred strains. Strains are kept in trial for three years before she judges whether they are commercially viable for her. Then she has customers do taste tests on them.

Sustainable Vegetable Production from Start-Up to Market

Before planting, the garlic bulbs are split open, or "cracked," by hand. The loose material is removed and 1,700 pounds of cloves prepared. A homemade unit with two planters pulled on the tool bar is used to set the cloves. It has a coulter that cuts through the oats, followed by a specially-made shoe that opens a trench without moving much soil, so that narrow row spacings can be used. A pipe serves as a tube to drop cloves behind the shoe, which is followed by a closing wheel that covers the cloves with about 2 inches of soil. There's a timing device on the hub of the tractor wheel that clicks when the tractor has moved 5 inches. Grace drops a clove into both tubes with every click, thus getting a uniform 5-inch spacing. Some of the cloves fall right side up, most end up lying on their side, but very few are upside down.

There are four rows on a bed, 9 to 10 inches apart. The planter makes one pass down a bed, then one pass back on the other side, planting two rows each way. There may be a little side slipping, depending on the contour of the field; but generally Grace ends up with the plant population desired. In the past, Grace has always done this without a driver, letting the tractor (Kubota 2250) drive itself in creeper gear. As a result, sometimes the rows weren't all that straight. This year, she had an apprentice driving, and planting was much better.

Planting takes place throughout the last three weeks of October. Grace has a family to take care of, too, so it takes that long to plant the whole acre. She has found that anything planted after the first of November doesn't size up well on her farm. After planting, leaf compost from her town is spread over the whole field; she puts on as much as she can get, which is usually a couple of dozen cubic yards. Then, large round bales of hay are unrolled over the beds. She gets them from a good farmer, so the bales are relatively weed free and uniform and unroll pretty well.

Grace still has to go back and cover certain spots, and at the same time hay is spread on the alley-ways between beds, too. That makes sure the crop will be protected in an exposed winter. Most years she could get away with only doing the top, but in some years the alleys need to be covered to protect the garlic rows along the bed edges. One year the center rows came up uniformly but the edge rows came up late and irregularly, indicating that winter damage had occurred in the exposed sides of the beds. Having an apprentice has really helped with chores like applying hay mulch.

The following spring, the mulch is left in place. It may slow soil warming, but Grace thinks "there are other things more important than the cold in my soils. When things dry out, the field turns to concrete, so mulch keeps it moist and soft. It also helps control weeds and moderate soil temperatures. It stimulates soil life by adding organic matter, too. And everything just looks better mulched, too." Grace has no desire to use plastic mulch, which she doesn't like.

Usually, the garlic pokes up in early April. Soon after that any winter-hardy weeds like rocket and dandelion are hand-pulled, and they are few and far between. Then the drip irrigation t-tape is put on, one line down the middle of each bed. This is run off a deep well in the field, which only gives 7 gallons per minute, so the system is divided up into zones. Grace waters five beds at a time.

Recently, tile drainage was installed in strategic places in the field. This drains into a pond at the bottom of the fields. When the pond gets low, Grace knows she needs to check the soil under the mulch. "I like to keep the soil moist—garlic likes uniform moisture. One of the critical things is to not let it dry out." She is considering getting an injector that would allow her to fertilize through the drip tape using kelp, seaweed, or fish emulsion in May.

Weeding is an ongoing thing; it's all done by hand because of the mulch and the close spacing. They start on one side and keep going, then turn around and come back if need be. Some years are worse than others, and Grace hopes that the new rotation will improve things. Thus far, there have been no insect or disease problems, so controls haven't been needed in the eight years of production on the farm.

Once the scapes appear, Grace waits for them to curl once, forming a 360 degree loop; then they are snapped off with fingers. There is no significant market for them in her area, although other growers have found ethnic markets near cities. Scape removal occurs toward the end of June and takes about a week, as varieties differ in their timing of scape development.

Next it's time to get the barn, equipment, and labor ready for harvest. In addition, cover crops have to be managed on other fields. It sounds like there's a lot of vacant time with garlic production, but there's always plenty to keep a grower busy.

"There are four ways to tell when the garlic is ready to harvest," says Grace. "I always leave a few scapes on as maturity indicators. When they have just about straightened out after their curling episode and bulbils at the end are bulging but have not burst their wrappers, it's usually time to dig. The second way is to look at the foliage: the stem should still be green; the bottom two leaves should be totally shriveled; and all the other leaves, including the top leaves, should have yellow tips. The third method is to do a test dig and look for bulging cloves in the bulbs, rather than smooth round bulbs. The fourth way is to peel a few bulbs and look for some signs of pink

Sidebar 19.5 Enterprise Budget for Garlic (per acre)

Variable Costs
Labor and Machinery Costs

	Labor hrs	Machinery hrs
Plow, harrow	3	0.5
Plant vetch and rye	2.5	–
Mow vetch and rye	2	2
Rototill vetch and rye	3.5	3.5
Hand cultivate for weeds	130	–
Plant sorghum-Sudan grass	1.5	–
Mow sorghum-Sudan grass 2 x	4	4
Rototill sorghum-Sudan grass	4	4
Plant buckwheat	1.5	–
Mow buckwheat	2	2
Transport, spread fertilizer and manure	50	50
Rototill	3.5	3.5
Form beds and sow oats	6	6
Crack garlic	170	–
Plant garlic	100	50
Apply leaf compost	20	20
Apply hay bales	60	2
Hand-weed early spring	5	–
Set up drip irrigation	15	–
Snap off scapes	50	–
Undercut garlic	5	5
Lift, harvest, hang garlic	225	4
Cut tops, trim roots, grade	250	–
Rototill field	3.5	3.5
Maintain equipment	50	–

Marketing

Prepare and mail catalog	20	–
Travel to, attend shows, fairs	120	–
Roadside stand sales	45	–
Recording and filling orders	100	–
Office and phone time	1,000	–

(such as marketing, payroll, taxes, purchasing, signs, posters, trial records, generating literature)

Total Hours	2,452	160
	@ $5 /hr	@$20/hr
	= $12,260	+ $3,200
Total Labor and Machinery Costs		
	= **$15,460**	

Materials

30 lbs vetch and 56 lbs rye seed	$50
40 lbs sorghum-Sudan seed	$40
60 lbs buckwheat seed	$20
3 bushels oat seed	$20
Fertilizers	$500
Leaf compost (turning cost)	$100
Hay bales	$450
Irrigation tape (per year basis)	$60
Snow fence (per ten-year basis)	$30
Onion bags	$10
Printing (catalog, cards, fact sheets)	$350
Catalog postage	$50
Total Material Costs	= **$1,680**

Total Variable Costs	= **$17,140**

Fixed Costs
(buildings, land, insurance, interest, office expenses, utilities, taxes, fees, permits)

	= **$ 675**

Total Costs	= **$17,815**

Gross Returns
average yield (pounds) x average price ($ per pound)

Premium	340 x 4.50	= $1,530
Extra Large*	2,000 x 4.00	= $8,000
Large*	2,200 x 3.50	= $7,700
Medium	1,700 x 3.00	= $5,100
Small	510 x 1.80	= $918
Total		= $23,248

Net Returns	= **$5,433**

*Not including seed saved: 1,000 pounds of extra large, 800 pounds of large. Total yield per acre: 8,550 pounds

on the clove skins of the Rocambole types. This varies from year to year but there should be some kind of color.

"Usually harvest starts about the third week of July. The softnecks come out earlier, but I only grow them in trial since I haven't found a variety that does really well in terms of vigor and sizing up. The first step in harvesting is to undercut the garlic to loosen it from the soil. This is done by removing the blade from the single shank subsoiler and replacing it with a 22-inch-diameter disk that is cut in half. The rounded side of the disk faces toward the tractor and is pulled down the center of the bed about 8 or 10 inches deep, so it loosens the soil but does not come close to cutting any roots. The soil is just lifted then dropped back into place. You can't see where the disk has been, and the plants are not disturbed. The result is that the plants can be lifted right out of the soil without any pulling."

Plants are lifted by the handful; the loose dirt is shaken off; and the crop is piled on the center of the beds, but not for long. To avoid sunburn, the garlic is collected as soon as possible. The tractor comes along with a wagon that is loaded up and taken to the drying shed. There, 8-foot-high walls of snow fence are used to hang the garlic for curing. Two pieces of 4-foot-tall fencing are hung onto screws in 2 x 4s to form the 8-foot-high wall. They stand vertically and are held in place by hooks that are attached to the barn's roof beams. That way, the roof does not bear any of the weight. Bricks go under the 2 x 4s so they don't touch the earthen floor. The garlic is hung up by placing the bulbs between the slats of wood on the snow fence, forming a solid wall of bulbs on one side of the fence and a solid wall of tops on the other. This way all the bulbs are exposed to the air for drying, and it's easy to inspect the crop for damage and size. The system is assembled and disassembled each year to make room for equipment storage in the winter.

All the bulbs hang for about three weeks, or until no green center can be seen when the stem is cut an inch above the bulb. Then she gets a crew in, and they just cut tops. They put the bulbs in 50-pound mesh onion bags. After all the bulbs are cut, the crew takes the bags to another work area and empties them out so that the roots can be cut off, and the bulbs separated into size grades. Then the crop is ready for market. Bulbs are never washed or rubbed, but most of the soil gets brushed off in the process of handling. Once they taste the garlic, nobody has objected to a little dirt on the bulbs.

After all this is done, Grace rototills the field to kill any weeds that got away, and at the same time also breaks the beds down. Then she spins on vetch and rye or oats, depending on the rotation, using a cyclone seeder. A spring-tooth harrow incorporates the cover crop seed.

"About 80% of sales are through my own catalog; another 10% are at shows and conferences; and the other 10% are through on-farm sales at a self-serve stand. My catalog mailing list has been developed by having people sign up at fairs and shows. I make an effort to change where I go each year, trying many different events, but I always attend the big Hudson Valley Garlic Festival. I'm lucky to have received a lot of free local publicity that I haven't looked for, such as articles in news-papers."

Green Beans— A Grower Profile

Chuck Armstrong
Fiddlehead Farm, Brownsville, Vermont
Chuck Armstrong grows 30 acres of vegetables, half of which are green beans, along with 25 acres of cover crops, on sandy loam and silt loam soils. He has been farming in this location for eight years. All his crops are certified organic and sold to wholesale markets, mostly through the Deep Root Co-op. Some produce is sold to a regional distributor and to local farm stands.

Crop rotation is mostly among beans, sweet corn, and winter squash, with a small amount of peas, potatoes, and other odds and ends. Chuck would like to treat cover crops with more attention as part of the rotation, rather than just putting winter rye on at the end of each cropping season. The few times he has used other cover crops, such as sorghum-Sudan grass, during the main season, he felt it really improved soil tilth.

In the early spring, winter rye is plowed down when it is about 6 inches tall, then disked. Field cultivating with a Perfecta II then smooths the field, provides early weed control, and incorporates a couple of hundred pounds of broadcast potassium sulfate. Soil tests consistently indicate a potassium need. Chuck also runs several hundred pounds per acre of an organic fertilizer blend such as 5-3-4 through the planter.

Planting starts around May 15 in central Vermont. Sequential plantings are aimed at getting a consistent supply of beans over the harvest period. A single planting provides about three days of harvest, at most; so many plantings are needed. In this case about fifteen plantings are done on 10 acres. He usually digs up a few recently planted seeds, and when they have sprouted, it's time for the next planting. The first few early plantings may be three to seven days apart. However, by around June 1, when the soils are warm and emergence is rapid, plantings are usually every two to three days. The last planting is in early to mid-July. Late plantings are somewhat risky, since early frosts are likely, and frequent rains and poor drying conditions often occur in September. In some years, however, late harvests have been among the best in terms of yield and quality.

A Monosem vacuum planter sows three rows between the tractor wheel tracks, which are 90 inches on center. Planting depth is about 1 inch. Chuck uses a 100-horsepower Ford 9030 tractor, which is also used for logging nearby woodland in the winter. The target planting density is 100,000 plants per acre, which on a 30-inch row puts seeds somewhere around 2 inches apart. He has tried different row spacings to facilitate cultivation and crop growth, but ultimately the planting arrangement must be suitable for the 48-inch, two-row mechanical picker he uses. He has tried narrow row spacings, both 15- and 20-inch rows, which resulted in good growth but also more disease in wet years, probably due to reduced air movement. Also, the harvester could not quite reach all three rows at once with the 20-inch spacing, since the beans tend to fall over somewhat. Planting too densely seems to encourage the plants to fall over, or lodge, which interferes with harvest.

"Over the years, I've tried a number of varieties," says Chuck. "So far the best one is Strike, because it has a good yield and holds well on the plant. I plant this one variety all season long in sequence. It does tend to pick 'trashy,' with more plant debris than other varieties."

For weed control, the Perfecta may be used for one or two pre-plant cultivations, although in some years Chuck has concerns about drying out the soil with this. "After planting, a Lely spring-tine weeder is used to control weeds. There are usually two 'blind cultivations' before the early season beans come up and one pass before emergence of later plantings, which come up quickly. Then, after emergence, when the plants are small, I have to be careful not to yank the plants right out of the ground, so I go lightly and keep a close eye on the crop to see if damage is being done. Flaming to create a stale seedbed could be an option in early plantings, when beans come up more slowly than some of the weeds. Once the beans are up several inches, I add Bezzerides spyders and torsion weeders belly mounted in front of the Lely. The spyders pull soil away from plants; torsion bars hill just a little bit; then the Lely gets in between the plants and finishes off the weeds that were knocked loose by the other tools.

"If necessary, when the plants have four or five true leaves, the Lely is removed. Shovels are mounted behind the tractor for wheel tracks; and

> *"After planting, a Lely spring-tine weeder is used to control weeds. There are usually two 'blind cultivations' before the early season beans come up and one pass before emergence of later plantings, which come up quickly. Then, after emergence, when the plants are small, I have to be careful not to yank the plants right out of the ground, so I go lightly and keep a close eye on the crop . . . ."*

spring-hoes are put on in place of the torsion bars to give more aggressive action alongside the plants. The spyder cultivators may have to be removed, too, because they start to catch the plants when they begin to bush out a little bit. For the last time through, Lilliston rolling cultivators are used. A single gang is used for each row, angled so as to avoid hilling up the soil around plants, which would interfere with the picker since it goes down close to the ground. I am careful to avoid root damage late in the season because it can encourage lodging and make for harvest problems.

A schedule develops from late May through early July that alternates planting and weed control in the field. On average, a field of beans may be mechanically cultivated three or four times after planting, although the first two or three plantings may be cultivated a couple more times with the Lely since they are slow to get out of the ground."

"Yellow nutsedge has becomes a serious problem on some parts of the farm, and it can really interfere with harvest if it gets too prolific. Mechanical cultivation has cleaned up many other weeds but has not provided season-long control of nutsedge. I've been experimenting with sweet potato production, since there is evidence from USDA research that sweet potato can provide allelopathic suppression of nutsedge. I've also tried a fungal pathogen product labeled for nutsedge control, applied to different sections of the field at three different times. There has been little evidence of control; however, our summers are pretty cool, and that may have reduced its effectiveness, since it is supposed to be used at warm temperatures."

Insects have not caused many problems in the beans, except for a recent year, in which potato leafhoppers destroyed the crop. By the time they were noticed it was too late for any treatment. In the future, Chuck plans to try using botanical pesticides if needed. Small numbers of Mexican bean beetle have been observed, but damage has never been significant. Similarly, a few plants each year get loaded up with Japanese beetles, but the problem has never spread.

"Diseases have been my biggest pest problem. In

some years, Sclerotinia (white mold) has caused major losses in several plantings; and in one year bean yellow mosaic virus caused real problems. To manage Sclerotinia, I'm trying more intensive

Sidebar 19.6 Enterprise Budget for Green Beans (per acre)

Variable Costs
Labor and Machinery Costs

	Labor hrs	Machinery hrs
Plow winter rye	0.5	0.5
Disk	0.5	0.5
Broadcast fertilizer	0.5	0.5
Perfecta field cultivation 1 x	0.5	0.5
Plant / band fertilizer	1	1
Lely "blind cultivation" 2 x	1	1
Lely + Spyders™, torsion bars 1 x	1	1
Shovels and spring hoes 1 x	1	1
Rolling cultivators 1 x	1	1
Hand hoeing	17.5	0
Mechanical Harvest	7.5	7.5
Dump, sort, pack (150 bushels)	40	0
Disk	0.5	0.5
Plant winter rye	1	1
Total Hours	73.5	16
	@ $10/hr	@ $20/hr
	= $735	+ $320

Total Labor and Machinery Costs
=   **$1,055**

Materials
Lime	$10
Potassium sulfate (200 pounds)	$45
5-3-4 organic blend (300 pounds)	$45
Bean seed (50 pounds)	$85
Boxes (150 1-bushel)	$100
Rye cover crop	$10
Total Material Costs =	**$295**

Marketing Costs
(20% of gross sales, fee to grower cooperative)
=   **$ 510**

Total Variable Costs   =   **$1,860**

Fixed Costs (buildings, land, insurance, interest, office expenses, utilities, taxes, fees, permits)
=   **$382**

Total Costs   =   **$2,242**

Gross Returns
(Average yield x average price)
= 150 bushels x $17 per bushel
=   **$2,550**

Net Returns   =   **$308**

rotations and improving drainage in wetter fields, and I may try raised beds. Changing planting arrangement to 20-inch double rows on 60-inch centers may improve air movement in the plant canopy."

"Deer have recently become a problem, too. For years they didn't touch the beans; then they seemed to have discovered them. This will probably require putting in some type of low-cost fencing, either single-strand, baited electric fence, or a double-strand T-fence."

Harvest of the main season crop is usually fifty-eight to sixty days after planting. Ideally, beans are harvested after the dew has dried, because if they are picked when wet some russeting can occur. Russeting was also a problem once when the beans were thoroughly soaked by a thunderstorm before harvest. A two-row MaxiHarvester with a 48-inch head is used. The company is not in business anymore, but the unit looks pretty similar to a Byron. It has large cleaning fan that does a good job of removing trash before beans go into a homemade trailer that holds up to 20 bushels. Harvest speed is pretty slow in order to do a good job, about ½ mile per hour, regardless of how many beans are there. With well-producing plants, it is possible to harvest about 20 bushels per hour, including the travel time to and from the field to unload. So that the beans stay fresh, Chuck doesn't harvest for much longer than an hour, regardless of yield, before bringing the trailer to the packing shed.

The trailer has a "live bottom" that slides out the back so can beans can be slowly released from the trailer via a hand-crank. They drop onto a vibrating sorting table, made by Pixall, and then the good beans drop into boxes at the end of the table. The vibrating table helps the people sorting to singulate the beans. This works better than a simple conveyor belt, on which the beans tend to clump up. Relatively clean-harvested beans flow right through the packing line, perhaps as fast as 10 bushels per hour. With more trash in the trailer, more people and time are required to pick out the stems, leaves, and any bad beans. If there's a lot of Sclerotinia, grading and sorting are much more critical, and they can go slowly.

Each box is weighed and filled to get to standard 25-pound pack, then put into the cooler at 40°F. There is a pretty short shelf life, perhaps a week. Beans are shipped out four or five days a week, mostly direct to the distributor that takes them to Boston.

"My yields vary between 100 and 200 bushels per acre, depending on disease, weed pressure, and weather. At the low end, it's not really worth it, since so much time is required to do the picking. However, it's often necessary to take a loss on an individual planting in order to keep markets consistently supplied with product. Prices average about $16 or $17 per bushel. If you picked by hand and had a lot fewer beans to market, you might get $25 a box."

After harvest the fields are disked once and seeded down to winter rye, by using a Brillion seeder or by broadcasting, depending on how much time is available. Chuck doesn't bother mowing the bean residue first; there isn't that much trash, given that the picker shreds most of it before putting it back on the field.

Kale and Collard Greens— A Grower Profile

David Marchant and Jane Sorenson
River Berry Farm, Fairfax, Vermont
David Marchant and Jane Sorenson farm in northwest Vermont, along the Lamoille river. The couple's farm is certified organic, with 40 acres of vegetables and 3 acres of noncertified, IPM-managed strawberries. Their vegetable markets are primarily wholesale, through the Deep Root Co-op, with some retail sales at farmers markets. The farm also offers some pick-your-own, especially for berries.

For early plantings of kale and collards, David tries to go onto ground that can be worked early because it has either a dead cover, such as oats, or clean ground that followed late lettuce or carrots and did not get cover-cropped. Later plantings usually follow a rye or vetch-rye plow-down. There really is no specific crop rotation plan because it is too hard to plan the placement of early crops; field conditions are extremely variable from year to year, in terms of what's wet or dry or ready to plant. However, David never plants brassicas after brassicas.

On all fields, 15 tons per acre of year-old, composted dairy manure is applied. The land is then worked with a field cultivator with large rolling basket attachments. If a particular field tends to be wet, raised beds are formed, otherwise planting is on flat ground. Later plantings follow rye or rye-vetch winter cover crop plow-downs.

It takes about three and a half to four weeks to grow transplants that are ready to set out, typically using 128-cell trays. Plants are hardened off for three or four days in a cold frame, then transplanted three rows to a bed on 18-inch centers, using a Lannen carousel cup transplanter. Plants are spaced 18 inches in the row. Beds are 4 feet wide on 5 ½-foot centers. Blocks of eight beds are separated by alleyways.

The collard varieties currently grown include Top Bunch, Flash, and Blue Max. David finds there is a large yield difference between hybrid and non-hybrid collards. The one kale variety grown is Winterbor. The first spring planting is always covered with floating row cover for cabbage maggot and flea beetle control. This costs about $700 per acre, but it also gains about two weeks earliness, as well as saving on the cost of pest control materials and labor; so it easily pays for itself. Using covers that measure 600 feet by 45 feet wide allows a whole block to be individually covered.

Four plantings are set out, on about April 15, May 15, and June 15, and between July 15 and August 1 for a late planting. An even later planting is possible if the harvest method was cutting and bunching entire plants rather than picking and bunching leaves. Each planting is about one acre, a half-acre each of kale and of collards.

After two or three pickings, the crops are sidedressed with Chilean nitrate at a rate of 30 pounds per acre actual N (the highest use of Chilean allowed by NOFA-VT certification standards). Other nutrients test high, but in late fall there may be a side-dressing with an organic P source to avoid purpling of leaves.

The three major insect pests each year are imported cabbageworm, diamondback moth, and flea beetle. Both crops do not tolerate much damage, since leaves with holes in them are not marketable. Collards are much preferred by the caterpillar pests, so more controls are needed. In addition, Kale doesn't show feeding damage quite as much because of its curly leaves. Organic pesticides are applied once the first flight of imported cabbageworm is observed or scouting of the crop finds immature larvae feeding deep in the plant.

"Getting controls onto the crop when feeding is just starting is key to minimizing losses to cabbageworms, especially when using Bt insecticides, which are most effective on small larvae. If flea beetles also need control, I'll apply a botanical insecticide . . . Since I'm concerned about the development of insect resistance to Bt, some alternation of insecticide is desirable."

"Getting controls onto the crop when feeding is just starting is key to minimizing losses to cabbageworms, especially when using Bt insecticides, which are most effective on small larvae. If flea beetles also need control, I'll apply a botanical insecticide instead of Bt. Since I'm concerned about the development of insect resistance to Bt, some alternation of insecticide is desirable. A coconut oil-based organic spreader-sticker is always added to the sprays. On average, each planting of collards gets three or four sprays per season, and kale gets two sprays. These are applied at dusk or dawn to avoid photodegradation of the pesticides. There have not been any serious disease problems with these crops."

Sidebar 19.7 Enterprise Budget for Kale and Collards (per acre—½ acre each)

Variable Costs

Labor and Machinery Costs

	Labor hrs	Machinery hrs
Plow, manure, form beds	5	5
Grow transplants	26	0
Transplant	12	6
Row covering	6	2
Cultivate 3 x (and fertilize 1 x)	3	3
Spray 3 x	8	16
Harvest, pack	200	64
Mow and sow cover crop	2	2
Total Hours	262	98
	@ $10 /hr	@ $20 /hr
	= $2,620	+ $1,960

Total Labor and Machinery Costs

= **$4,580**

Materials

Seed, potting mix, trays	$80
Greenhouse utilities	$20
Compost (on-farm, 15 tons)	$150
Row cover (2 years)	$350
Insecticides	$100
Cover crop	$10
Boxes @ $1.25	$1,062
Cooling/ice	$85
Total Materials Costs	= **$1,857**

Marketing/trucking fee
(18% of gross sales, fee to co-op)

= **$1,912**

Management costs = **$200**

Total variable costs = **$8,549**

Fixed Costs
(buildings, land, insurance, interest, office expenses, utilities, taxes, fees, permits)

= **$618**

Total Costs = **$9,167**

Gross Returns
Average price per box collards: $13.50
Kale: $11.50, = $12.50 x 850 boxes

= **$10,625**

Net Returns = **$1,458**

To apply the sprays, a Pak-tank 100-gallon, three-point hitch, 24-foot boom sprayer is used. The tractor has 38 x 13.6 rear tires which allow approximately 22 inches of ground clearance. Driving over the rows, one pass with the sprayer can cover four beds, or an eight-bed block can be sprayed in two passes.

"Weed control is accomplished with mechanical cultivation, primarily using sweeps. The one problem with this approach for the early plantings is getting the row cover off in order to cultivate. If this can't be done in time, early plantings may need to be hand-hoed. If it rains excessively, other plantings may have to be hand-hoed as well, since timely cultivation will not be possible. Four 6-inch wide sweeps are belly-mounted on a high-clearance tractor, so that there's a sweep on the outside of rows, and one in between each row. If soils are a little wet, this may not achieve enough soil movement, so I'll move the inside sweeps closer to the middle rows, then add a 2-inch-wide shovel close to the inside edge of the outside rows to assure complete cultivation of the soil. I've got to be careful to avoid root damage if I go too close to the plants. If some weeds are missed, after picking and removing much of the crop canopy I'll use beet-knives to undercut weeds, especially grasses, close to the plant."

"Harvesting is done by hand, picking six to ten leaves and bunching them with a rubber band in the field. All leaves are removed down to the center whorl, leaving two or three leaves the size of a hand. Plants are also stripped below where leaves are picked to remove all yellow leaves, which makes picking easier next time. The stripped leaves are just dropped in field. Usually one person can cover two or three rows, depending on how lush the growth is. Bunched leaves are placed on a conveyor belt that carries them up to a wagon pulled by a creeper tractor without a driver. The tractor runs in the alleys between blocks of beds. This systems works well with four or five pickers at a time, so three or four beds can be harvested in a pass. One person can pick five to six cases an hour. The center of the eight-bed blocks can be reached from the alleys with the 28-foot-long conveyor.

"One person stands on the wagon packing twenty-four bunches to the box. A 1 ⅔-bushel box or wire-bound crate is the standard for wholesale markets. In cool weather, workers pick until the wagon is full. In warm weather, after picking thirty or forty boxes, they run them into the packing shed, hose them down with cold water, then top ice. If it's really hot, they bring ice to the field and apply it to the boxes on the wagon."

David would like to have a slurry ice system so they would not have to unload the stacked pallets to apply the ice, as they must do now for top icing. Before placing pallets in the cooler, boxes are spread apart to allow air to flow between them. Storage is at 34°F.

All sales are through the Deep Root Co-op. There is little variation in prices over the season. The co-op sets a price and sticks with it. Harvest starts about June 15 and continues until the end of October. After harvest, fields are flail-mowed to chop up the thick stalks and help them to break down. All fields are then disked and cover cropped with winter rye, except very late fields, in which the stems are left in place to provide some erosion control.

Leeks— A Grower Profile

Cliff Hatch
"Upingill," Gill, Massachusetts

Cliff Hatch farms about 40 acres of varied soils in western Massachusetts. Most of his truck crops are grown on silt loams that hold their moisture well and have a high pH for the area. He grows strawberries, onion-family crops, herbs, potatoes, and pumpkins, as well as small grains. He has grown up to 2 acres of leeks but finds that half an acre is better in terms of marketing. The whole farm is certified organic by NOFA-Massachusetts.

Crop rotation is driven by the strawberries, which are the principal moneymaker. Cliff follows two to three years of berries by a year or two of leeks and onions with a half-acre of cilantro. Then, cover crops are grown for at least one year before going back into strawberries. For cover crops,

Cliff is interested in suppressing nematodes as well as maintaining soil fertility; he's grown a lot of sorghum-Sudan grass and buckwheat in the past, and he may try marigolds. After the summer cover crop, winter barley or rye is planted. These are then harvested for hay or straw and grain.

Cliff generally grows two varieties of leeks, an early and a late type. For early, he uses Titan or King Richard, which produce a nice big tall plant. However, all the short-day summer types are susceptible to purple blotch and other foliar diseases and tend to deteriorate fast after a couple of frosts. In particular, Cliff dislikes Poncho, which has purple blotch problems, and Unique, which has very brittle leaves. For late season leeks, 107 to 120 days, Cliff likes any of the blue-leaf types, such as Nebraska, Arkansas, and Carina (which he has not been able to get for a couple of years). These blue-green leaf types have a shorter shaft but are much more attractive than the summer types, and they hold up well late into the season. Cliff has no problem growing late maturing varieties. "I don't find that people buy many leeks before Labor day, anyway."

"Unless I have a pH of 7 to 7.5, I don't grow onion crops, as they don't grow well in their early growth stages, so I'm more likely to lose them to weeds, which is the main reason we have lost crops. We cover crop all our land and use no animal manure, no matter how long it has been

"A lot of recommendations talk about starting leek plants in February and getting them in by May and out by August. Around here, the humid summers can promote foliar diseases. If you take your time and don't plant until June, you can avoid much of the summer disease pressure. Having the leeks mature in the middle of summer is not necessarily such a great idea, especially since they will continue to size up in the cool weather of fall."

composted, since I don't trust it to be weed-free. Using buckwheat and sorghum-Sudan grass as summer covers helps with weed control, too. We don't make a big practice of using legumes since they can carry viruses and soil nematodes to our strawberries. Instead, I provide nitrogen and other nutrients by using bagged organic fertilizers. Right now I apply a 7-2-4 blend and almost always add sul-po-mag, too, which helps with better leaf health. We do regular soil testing every season on every field."

"Tillage before leeks is moldboard plowing and clod-busting in one operation when plowing down the winter cover crop, as early in the spring as we can get on the land. Clod-busting smooths the land right away and avoids moisture loss. Then the field sits fallow for a couple of weeks, allowing weeds to sprout before disking. If it's dry, I'll even irrigate to encourage weed germination."

After another two or three weeks, rows are marked and fertilizer is drilled into shallow beds about 2 inches high. A potato planter makes a nice bed and adds the fertilizer. Cliff likes to be ready to plant leeks by the first of June, mid-June at the latest. "But I've planted them a lot later in bad years. A lot of recommendations talk about starting leek plants in February and getting them in by May and out by August. Around here, the humid summers can promote foliar diseases. If you take your time and don't plant until June, you can avoid much of the summer disease pressure. Having the leeks mature in the middle of summer is not necessarily such a great idea, especially since they will continue to size up in the cool weather of fall."

Leek seedlings are started in plastic seed trays outside, on top of black plastic laid on the ground, with a perforated row cover over them. "If you were further north you might need a cold frame." A compost-based potting mix is used, sometimes enriched with the 7-2-4 blend, other times top-dressed if the color of the leeks is poor. "Topdressing seedlings can be tricky. One time I burned them with cottonseed meal!" The plants are ready to set in the field by the first of June, which results in a harvest period that starts shortly after Labor Day.

After the beds are prepared, they are flamed and planted in one pass. Flaming using a hand-flamer attached to a propane tank in a wheelbarrow is done directly ahead of the two-row Holland 2004 onion planter. One person pushes the wheelbarrow and another person holds the wand over the row. They flame the plant row, not between rows, as weeds in that area can be handled with subsequent cultivation. "Our planter is designed for celery and onions, with twelve fingers on the wheel that sets plants at 6 inches apart, about 2 inches deep, and it continuously waters in as plants are set. We can plant about 1,000 plants in 15 minutes when it's set right. It was the best thing I ever bought: in an hour we can put in what used to take a week. We plant 25,000 plants per acre, but it is possible to pack them in a lot more like onions. We use 36-inch rows so there is room and soil to work with for hilling later on. If you weren't fussy you could use narrow rows and not hill up the leeks as much, but there would be less blanched stem that does not turn green because it is covered by soil.

"The transplants are only ⅛ inch or less in diameter, and we always trim all the tops to make them uniform in length, about 2 or 3 inches. Longer tops tend to fall over and get in the way of the cultivator, and they also lose water more easily. We severely rogue out any small plants. We never plant any small ones because they don't size up and you can't make any money selling small leeks. If there is too much root growth, we will trim roots down to make them all the same length, about 1 ½ inches."

"One of the most important things you can do for leeks and many other crops is get into the field the next morning after putting them in and hoe the dry dusty soil on either side of the packing wheel into the row. The packing wheel leaves a moist, compacted zone that grows weeds like crazy, and throwing some soil over it to 'dust mulch' will suppress weed germination."

"Timing the first cultivation is difficult. If you go in too quick and things aren't set right, you can bury the tiny plants. We usually have to do a hand cultivation no later than ten days after planting since we can't get in and cultivate too close. Early on, I go down the middle of the rows, two rows at a time, with a four-gang Lilliston rolling cultivator; but I don't try to get close to the crop until after about six weeks. It's important to be on ground that has been well cultivated for a few years ahead of the leeks. There's an old expression I like: never try to grow onions on land that hasn't been under the hoe for at least three years."

The crop gets at least three hand-hoeings—a couple early and one to clean up the weeds later in the season to keep weeds from going to seed or getting in the way of harvest. Cliff tries to use the Lillistons as much as he can, cultivating weeds every ten days or so and aggressively hilling the crop three times, about three weeks apart, starting when the leeks are half an inch in diameter. Once the plants are too big, cultivation has to stop so the leaves don't get damaged. By the end of the season, Cliff likes to have the leeks well covered, in effect having made a raised bed about 10 inches high. "The process of hilling leeks eliminates a lot of the weeding problem you get into with other onion crops, and makes them easier to grow organically."

"I have used an organic fungicide rarely, but I don't rely on fungicide because I just prefer not to. To minimize purple blotch and other leaf diseases, we plant our leek rows oriented north to south so that the early morning sun dries one side, then the afternoon sun dries the other." Cliff has never had any problems with insect pests on leeks—no thrips or onion maggots. In nine years of growing leeks he has never sprayed a single insecticide.

Like any onion crop, leeks need an inch of water per week, and if they don't get that naturally Cliff irrigates to give it to them. For all his truck crops, irrigation consists of overhead guns on tripods, 150 feet apart, attached to flexible lay-flat pipe off 4-inch mains. The 55-horsepower pump is rated for well over 500 gallons per minute. The guns easily cover a 100-foot diameter circle. "We can pick the system up and move it pretty easily once you get the water out of it. You have to watch it if the tripods fall over; that can be a real horror story because of the erosion!"

"We start harvesting in September and go right through November. Sometimes we're harvesting after the ground has frozen a few times and then thawed. It can get miserable out there, so I like to be done with the crop by November 1 if possible. We've done machine harvesting using a potato

Sidebar 19.8 Enterprise Budget for Leeks (per acre)

Variable Costs

Labor and Machinery Costs

	Labor hrs	Machinery hrs
Prepare mix, fill trays, plant seeds	3	–
Cover trays, keep watered	3	–
Soil test field	1	–
Plow and clod bust	1	.75
Disk	1	.75
Form and fertilize beds	2	1
Trim transplant tops, roots	2	–
Set transplants	18	6
Hand hoe (3 x)	48	–
Irrigate (6 x)	1	9
Lilliston cultivate and hill (6 x)	6	6
Harvest and trim	50	–
Sort, pack, and wash	25	–
Marketing and delivery	25	15
Total Hours	186	38.5
	@ $7.50/hr	@ $20/hr
	= $1,395	+ $770

Total Labor and Machinery Costs
= **$2,165**

Management Time
60 hours x $10/hr   = **$600**

Materials

Soil test	$10
Seed (2 ounces @ $10 per ounce)	$20
Black plastic and row cover on seedlings	$10
Potting mix (50% = two years)	$25
Trays (20%= five years)	$20
Bagged fertilizer @ $500 per ton	$250
Crates and boxes 300 @ .75	$225
Winter rye	$10
Total Materials =	**$570**

Total Variable Costs   = $3,335

Fixed Costs
(buildings, land, insurance, interest, office expenses, utilities, taxes, fees, permits)   =   **$160**

Total Costs: = $3,495

Gross Returns
$1 per pound x 5,500 pounds   =   **$5,500**

Net Returns   = $2,005

digger to lift the leeks, and we've just pulled the crop by hand. Hand pulling is actually just as efficient, since we have to shake soil off the crop after potato digging anyway. Now we have someone cut the tops with a big pair of shears, then people come along and dig the crop, shaking off the soil, stripping the leaves and trimming the roots in one operation. All the organic matter is left in the field. It is critical that the plant is upside down when you do this so that the crown does not catch the dirt. The leeks then go into bins and are transported back to the shed to be washed."

After early harvests barley is sown as a winter cover. Since barley won't germinate in cold soils, winter rye is used after October 15.

The nonuniform-size leeks are just washed in a wheelbarrow, in preparation for sale at farmers market. For wholesale markets, the crop gets sorted and washed right in the crates. Again, the plants should be upside down when washing.

Everything is packed and shipped the same day; nothing is held on the farm. "For a couple of years now, the wholesale price has been around $20 for a 20-pound crate, which contains about thirty-six loose leeks. We don't bunch since it takes more time, and it's fairer to the seller and the buyer to sell by the pound. Also, retailers tend to sell more leeks when they allow the customers to take what they want instead of making them buy bunches."

"Yield averages about 10,000 marketable plants on a half-acre, or 275 crates. Late blue-green leeks have lots of top—you are selling greens. Early varieties have less top and lots of shaft, and these don't fill out crates so well. Depending on disease and fertility levels, about 14,000 plants per half-acre are set out, but about 1,000 are lost to injury or carelessness; another 2,000 don't size up; and 1,000 are sold as seconds."

"When I first started vegetable farming I was going to make my living on leeks, I but soon found out there wasn't a market for two acres of leeks. The first year we shipped to Boston and took a real skinning due to brokers' practices—selling short at the farmer's expense. Now people

come here looking for strawberries, but nobody ever comes looking for leeks. Growing lots of leeks is tough; I know because I tried it! But because they fit into our cropping system at a smaller scale, they make sense."

Lettuce— A Grower Profile

David and Chris Colson
New Leaf Farm, Durham, Maine

David Colson and his wife, Chris, farm near Portland, Maine. David handles most of the crop production and Chris manages most of the marketing. Their farm is certified organic by the Maine Organic Farmers and Gardeners Association (MOFGA). Of their 45 open acres, only 12 are suitable for cultivation because of drainage limitations. The rest are in hay. The tillable land has been in a four-year rotation: two years of mixed vegetables followed by wheat under-sown to red clover; then a full year of clover alone. Recently, the rotation has been changed to just a single year of vegetables, as the land in vegetable production has been reduced along with an increase in crop specialization. Oats are used as the winter cover crop after vegetables.

The major crops in the 3.5 acres of field vegetables are lettuce and other leafy greens, broccoli, tomato, peppers, summer squash, and winter squash. Wheat covers 1.5 acres, and the other 7 are in clover and other green manures. There are also four 14- by 96-foot high tunnels, a few dozen perennial herb beds, and another half-acre or so of high-value crops such as annual herbs. Marketing is entirely wholesale, with biweekly deliveries to three specialty stores and eleven restaurants in the Portland area.

The green manures provide most of the fertility for field vegetables. Animal manures are used only to make compost for the high tunnel crops and the half-acre of high-value crops not in rotation with legumes. Over the years, calcium, magnesium, and potassium levels have been increased with lime and sul-po-mag. Now David is also working on raising available phosphorus levels. He prefers to use bone meal rather than rock phosphate, since reserve P levels are OK, and he feels he gets more bang for his buck in terms of availability.

About a half-acre of lettuce is grown, in sequential plantings every two weeks to provide his markets with a steady supply over six to seven months. The first seedings of transplants are made in mid-March in the greenhouse, for setting in the high tunnel. In the greenhouse, bottom heat is used, along with nighttime "tents" over the flats to minimize the need for heating the whole house. The earliest plantings are grown in the greenhouse for three to four weeks in Speedling flats with 1-inch cells before being placed in the ground in a high tunnel, where harvest may begin as early as the end of April.

David begins setting out in the field the next set of transplants in early May, after one week in a cold frame to harden-off. Two types of cold frames are used: traditional wood and fiberglass, as well as PVC hoops covered with clear plastic at night. Direct-seeding of lettuce in the field begins around mid-May and runs through mid-July. For late-season harvest, lettuce is direct-seeded into a high tunnels in August, and harvest continues through mid-November.

Direct-seeding of lettuce is done with a Planet Jr. seeder. After plowing under the clover in early May, the field is disk-harrowed and fertilized with mineral nutrients. Four-foot-wide beds are formed a week or two later. Lettuce is grown in triple rows on the beds, 16 inches apart with about 15 inches between plants, which are staggered in the rows. Wide spacing and raised beds help control bottom rot.

Transplanting is done with a homemade unit pulled by the Kubota high-clearance tractor with a creeper gear. The transplanter is set up on a tool bar with two seats facing backward, one on each side of the 4-foot bed. Narrow, 1-inch shanks open small furrows into which the seedlings are planted by hand. Transplants are carried on a rack in front of the workers. About 1,200 plants per hour can be set this way.

"We grow many lettuce varieties, but my current favorites include Vulcan, which I consider the best red leaf type overall in terms of color and heat tolerance; Simpson Elite and Vanity (which are green leaf types); Romulus (a romaine type); and Red and Green Salad Bowl for the mesclun mix. Some varieties, such as Simpson Elite and all the romaine types, are more susceptible to tarnished plant bug, or TPB, damage than others. TPB is a serious insect pest of lettuce for organic growers, as it "stings" the leaves, causing brown spots and making heads unmarketable. The pest is a general feeder, living in nearby hayfields. When my neighbor mows his adjacent 80 or so acres of hay, the TPB moves into our vegetables, and in some years has devastated the lettuce crop."

"I've tried using botanical insecticides to control TPB, without much success. I prefer to avoid these materials anyway as much as possible because they are harsh on beneficials. Recently, I've experimented with modifying the farm environment to manage TPB habitat as a means of minimizing damage. By managing my crop of red clover so it is succulent about the time my neighbor will be haying, I provide an alternative habitat for TPB emigration. This technique has worked well to keep TPB damage low in the past few years."

Weed pressure on the farm is minimized by avoiding the use of animal manure and by strict rotation of vegetables, small grains, and legume sods. Of course, there are still weeds, and these are controlled mechanically as much as possible. About three weeks after transplanting or four

> *"The fresh-picked quality and the custom order and delivery service are key to attracting and retaining restaurants and upscale food markets as customers. Chefs talk to each other, and word of a good product spreads. In the winter, we visit all our accounts to get feedback . . . "*

weeks after direct seeding, a basket weeder cultivates close to the crop. Then one hand-hoeing is needed to get weeds in the row. A couple of weeks before the crop is harvested, before it gets too big, there is a final cultivation using shovels between the rows and half-sweeps on the outside of the rows. After harvest, either buckwheat or oats is sown promptly to suppress weeds and build the soil. David has switched from winter rye to oats for all his early and late cover crops, as the oats are easier to incorporate before the next crop.

Deer damage is prevented by using half-inch nylon and wire "hot tape" mounted 28 inches off the ground, all around the field. The system is portable and is moved to the field that is in vegetables each year. It is powered by connecting to electricity from the barn.

"We irrigate only at critical times, when stress would be rather severe. Our water supply is a shallow well. A 3-horsepower gas-powered pump fills a head pipe along the edge of the field, with outlets every 40 feet for attaching sections of 2 ¼-inch plastic pipe with Rainbird impact sprinklers on them. The sprinklers are spaced at 40-foot intervals along the plastic pipes, which are detached and moved through the field of lettuce, which is irrigated one swath at a time."

"Harvest is done in the early morning, while the crop is still cool. Lettuce is placed in boxes and moved to the washing shed, where it is dumped into a tank of water to get all the soil off. It then goes into a clean box and into the cooler overnight for delivery the next day. A night in the cooler has the heads in top condition with all field heat removed prior to delivery."

Harvests are made twice a week, on the days before deliveries. Chris calls all clients the day before harvest and gets their orders. That way, David knows exactly what needs to be harvested, and crop waste is minimized. On harvest days, a crew of five or six people work a full day to gather and prepare all the crops for delivery. David and his father switch off on making deliveries, each driving the truck once a week.

"The fresh-picked quality and the custom order and delivery service are key to attracting and retaining restaurants and upscale food markets as customers. Chefs talk to each other, and word of a good product spreads. In the winter, we visit all our accounts to get feedback, identify new crop needs, and determine trends so that next year's planting can be planned accordingly. As a result, the crop mix on our farm has changed. Ten years

Sidebar 19.9 Enterprise Budget for Field-Grown Lettuce (½ acre)

Variable Costs
Labor and Machinery Costs

	Labor hrs	Machinery hrs
Seed clover	2	1
Plow and harrow clover	1	1
Seed, water, harden transplants	15	–
Apply fertilizer, form beds	1	1
Set transplants	40	8
Water transplants	2	–
Tractor cultivate 2 x	2	2
Hand-weed 1 x	6	–
Harvesting 2 x/week, 12 weeks	96	–
Washing and packing	96	–
Taking orders, trucking, delivery 2 x/ week	48	19
Seed-down buckwheat or oats	1	1
Total Hours	310	33
	@ $5/hr*	@ $20/hr
	= $1,550	+ $660

Total Labor and Machinery Cost
= **$2,210**

Marketing
(one day of winter visits with customers)
= $80

Materials
Lettuce seed	$39
Trays and potting mix	$76
GH fuel for heat	$20
Fertilizers	$100
Red clover seed	$20
Buckwheat and oats	$8
Deer tape (20% = five years)	$10
Irrigation (20% = five years)	$60
Boxes (recycled for five years)	$17
Total materials cost	= **$350**

Total Variable Costs
(labor, machinery, materials, marketing)
= **$2,640**

Fixed Costs
(buildings, land, insurance, interest, office expenses, utilities, taxes, fees, permits)
= **$1,400**

Total Costs: = **$4,040**

Gross Returns
(= 40 dozen x 12 weeks x $9.60/dozen)
= **$4,608**

Net Returns = **$568**

*Average of apprentice labor and farmer labor

ago, lettuce accounted for 50% of sales, now it is 10% and mesclun is about 25%."

Prices are maintained consistently over the season for all crops except tomatoes, which bring a higher early-season price. Lettuce sells for an average of $9 to $10 per dozen heads, and the average weekly sales are 40 to 50 dozen.

Muskmelons— A Grower Profile

Pooh and Anne Sprague
Edgewater Farm
Plainfield, New Hampshire

Edgewater Farm includes 65 cultivated acres in western New Hampshire, mostly along the Connecticut River on sandy and silt loam soils, with some heavier soils inland. Crops include 10 acres of strawberries, 35 acres of vegetables, and 20 acres of cover crops. Melons are grown on approximately ¾ of an acre.

Field preparation prior to plantings of melons can vary somewhat. Pooh Sprague always uses fields that are near irrigation and have not had melons in them for at least one year before. If following winter rye, he may rotavate 5-foot-wide strips of rye on 10-foot centers to create planting beds, leaving the untilled rye strips to grow up as windbreaks. If the field has crop residues but no cover crop, he will disk and harrow the whole field. In either case, black plastic mulch is then laid down on 10-foot centers, and a synthetic blend of fertilizer is applied right under the plastic, at a rate of 60–90 pounds per acre actual N. Sometimes drip tape will be laid if the field is not near a large water supply that can feed solid-set irrigation.

When winter rye is left in between rows of melons as a windbreak, it is mowed and incorporated when it starts to form a seed head; and then Dutch white clover is Brillion-seeded in these strips. A high rate of about 30–40 pounds of seed per acre is used to try to get a good stand. If bare ground was prepared in fields without winter rye, Pooh tries to plant the clover as early as possible, in order to get a better stand. In this case, clover may

be three inches high by the time melons are transplanted.

"Clover does not tend to establish well in the rye stubble," says Pooh. "Any clover, white, red, or sweet, can be used, as they will all tolerate mowing in the first year; but I prefer using Dutch white because it fills in better with its stolons. This competes with crabgrass later in the season. The clover gets mowed when it gets to be 4–6 inches high, using a 16-horsepower garden tractor with a flail-mower which drops the clippings right on the clover strip. Keeping the clover low helps control broadleaves, improves the working conditions in the field for the workers, and makes a nice harvest situation. Using the clover also improves the soil tilth as well as fixing nitrogen."

Pooh transplants all his melons with a water-wheel transplanter. He tried direct-seeding but it led to erratic stands and slower maturity. Transplants are grown in old Speedling trays with 2 ¼-inch cells, or 606-cell pack trays filled with soil-less mix. He recently tried a compost-based mix, which appeared slower to start but gave good results by the time plants were ready to set out.

The first muskmelon planting of early varieties is sown around the last week of April to be planted out the third week of May. The second planting is seeded into trays about three weeks later, from May 10 to 20, using mid- and late-season varieties; and these are set out about June 10 to 15. To harden-off seedlings, they are put on wagons outside for a week before transplanting. When they are outside, the transplants are getting air movement and more direct sunlight but can be covered at night when necessary.

"Plants are spaced 18 inches in the row. This is a tight spacing, but growers in the area have learned that the melons you will harvest will be

> *"Plants are spaced 18 inches in the row. This is a tight spacing, but growers in the area have learned that the melons you will harvest will be the early ones—those that set up on the plastic."*

the early ones—those that set up on the plastic. The side vines are really just useful for energy and sugar production. Tight spacing also makes better use of our limited field space.

"Transplants are set in the plastic mulch and simultaneously watered in with at least a quart of water plus a little bit of soluble starter fertilizer. Transplanting is best on a cloudy, warm day. On a sunny day the plants will cook on the plastic, no matter how well they have been hardened off. Additional movement from the wind hardens them up a bit for a day or two after setting, then they are watered in again with about a quart of water each, using the transplanter, before they are covered with 4-foot-wide spunbonded polystyrene floating row covers.

"Spunbond row covers may not give the growth enhancement response of clear plastic cover, but I find them more friendly to the plant—they are not as hot inside and do not tend to blow off in wind as easily. However, I've recently been experimenting with perforated (not slitted) plastic row covers. I'm always seeking to fine-tune my production system.

"Wind can really be a problem in the fields that don't have the rye windbreaks. The row covers are supported with metal hoops made of number 9 wire cut to 38-inch lengths and bent over to hold up the cover. All edges of the cover must be buried, which used to be done with a hand-pushed hiller. Now, a disk mounted behind the rear tire on a tractor is used to throw soil over the cover edge much more quickly.

"Giving at least a quart of water to each plant at transplanting and then again a couple of days later, just before covering, will carry them quite a long time, especially if the plastic mulch was laid on moist ground, as it should have been. Rarely is it necessary to irrigate when row covers are on; but if it doesn't rain, it might be. The covers stay on until about the Fourth of July, when vines are running and some blossoms are visible. Because strawberry season is slowing down by then, labor is available to work with the row covers. There is some flexibility in timing the removal of row covers, but I want them on as long as possible to

promote growth. After some female blossoms are present (which is shortly after the first few male flowers appear), and when the vines are pushing against the sides of the row cover, I will remove the covers.

"Workers take the covers off by hand, roll them up, and store them in apple bins. They are useful

Sidebar 19.10 Enterprise Budget for Muskmelons (¾ acre)

Variable Costs
Labor and Machinery

	Labor hrs	Machinery hrs
Plow and harrow or rotavate rye	3.5	3.5
Seed clover	1	1
Seed, water, harden transplants	10	0
Lay plastic and band fertilizer	1.5	1.5
Set transplants	18	6
Water transplants	3	1.5
Set hoops and apply cover	6	0.5
Remove cover and hoops	4	0
Cultivate (+ sidedress) 2x	1.5	1.5
Mow clover 4 x	4	4
Hand-weed 1 x	5	0
Spray 2 x	3	1
Harvesting	110	20
Remove plastic mulch	3	0.5
Seed down winter rye	0.5	0.5
Total hours	174	41.5
	x $10/hr	x $20/hr
	= $1,740	+ $830

Total Labor and Machinery Cost
= **$2,570**

Materials
Seeds	$100
Trays (used) and potting mix	$150
Fertilizer blend	$50
Starter fertilizer	$10
Calcium nitrate	$30
Black plastic	$75
Row cover (50% = 2 years)	$200
Hoops (20% = 5 years)	$10
White clover seed (30 x $5)	$150
Fungicides (2 x)	$40
Winter rye seed	$25
Total Materials Cost =	**$840**

Marketing Cost
(stand labor, cooler)   = **$130**

Total Variable Production Costs = **$3,540**

Fixed Costs
(estimated at 15% of variable production costs)
= **$531**

Total Costs   = **$4,071**

Gross Returns
(average marketable yield) 15,000 pounds
x (average price) .55   = **$8,250**

Net Returns   = **$4,179**

208

Sustainable Vegetable Production from Start-Up to Market*Sustainable Vegetable Production from Start-Up to Market*

for an average of two years before too many tatters become a problem. After taking the wires out of the rows, there is heavy weed growth on edges of the plastic mulch to deal with. By going through with belly-mounted half-sweeps set close to the plastic edge, large weeds up to a foot tall can be uprooted and turned over almost in a plow-like fashion. After a few days, another pass may be needed. The first time through, the melons are also side-dressed with about 200 pounds per acre of calcium nitrate.

"At this stage, the crop is regularly irrigated. I feel the soil for moisture, and I look at the growth of the cover crop and the condition of the mowing residue, too. For melons, it is important not to allow any drought stress on the plants, and I don't wait to see any leaves starting to appear flaccid before I irrigate. Ideally I'd use a drip T-tape, but I rely on overhead irrigation because it's quick and allows the crew to irrigate a lot of crops in a short amount of time."

"Natural pollination hasn't been a problem in the past, but it is now. A neighbor has an apple or-chard, so there have been enough bees in certain locations. Now, however, beekeeping is becoming part of the requirement to growing good melons. I'll be paying more attention to this in the next few years."

"If the crabgrass looks bad in the clover crop early in the season, an application of a selective grass herbicide will be made in mid-June. After several early mowings, broadleaves have been sup-pressed, but the crabgrass grows too flat to the ground to be mowed off. After the herbicide application, the clover usually fills in and shades out any further weeds that might germinate. By the beginning of August the clover has formed a thick mat, free of weeds except for the occasional one that gets away and has to be hand-pulled."

"There never seems to be much problem with cucumber beetles, because the plants are pretty good sized by the time the covers come off, and beetle pressure is usually low. In some years an insecticide spray will be needed. I keep an eye out for disease, which tends to show up at about the time first picking starts. Powdery mildew and downy mildew are the key diseases. I use one of several fungicides, depending on the year and the diseases. Usually spraying once or twice is all that is needed. I never did spray fungicides until about six years ago, when I had a problem with powdery mildew and all the plants went down. The inoculum buildup after you've been growing a crop for a number of years changes how you do things."

"Getting into the crop to harvest is pretty easy since all the runners that get in the way are cut off as clover is mowed in the 5-foot-wide alley. Pickup trucks can drive right into the field, which saves on the back and speeds up harvest. The melons are loaded up with baskets, and the crop is put right into our farm stands or delivered to other growers. If the harvest is heavy, some melons are stored in a 50°F cooler for a couple of days at the most.

"Each planting is harvested for about three weeks. Fruit quantity and quality are still high for that period; then they start to go downhill rather fast. The two-planting system was initiated to prolong the season. Harvest of the second planting begins two to three weeks later than the first planting, even though the second planting is set out fully three weeks later. In most years, picking starts in early August and continues into the second or third week of September."

"Varieties for early planting include Early Gold, Earliqueen, Rising Star, Starship, and Passport; but the latter doesn't sell very well because of its green flesh. Super Star has been used; even though it gets too big and may have to be cut for sales, it does taste good. For the later planting, I use Starsweet, Superstar, Saticoy, and Rising Star again. Gold Star was a good variety but had a lot of disease problems on this farm. The heavy-netted Harris varieties have performed well and shown good disease tolerance."

"After harvest, the field is brush-hogged to chop up residues; plastic is pulled up; and winter rye is seeded with a Brillion between the clover strips. That way a complete cover crop will be in place until next spring."

The farm makes the most money on bedding

plants and strawberries, and that is where the most effort is placed to keep track of costs and returns. Other crops must be grown to have at the stand, but Pooh doesn't bother to keep close track of costs and returns on crops like melons because the farm is so diversified, with half-acres of dozens of crops. However, below is an estimated budget for growing muskmelons based on typical labor and machinery time, materials, and sales.

Parsnips— A Grower Profile

Doug Jones
Birdsfoot Farm, Canton, New York
Birdsfoot Farm is an "intentional community" in upstate New York. Located on silt loam soils, it is certified organic, with about 5 acres in cultivation. Doug Jones and his partners grow a wide variety of crops for local markets but also enjoy the profitability of shipping downstate such specialty root crops as burdock, horseradish, Jerusalem artichokes, celeriac, and about ⅛ acre of parsnips. They have been growing many of these crops since the community started twenty-five years ago. Their market has been mostly wholesale, through the Finger Lakes Organic Growers Cooperative (FLO), with just a little bit of local retailing.

For parsnips, they try to use a field that was in a heavy-feeding crop the previous year, and one where weeds were well controlled, since germination and early growth are slow. To prepare the ground they use a homemade chisel plow, which is an old corn cultivator with some tines removed, pulled by a Ford 800 tractor. The goal is to till at least 10 or 12 inches deep to loosen the soil. Then, after disking, the soil is hand-raked to level it and remove trash that would clog the seeder. Finally, a cultipacker or a hand-pushed roller is used to create a firm seedbed. The hand-roller seems to cause less compaction than a tractor-pulled roller but still creates a sufficiently firm seedbed.

By following a heavy-feeding crop that got a lot of cover crop (mammoth red clover, hairy vetch, or yellow sweet clover) or compost incorporation,

Doug and his partners take advantage of residual nutrients, so no soil amendments are needed. "Our soil is already right up there on all major nutrients according to soil tests, so parsnips seem to do well without any other fertilization," says Doug. In general, they use a minimum of three to four years of crop rotation. That includes a one-year fallow with a sod crop. "We would like the parsnips to be the last year before the sod, but since we establish the sod by undersowing, that is not possible with parsnips due to all the digging at harvest. We usually follow parsnips with peas or beans, and then a sod is established that year."

"It's very important to be aware that parsnip seed has a short shelf life, so it is standard practice to use fresh seed every year. It's just too risky to use more than one-year-old seed . . ."

"We try to plant in the last week of May, so that there is still a lot of moisture in the ground, which is critical for germination. It takes ten to fifteen days to germinate, so you really have to keep the soil surface moist. If we have a dry June, we irrigate to prevent crusting that can be lethal. You could plant earlier, but we are usually too busy. The end of May leaves adequate time to get a full crop; there's no point harvesting before the middle of October. Prior to that, the crop doesn't yet have the sugar taste we are looking for. Parsnips get even better into November, but of course you can't leave all of your harvest till that late."

An antique Planet Jr. planter is used to sow seed; it doesn't have plates but a gravity-feed opening with a brush inside that stirs the seeds. It's really heavy-duty and works well. They aim for a depth of about ¾ inch and a spacing of three seeds per inch. That's heavier than recommended, but they prefer to have to thin than to be stuck with gaps in the rows. "It's very important to be aware that parsnip seed has a short shelf life, so it is standard practice to use fresh seed every year. It's just too risky to use more than one-year-old seed; and even that is not really worth it since seed is a minor cost." They use about an ounce of seed per 250 feet of row.

Rows are spaced 18–20 inches apart on flat ground; no raised beds are used. That gives ample room for growth and digging. The planter has a row marker that helps keep the rows parallel, which is important for cultivating.

"Harris Model has been our main parsnip variety, as it's been reliable for us. We've tried Lancer but have not seen much difference. Andover is a new one we plan to try. It has rounded crowns, and this should make trimming the tops easier compared to most other varieties, which have concave crowns and make close topping a challenge."

"The crop is thinned after everything has germinated. The ideal density is an average of 3 inches between plants. A lot of seed doesn't come up, so in general half or less of the plants that do come up are removed. In some years, very little thinning is needed at all."

"Cultivation is done by wheel-hoes with Real-type oscillating blades. The first cultivation may even be done preemergence, if high weed pressure is expected, staying to the side of the marks made by the planter, and going as close as we dare. Usually, our first cultivation is shortly after emergence, when there are two true leaves per plant. Using walking tools, one can get quite close to the plants. Cultivations continue as needed, usually three or four times, until the canopy is too large and prevents passage with the hoes. A thorough hand-weeding is usually performed when the plants have one or two true leaves; and another is done in July, to get anything that was missed earlier."

"There have been very few insect problems with this crop, just the occasional carrot rust fly larvae, but nothing serious over all the years we have been growing parsnips. We do have a small problem with a rust-like surface discoloration and we're not sure what is causing it. This is responsible for an average of 3–5% culls."

"We've had very little damage from rodents, but deer have become more of a problem over the

Sidebar 19.11 Enterprise Budget for Parsnips (⅛ acre)

Variable Costs
Labor and Machinery Costs*

	Labor hrs	Machinery hrs
Chisel plow (two passes)	1	1
Disk (three passes)	1	1
Hand-rake seedbed	5	–
Seed parsnip	3	–
Irrigate	3	–
Cultivate 4 x (wheel-hoe)	10	–
Hand-pull weeds	45	–
Hand-harvest	65	–
Wash and grade	45	–
Pack and store	15	–
Marketing	5	–
Office work, intern program, promotion, mammal control	55	–
Total Hours	253	2 (@ $15)

*Labor/machine cost (includes 84 hours of intern labor @$2/hr =$168 + $30 machine time; community partner labor is not included here but is accounted for as hourly return below)

Total Labor and Machinery Costs = **$198**

Materials, Marketing

Shipping costs	$120
Seed	$12
Compost	$20
Bulk bags	$15
Hand tools (prorated)	$15
Miscellaneous	$5
Total Materials and Shipping =	**$187**

Fixed Costs
(organic certification, internship program, community living costs, utilities, office)

= **$40**

Total Costs = **$425**

Gross Returns
= 2,420 pounds @ .85

= **$2,057**

Net Returns
(over intern pay and all costs but not farmer/owner labor) = **$1,632**

Hourly return to community partners
for 169 hours

= **$9.66/hr**

years. A few years ago the deer started to eat the tops off the crop in the fall. In winter they actually ate them out of the ground, down to 2 inches deep when they were hungry. To deal with the problem we built a 10-foot-high deer fence around our 5 acres of vegetable fields."

In most years, they have not found irrigation necessary after germination, since their soils are high in organic matter, and there is a long fall season for recovery from a slight drought. If there is no rain for more than a couple of weeks, then drip irrigation or overhead sprinklers are used.

"Our basic harvest season is from October 15 to November 15. It's not the freezing of the ground, but just the prolonged cold weather that creates the sugars from starch in the roots. We hesitate to dig too early even though the market wants our parsnips, since we want the product to be at full flavor. It is possible to dig roots and hold them in cold storage to sweeten them up. We leave only 10% of the crop in the field for spring harvest, since the risk of loss is great if there is an open winter. On average, about 10 to 15% of roots overwintered are damaged by exposure to cold and have to be culled. Our area does not have a lot of snow cover relative to other cold growing areas. The market season for spring harvest is also short, since shelf life is not long.

"We've tried a lot of different techniques for hand harvesting. If you were going to use a mechanical lifter, it would have to be set deeper than 12 inches. We use a broad garden rake to pull all the leaves to one side of the row, and then dig a trench alongside the row with a regular round-point shovel, enough to get two hands on the parsnips. They are really rooted-in and require a lot of force to pull out. They are then topped in the field with a knife, close to the crown, to delay sprouting. If the crop is dug in the spring, then the leaf crown is dug out completely, since the parsnips really want to sprout by then."

The roots are put in waxed produce boxes and removed from the field in garden carts. The crop is always washed right after harvest, within an hour or two of digging. Pressurized water through a spray gun on a hose is applied on a wash table. The roots are then bagged in 20- or 25-pound bags. Early harvests are placed in a cooler in the barn that holds them at 40°F or so. At this temperature they will continue to sweeten until shipped. The roots do tend to discolor in storage. Usually within a couple of weeks they have a tan color instead of white, but they are still marketable. Later, when the barn is freezing, harvests will go into the root cellar, which doesn't really get cold enough until Thanksgiving. Storage can be tricky; but the parsnips are usually sold within a few days of digging, so they are not stored on the farm very long. Customer feedback has been positive about quality.

Roots with more than a little cosmetic discoloration are culled, as well as any that are damaged during harvest. Forking of the root is acceptable, if it's near the top and both branches look good, but not more than a few percent would be included in the total marketable harvest. A minimum root diameter of 1 inch and a minimum length of 8 inches are considered a "grade A." Weird shapes are also removed. Culls are then fed to their cow, or eaten by Doug Jones and his partners or by local customers; or they are given away or composted if necessary.

Average yield is about 1 pound of grade A roots per row-foot. Over the last four years, wholesale price has averaged about 85 cents after a 30% marketing fee is paid to FLO. If Doug sells locally to stores, they still sell for about $1 or so. On average the price for parsnips is about 60% higher than carrots, perhaps due to the frequency of poor stands, a longer growing season, and the difficulty of digging them.

"The market seems to like our big roots, which average 2 inches at the crown and 12 inches long, with a very gradual taper. The future of our parsnip production is uncertain, since FLO is having organizational challenges. This may not be such a bad thing for us, since we would like to try and market more locally, and we have not fully exploited the local potential of other crops than the specialty root crops we have emphasized in the past."

Potatoes—
A Grower Profile

Rob Johanson and Janice Goranson
Goranson Farm, Dresden, Maine

Rob Johanson and Janice Goranson farm 37 acres of river bottom fine sandy loam in mid-coast Maine, not far from Augusta. The farm was purchased by Janice's father and mother, who grew potatoes primarily for wholesale markets. The next generation has inherited a paid-off property along with older machinery in good shape. Since taking over in the late '80s they have diversified the farm and developed retail markets that include a farm stand, restaurant sales, and farmers markets four days a week in season. They wholesale only their excess production. Janice's primary responsibilities include marketing and greenhouse production, while Rob manages most of the field work, maintenance, and repair.

The crop mix is widely diversified and includes vegetables, maple syrup, strawberries, greenhouse tomatoes, flowers, and herbs. Marketing is mostly retail through the farm stand and farmers markets, with 16% of gross sales to restaurants and just a few percent as wholesale. Janice says, "We also have a CSA, which has worked very well for us. We have 170 families in our summer program and it's made a huge difference in our farm because it amounts to about 22% of our total sales, essentially presold. It's a little different than the typical CSA because ours is a credit with the farm. Depending on the size of the share, they either get a 3, 5, or 7% discount. Shares range from $100 to $400 a year. Members can shop for whatever they want. We also do a winter share with 45 families. That is more like a traditional CSA where they get a box of produce."

"On average, we have about 8 acres of land in potatoes. Roughly 12 acres of the tillable land is taken out of production each year and planted to Japanese millet or sorghum-Sudan grass, followed by hairy vetch plus winter rye or oats, depending on what crop is going in the following spring. The winter rye can be a problem because of the root mass; it doesn't like to break up and till in, and the oats leave a smoother seedbed," says Rob.

"Potatoes are grown in a three-year rotation with sweet corn and the cover crops. Soil tests are taken every year before planting cash crops, and fertilizer is custom-blended to meet the nutrient recommendations. Growing hairy vetch in the rotation supplies a lot of N to a subsequent potato crop, but some fertilizer N is still applied to much of the crop. The timing is perfect with the release of vetch N in terms of when the potato crop needs it, but I'm still side dressing late-season varieties like Green Mountain and Burbanks to assure that we get the size our markets desire. There is a lot of demand for big 'bakers' with these two varieties. With the early reds I usually don't apply any N at all. With mid-season varieties I'm still experimenting to get the right rates. The quality of the green manure stand, when we get to tilling it in, the weather, and other factors affect how much fertilizer will be needed. Nitrogen fertilizer application is usually split, with some in the band at planting and the rest just before the crop canopy closes. All the P and K is applied at planting."

"We grow our large crops on 3-foot centers and set up the equipment to cover two rows at a time. All our tractors are on 6-foot centers, so most crops are either 36 or 18 inches between rows. Primary tillage is performed with a 130-horse-power International. We're plowing more and rototilling less. We still run the rototiller over the top of the plowed ground to create a fine seedbed. The International is also used to run the irrigation. We have both hose-reel and solid-set, which we use mostly for frost control and for irrigating fields we can't get to with the hose-reel system. The reel avoids the problems with overlapping water application that we have with either the solid-set or with the big irrigation gun we used for a while."

> *"In farming, you have to have goals, but you also have to be process oriented to keep at it. Every year is a learning experience; every year is an experiment. It helps to have the desire to keep . . . tweaking your system to make it better."*

"We cut any large 'seed' by hand. This gives a better quality seed piece than using the seed cutter, which requires pretty round potatoes. We get less sliced pieces and more consistently blocky pieces. We put them right in the ground without curing or fungicides, using a two-row Lockwood planter. Spacing varies with variety; the reds are planted 6 inches apart, and Russet Burbanks 15 inches apart, so every variety requires a different amount of seed. We go by University recommendations as well as our own experience. Where we want larger-size tubers, we spread out the spacing."

"We used to grow 3 acres of red 'Bs'; the wholesale price for these small, early potatoes is good but still not enough to justify growing a lot, given our production costs. Also, the timing of the work for the wholesale market is not good because it comes at a time when all our retail markets are busy; and it strains our whole system. So we got out of wholesaling new potatoes, and now we retail about half our red acreage and sell the other half to restaurants over the winter. Besides the red 'Bs,' we sell a lot of US #1 Green Mountain, Russet Burbank, and Kennebec, as well as Red Clouds, which keeps well for a red variety. We retail all these varieties for winter keepers. There's also a high demand among consumers for the largest potatoes, or 'bakers,' but restaurants actually prefer the smaller ones."

Over the years Rob has been cutting back on the use of herbicides. "We stopped using herbicides on our greens and other small crops in the late 80s, due to the complexity of getting applications just right, avoiding drift, mixing different materials for the areas of different crops. It was just a nightmare. Now we use a flame weeder, a basket weeder, and a Lilliston rolling cultivator for weed control in most of our crops. But with the sufficient acreage of potatoes and sweet corn it has made sense to avoid labor costs by using herbicides. We apply low rates whenever possible. In order to get everything cultivated in a timely fashion I would need to invest in some additional equipment, probably a tine weeder for early-season control. Then I'd follow with the Lillistons and then hilling. This year for the first time we are going to do our 5 acres of sweet corn without

herbicides. The rotation system is really critical to keeping the fields clean and making it possible to give up the herbicides. We're taking it one crop at a time as we transition away from herbicides. Potatoes will be the last one."

"We've been working with the University of Maine on a biological control program for CPB (Colorado potato beetle). This will be the third year in a row without any 'hard' insecticides applied. At the beginning of the season, if the population is high enough I'll go out and flame the adults with a tractor-mounted vapor unit with one burner. It's crude, but I still get over 80% control, which is as good as I can get with a chemical. If I had two burners I could probably get 90% control. I just flame the outside rows, so even though it's one row at a time, it only takes about an hour to do that first half acre, which is where most of them are. I use the same flamer for weed control, flaming over the row just before emergence, and if we need to, we flame vines, too, at the end of the season, although usually we get natural senescence.

"Then, we scout for eggs, watch for the hatch, and get prepared to go in with Bt (*Bacillus thuringiensis*). We have also been using *Beauveria bassiana,* another biological insecticide, generally in combination with Bt, on an experimental basis. We started with plots set up by University of Maine researchers, then we received a SARE (Sustainable Agriculture Research and Education) farmer grant to look at different combinations of biological treatments. Our conclusion so far is that the Bt works, but the Beauveria gives the added boost of long-term control. If you inoculate your fields with Beauveria, the CPBs are constantly risking infection when they come in contact with the soil, so the population pressure is kept down. After this year, all our potato fields will have been sprayed with Beauveria, but it's not a knock-down type of material, and it doesn't provide enough control alone, so we still need to spray something else. We usually put on four to six sprays of Bt, depending on timing of egg hatch; and that provides excellent control. As far as aphid control, we don't get too excited since we now have a tremendous population of lady beetles and spiders, too, as a result of avoiding nonselective insecticides. We have had to spray for leafhopper, and we use organic sprays. Pyrenone knocks them down, but in a bad year you've got to keep spraying as long as they keep flying in on the winds."

"Disease control is accomplished with rotation, sanitation, and fungicides. We watch the extension reports, and we scout. Of course, once you see

Sidebar 19.12 Enterprise Budget for Red "B" Potatoes (per acre)

Variable Costs
Labor and Machinery

	Labor hrs	Machinery hrs
Sow cover crops	1.5	1.5
Plow cover crops	.75	.75
Soil test	.25	–
Shallow rototill	1	1
Cut seed	2	1
Plant seed, band fertilizer	2	1.5
Apply herbicide	.75	.5
Scout for CPB adults	.25	–
Flame CPB in field edges	1	.5
Scout for CPB egg hatch	.25	–
Spray Bt 4 x	3	2
Hill up potatoes 2 x	2	2
Spray fungicides 3 x	2.25	1.5
Mow tops	.5	.5
Machine dig and hand lift	16	4
Brush, grade, wash, and pack	17	12
Marketing	50	–
Total Hours	100.5	28.75
	@ $6.50/hr	@ $17/hr
	= $653	+ $489

Total Labor and Machinery Costs
= **$1,142**

Materials	
Cover crops seeds (vetch and rye)	$40
Potato seed	$288
Fertilizer	$68
Fuel and oil	$127
Propane	$20
Insecticides (4 x)	$60
Fungicides (3 x)	$54
Bags and quart boxes	$418
Miscellaneous supplies	$5
Total Materials	$1,080

General Management Costs
(20 hours @ $12/hr)   =   **$240**

Fixed Costs
(buildings, land, insurance, interest, office expenses, utilities, taxes, fees, permits)   =   **$440**

Total Costs   =   **$2,902**

Gross Returns
yield 10,000 pounds (= 6,154 quarts) x average price $2 per quart   =   **$12,308**

Net Returns   =   **$9,406**

much disease you're in trouble. Knock on wood, we haven't had any late blight, which has become a big problem in the northern part of the state, where much of the seed potatoes come from. I'm really afraid one of these days it will come in on seed stock. As a precaution, we are going to enter the state program so we can grow our own certified seed. We've had good suppliers, but the problems are getting worse up north, and much of the seed is pretty beat up compared to how carefully we can handle it. We just received some foundation seed stock, so we're getting going this year on growing our own seed for next year's planting."

"We disinfect all tools and surfaces between seed lots when cutting, and if we see any disease we sterilize anything that's touched those tubers. The planter is disinfected between seed lots. The storage is cleaned up well and we do everything we can to keep sources of inoculum down."

"Harvest starts the first of July with reds for the new potato market. All the 'B' potatoes are lifted with the two-row digger and picked up by hand. Once they reach 1.5 inches in diameter, the tops are killed back by mowing, which allows the skin to toughen up for easier handling. We don't use the mechanical harvester because we lose too many through the chain. All the other potatoes are lifted with a Lockwood two-row harvester that's old but functional. It lifts the potatoes and carries them into a bulk body truck, which takes them to the packing line with a brusher, sizer, and grading table. They are bagged off the table into 10-, 20-, and 50-pound bags. The bulk of the fall crop is 50s. We do a lot of 3- and 5-pound bags of reds and Yukon Golds early in the season. Most of the red 'Bs' are sold in quart boxes."

"We have a potato barn for storage; it's not fancy but it stores them well until June. We don't use any sprout inhibitors. Yields are up around 225 to 275 hundredweight, depending on variety and weather. Irrigation just doesn't substitute for rainfall, since we can't be timely enough with it, but it is necessary some years to avoid a disaster."

"In farming, you have to have goals, but you also have to be process oriented to keep at it. Every year is a learning experience; every year is an experiment. It helps to have the desire to keep modifying what you're doing, tweaking your system to make it better."

Pumpkins— A Grower Profile

Jim Barber
Barber's Farm, Middleburgh, New York
The Barber family has farmed this land in east-central New York for about 150 years. The soils are sandy and silt loams, about 10 feet deep. There are 500 acres on the farm, 150 of which are in vegetables. The rest is alfalfa and field corn for the 150-cow dairy. The Barbers grow 65 acres of sweet corn, 20 acres of potatoes, 8 acres of melons, and 15 acres of pumpkins, plus a variety of other vegetables. Of the vegetables, about 90% are sold retail through a stand on the farm and a few satellite stands for summer sales off trucks. Pumpkins, however, are about 60% wholesaled to other vegetable stands and retailers in the area.

Jim's crop rotation plan is not rigid, but routinely the vegetable fields go into alfalfa for about four years; then vegetables are grown for six to eight years. Within the vegetable cycle, he rotates away from the same family of crops. Long-season vegetable crops such as tomatoes, peppers, and melons go on the best ground right after alfalfa, then cole crops, potatoes, and other vegetables follow in subsequent years. Pumpkins are grown toward the end of the vegetable rotation. It is tricky to juggle all the crops and match them to appropriate field conditions. "The key to the success of the rotation is to get the alfalfa in there for three or four years," says Jim.

Winter rye is sown on all the vegetable fields when possible. However, some crops, such as field corn, are harvested too late, and there's not enough time left to get rye going. On fields that were not cover-cropped, dairy manure is applied at about 10–12 tons per acre before vegetables. Then the fields are plowed and fitted by disking and dragging. Depending on when the fields are plowed, planting may be right away; or weeds may be allowed to grow and then harrowed a few times. Jim tries to plant pumpkins around Memorial Day.

"This year some of the pumpkins were planted into a dead rye mulch, but it didn't work out too well in terms of weed control. We used a four-row John Deere Maximerge 7000, planting every other row using no-till coulters; but every time you turn around you have to pick up a different planter box so that only two of the four rows get planted. The other two still get cut and fertilized, which resulted in weeds in those rows. It would be easier with a two-row planter. Also, the soil warms a little slower under the killed rye, which slows the plants and gives those early weeds an advantage. Our rye stand was also a little thin, since we didn't plan to use it as a dead mulch when it was sown the previous fall. Next year we'll plant the rye thicker and plant the pumpkins a week later to let the rye get up to 30 inches tall before we kill it.

"A second pumpkin planting is put in two weeks after the first to keep quality up throughout the harvest period. The first field tends to run down in quality before the season is over. If the dead rye mulch system is used with the first planting, the second planting should probably be one week later since the rye will slow the first planting down. Fertilizer is banded at planting. We apply a custom-blended fertilizer, and that supplies about 80 pounds of actual N per acre. No side-dressing is applied."

Howden is the only variety Jim grows, except for some small-scale experimentation. "It's a heavy, rugged pumpkin that lasts. It doesn't rot on the customer's lawn, and it has a strong handle. It's also thick-skinned, so the frost doesn't seem to bother it much." The seed is sown in rows 6 feet apart, in blocks of six rows separated by a 9-foot

> *"I have my market all set before I plant anything. One year a fellow I didn't know came by and asked me to grow 7 acres of pumpkins for him. I put in 4 and he never showed up. A good relationship with your customers is important."*

alley. A seed is dropped roughly every 2 feet in the row. Later, they go back and thin to about one plant every 4 or 5 feet during the first hand-hoeing.

As soon as the pumpkins start breaking through so you can see the rows, cultivation starts, using an old Farmall H with disks that pull soil away from the row, one row at a time. This is done twice, and the small hills that are formed on either side of the rows make it easier to hand-hoe in the row. Hand-hoeing (and thinning) takes place once the plants have a couple of true leaves and the weeds are an inch or so tall. "The trick to hoeing is get ten to fourteen kids out there so it goes quickly and looks like they are getting a lot done." Once the plants are bigger, with at least four true leaves, Jim cultivates with a four-row Lilliston rolling cultivator that covers two pumpkin rows at a time. Usually two passes are made, throwing soil into the plant rows. Once the plants are too big for that, Jim goes through with drag pulled by a narrow International tractor that is only about 4 feet wide so he can sneak between the rows. This is done twice or more, depending on how much the vines are running. Unless there are some bad spots, there will be no more time spent to hand-pull weeds.

Jim doesn't worry too much about cucumber beetle and only sprays for it once every three or four years. If the pressure is heavy and plants are small, he will go through with a banded spray just over the row by putting in blanks on the spray boom, which covers three rows on each side of the alley. Later in the year, when he starts applying fungicides, he'll put in an insecticide to control aphid or squash bug if necessary. Scouting is as regular as possible given that he does it himself. "Once a week I try and get around and see what everything looks like; it depends what stage the crops are in."

For foliar disease control, several fungicides are alternated. Weather and disease pressure dictate how often sprays are made. The first spray is usually in August, and about once a week after that, with an average of four sprays applied. "Up until a few years ago we didn't spray fungicides at all, but now that we are doing more wholesale we

need to keep the quality up and have the insurance that we'll have a good crop. I can't say for sure that quality has actually improved with spraying, but the last few years have been unusual in terms of weather and disease pressure—either quite dry or quite wet."

Sidebar 19.13 Enterprise Budget for Pumpkins (per acre)

Variable Costs
Labor and Machinery Costs

	Labor hrs	Machinery hrs
Sow rye in fall	.1	.1
Plow rye	.25	.25
Disk, drag	.25	.25
Plant and fertilize	4	4
Disk cultivate 2 x	1.5	1.5
Hand-hoe 1 x	7	–
Lilliston cultivate 2 x	1.5	1.5
Drag between rows 2 x	1.5	1.5
Spray fungicides 4 x	6	6
Harvest and load fruit	18	–
Transportation	3	3
Marketing	1	–
Total hours	44.1	18.1
	@ $8/hr	@ $20/hr
	= $353	+ $362

Total Labor and Machinery Cost
= **$715**

Materials
Rye seed	$10
Pumpkin seed	$40
Fertilizer	$25
Fungicide	$100
Total materials =	**$175**

Total Variable Costs = **$890**

Total fixed costs –
(not included in this budget)

Gross Returns
average price wholesale x 60% of average yield (22,000 pounds)

= .10 X 13,200 = $1,320

+ average price retail x 40% of average yield

= .15 x 8,800 = $1,320

= **$2,640**

Net Returns (after paying variable costs; fixed costs not included in this budget)

= **$ 1,750**

Harvest starts in late September, when people start to want pumpkins. "We don't put them in storage, just pick them when people ask for them. We load directly onto a trailer that holds about 6 or 7 tons, stacked loose, not in bins, and deliver them to the wholesale accounts. For our stand, harvest is in pickup trucks or flatbed wagons. The stems are cut just below the notch, about 6 inches long, using loppers."

Most of the hired labor on the farm is local high-school help, and usually a few local adults in the fall. "Now we also use international students on agricultural internships. It is a loose arrangement where the students spread the word for us and new ones write asking to come and work here. First we had students from Holland; then we tried migrant workers for a few years, but that was too expensive. Now most of our student workers come from the Czech Republic. They work for room and board, and they already have their own paperwork to enter the country. All they need from us is a letter inviting them over, and then a letter explaining that their work was satisfactory since they need to do this for credit for their agricultural education. In general their work is pretty good."

"Pumpkin prices have not fluctuated much over the years, although we try to nudge them up slowly." If wholesale accounts pick up at the farm, the price has been 8 cents per pound; and it's 10–12 cents delivered, mostly to other stands that are pretty close by, although one is 130 miles away. Our average yield is about 10-12 tons per acre."

"We do pretty well with pumpkins, since they are pretty low maintenance. There are a lot of people growing them out there, so if you get into it now it may be at the back end of the boom. I don't have to deal on the open market; I have my customers and we rely on each other. If you have a good set of customers like that, it works out fine. I have my market all set before I plant anything. One year a fellow I didn't know came by and asked me to grow 7 acres of pumpkins for him. I put in 4 and he never showed up. A good relationship with your customers is important."

Rutabagas— A Grower Profile

Dennis King
King Hill Farm, Penobscot, Maine

Dennis King started farming from scratch twenty years ago on a hilltop farm that had been abandoned in the 1950s. He slowly built up his animal and crop production, improving the soil over the years with lime and compost. In the first few years, he spent $500 to $1,000 on used equipment, using mules for tillage and cultivation. Slowly, he has become more mechanized, keeping in mind his goal of creating employment for himself without having to become a field boss of a lot of people or having to do a lot of paperwork. As he puts it, "the farm has gone from 1850s to 1950s technology" in the time he's run it.

The farm is certified organic and covers 40 rocky acres of shallow soil. About 4 acres are planted to vegetables each year, and the rest is in pasture and small grains and forage cover crops. Another 30 acres off the farm are farmed, mostly for hay and small grains, and an acre or so of sweet corn. Dennis raises thirty sheep and four or five beef cattle each year that are sold locally.

The vegetable market garden is grown on ten ¾-acre strip-plots, with half the plots in vegetables in a given year. There is a five-year rotation plan that starts with small grain and an alfalfa/grass mix in year one, alfalfa/orchard grass in year two, then vegetables for two years. Having a combine allows the small grain to be harvested for human or animal feed. Dennis has a local market for organic bread wheat and gets about half a ton off a ¾-acre strip. On land where vegetables are harvested early, forage brassicas (typhon, rape, and kale) are sown for sheep to graze on after the intensive pastures have stopped producing. Sheep also graze off late vegetable crop residues.

The animals provide manure that is field-stacked and turned two or three times with a bucket loader during the summer before being applied the following spring to the vegetable strips at a rate of 25 to 30 cubic yards per acre. Sul-po-mag, boron, and rock phosphate are added to the soil, based on soil test results. This compost and the alfalfa plow-downs supply the nitrogen for the vegetables.

Within the ¾-acre vegetable strips, there is no particular vegetable rotation. "It's more like an exploded home garden, with lots of little stuff grown in a few beds of each crop." Most crops are marketed locally to farm stands, restaurants, and food co-ops. A few crops, including carrots and rutabagas, are grown in larger quantities of about ¼ acre each and sold to a wholesale distributor of organic food, Northeast Cooperatives.

"Rutabagas are well adapted to the cool growing conditions in down east Maine. Yields of 40 tons per acre are common, and prices have gone up over the past few years, getting closer to what carrots bring. This past year both organic carrots and rutabagas were selling wholesale for around $14 per 25-pound bag, whereas rutabagas used to bring half that."

Dennis direct-seeds all his rutabaga. Laurentian is a variety that he finds uniform and very good quality. He delays planting until early to mid-July. This helps keep the size down, since big rutabagas don't sell well, and avoids early flights of cabbage maggot flies. After plowing and field-cultivating, a Buddingh basket weeder is used to mark the rows. Then a single-row precision seeder is used to plant three rows to a bed, 1 foot apart. In-row spacing is 3 to 6 inches. The high planting density helps keep size down and promotes a thick canopy that helps suppress weeds.

The farm was inherited with a relatively small weed seed bank, since the farm had been in pasture for decades. Dennis has tried to keep it that way with timely cultivation, composting of manures, and hand-weeding as necessary to keep weeds from going to seed. Originally, animals were used to cultivate using wide sweeps, but after acquiring an old Allis Chalmers G cultivating tractor and the Buddingh basket weeders, he changed planting arrangements to take advantage of these tools. Normally, two passes with the Buddingh, then one with 6-inch sweeps is all it

takes before a solid crop canopy has formed, which suppresses weeds for the rest of the season.

On brassicas, cabbageworms are controlled with Bt using a backpack sprayer, usually two or three times, when small larvae or feeding damage is seen. Since rutabagas are planted later, and since above ground parts are not marketed, they may get fewer sprays that other cole crops. If flea beetles are severe, a botanical insecticide will be applied to control them. This can require spraying every two days for a week or more in a bad year.

"Harvest takes place toward the end of October, when the roots are baseball- to softball-size or a little larger. The plants are topped to within 2 inches of the root; soil and small feeder roots are knocked off; and the roots are put into bags and stored in a root cellar. They are washed with a carrot washer and repacked into 25-pound poly bags before shipping to the wholesaler as needed."

There is no reliable source of water on the farm, so movable drip lines fed from the household well are used in an emergency to keep small plants alive. The variety of crops, animals, and markets and the low capital investment on the farm help Dennis weather the rough years and profit in the good years. Not a fan of paperwork, Dennis does not keep detailed records; that's one reason he gave up an earlier career as a "bureaucrat." However, he has built a farming system that minimizes operating and fixed costs through wise investment in inexpensive equipment and minimal reliance on off-farm inputs. In a good year, he estimates he grosses $10,000 an acre on the vegetables; in a bad year, maybe $6,000 or $7,000. He has no desire to generate enterprise budgets for individual crops.

Dennis grew up on a farm, and the skills he learned, such as how to slaughter animals and improvise with equipment, are helpful. He has

"Confidence is critical," Dennis says, "in balance with knowledge."

hosted many interns that are initially lacking in such skills but are now pursuing agricultural endeavors of their own. "Confidence is critical," he says, "in balance with knowledge."

Spinach— A Grower Profile

Robin Ostfeld and Lou Johns
Blue Heron Farm, Lodi, New York

Robin Ostfeld and her husband, Lou Johns, grow 12 to 15 acres of certified organic vegetables on heavy soils in the Finger Lakes region. Typically they grow an acre of spinach in succession plantings. Some of their fields are sloping; some are flat and not too well drained. Their markets include the Ithaca Farmers Market and a small CSA. They also wholesale to stores and restaurants both locally and in big cities. They have been farming at this site since 1986.

Because they grow twenty kinds of vegetables, they don't have an exact system of crop rotation. They have permanent beds that are mapped and numbered, and these are never planted to crops in the same family more than once every three years. They also use a variety of cover crops in the rotation, and all beds get a cover crop at least once a year, mostly as winter covers; but some summer and fall covers are used, too.

They set up the permanent bed system a few years ago by setting the wheel spacing on all implements so that they were the same. Thus, tillage, fertilization, seeding, and cultivating are all done on the same 6-foot-wide wheel spacing. The beds that pass under the tractors are never driven on. Each bed holds four 16-inch rows. There's a 2-foot-wide alley for tire tracks between the beds. This system avoids wasting fertilizer, and it protects their soils that are prone to compaction. On sloping fields, it prevents erosion. It also helps with driving and walking through the fields, because there is always a solid place for traffic during wet conditions.

The drawbacks to the bed system are that precision is required in all operations to maintain the beds exactly in place; that the wheel tracks (which are planted to white clover, but include native grasses, clovers, and perennial weeds) have to be mowed about every three weeks in the summer; and that sometimes there are minor slug problems.

Soil tests are done every three years, and lime is added as needed. Phosphorus and other nutrients are usually OK. Any amendments Robin and Lou use are added to a commercial composted chicken manure product that is applied at 1 ton per acre, more or less. Since the product is very dry and only ⅔ of a given acre is in beds, the application rate is not as low as it seems. It amounts to a layer about ½ to ¾ inch thick on the beds. This is spread and then rotavated in a couple weeks ahead of each spinach planting, but it doesn't always work out that way. They try to spread the compost, till, allow weeds to sprout, rotavate lightly again, and then plant.

Seeding is done with a four-row Planet Jr. that is belly-mounted on a very light cultivating tractor. In the spring when soils are cool, in-row spacing of seeds is eight to ten per foot. The in-row spacing is closer from late May through August, when the seeding rate may be doubled because the germination rate is lower.

Indian Summer is their primary spinach variety because it is disease tolerant, very resistant to bolting, quick-growing, and flavorful. They have tried many others, and currently the only other variety they use is Melody, which is planted in the fall when bolt resistance isn't so important. Savoy leaf types do better for them because they don't sell bunched spinach.

"Our wholesale markets are limited by the fact that we don't bunch. But it is really time consuming, and we don't see how we could do it and make any money. It limits who we can sell to, so we are really focusing on retail. We used to grow 2 acres of spinach a few years ago; we grow half that much now but make about as much profit on it."

Seeding depth is about ¼ inch when soils are cool, and up to ½ inch when soils are warm and dry out quickly. Most of the seed they use is sized. Fourteen or fifteen plantings are made. The first six cover 2,400 to 3,200 row-feet each, or three to four beds. These are sown ten days apart, starting in mid-April or even earlier if conditions permit. From mid-June to early August, three or four smaller plantings of two beds are made, and Robin crosses her fingers, hoping to get something. Sometimes these plantings don't germinate; sometimes they do; and they can produce a nice crop at a time when local spinach is not widely available. Starting in early to late August, another three plantings of seven or eight beds each are made. These are larger because there is a longer harvest period in which bolting is not a problem; they often last until early December.

Usually two plantings are made for overwintering, in mid-September and early October. The first planting is mulched with straw in December, then raked off in March. The timing is important, as the mulch has to be removed in time to keep spinach from rotting; but if mulch is taken off too early the spinach may heave out of the ground as it freezes and thaws, even if the spinach is large. The second planting is preceded by drilling oats in mid-September. When oats are up about 2 inches, Robin seeds the spinach directly into them. The oats winter-kill and act as a mulch, which helps keep the spinach from heaving. Success with overwintering has been variable; it works about two-thirds of the time. When it does, harvest begins around the first of May, and it's particularly sweet.

The earliest spinach grown on the farm comes from two unheated hoop houses, or high tunnels, with roll-up sides; each measures 13 by 72 feet. In February the seeds are sown tightly in rows about 3 or 4 inches apart so that space is well-utilized and a dense canopy develops. When it's time to harvest in April, you see nothing but spinach. Bolting resistance is an issue, so the roll-up sides are important for keeping the house cool, and Robin prefers the variety Indian Summer for its resistance to bolting.

Weeding isn't a big input with spinach because it grows so fast. There is no hand-weeding at all in the spring plantings. Shortly after the crop is up they cultivate with beet knives that are belly-mounted under the tractor, one pair around each row. These get close to the plants, cutting weeds off just below the soil surface. When plants are bigger, one more cultivation is made with a rear-mounted Danish S-tine cultivator. In the May and June plantings, one hand-weeding is necessary, mostly for pigweed. Chickweed grows rampantly when it's too wet to cultivate, and this can really choke out the spinach. This has been more of a problem in the late fall plantings and overwintering crop.

Occasionally, there have been leaf miner problems, but only once in the last ten years was it a big problem, and only in the spring crop. Cucumber mosaic virus can take out a lot of spinach in the warm weather in some years. If the soil get too wet, root rots can cause a lot of damage.

To deter deer feeding, tin pie pans on stakes were effective for a while. Then a single-strand electric fence was tried, which didn't work that well. Planting beds of "trap crops" such as beets or soybeans had some success in protecting other crops but was not reliable. Now Robin and Lou use electric fence with a single strand on a post about three or four feet off the ground, in conjunction with another three-strand fence, 2 to 4 feet in height, on a post placed about 6 feet inside of the outer strand. If the deer do jump over the first strand and hit the next fence, then they tend to panic and leave. "We buy a lot of wire and a lot of fence chargers, but it has saved us thousands of dollars in losses." The system has worked on lettuce, chard, and beets as well—crops that the deer seem to prefer.

Irrigation is really important in the summer to keep the spinach growing and to prevent bolting. They use an overhead system in the field, drip tape in the hoop houses. When it's really dry, they are moving pipe all the time, and it's hard to give everything as much water as it needs. However, spinach is an irrigation priority because it can't handle a period of drought as well as many other crops.

Harvest is based on size and begins when the leaves are at least 3–4 inches long. Robin and Lou don't wait till the plants are full-sized; that way the whole planting doesn't have to be harvested at once. To cut the plants, square-bladed spades are used, and these are kept sharp. Workers cut the crop right below the soil surface. Then, handfuls of plants are picked up; any brown leaves discarded; and the rest are put in boxes. These are then emptied into cold water in a big stock tank in the packing shed, where gentle agitation gets most of the dirt off. The plants are then re-boxed—loose rather than bunched or bagged, so that excess water can readily drain out. The boxes go into a walk-in cooler with paper on the top of the leaves to keep the top layer from drying out.

After harvest of a bed is completed, a cover crop is sown as soon as possible. Early plantings may be followed with a summer cover like buckwheat, or be replanted to rutabaga or bok choy. Later plantings will be sown to rye and hairy vetch, depending on when harvest is complete. All cover crops are drilled into the beds using an old grain drill.

"The direct market for spinach is huge in the fall, when the early-season glut subsides and most growers have not replanted for later harvests. Spinach is one of the crops that people seem to elbow their way to buy. It's funny, but I never thought spinach was a crop that people would get so excited about. I think it's because it's so different than the packaged or bunched spinach you can get in the store—the flavor is much better. We allow people to pick it out themselves so they get exactly what they want, and people really like that."

"Our wholesale markets are limited by the fact that we don't bunch. But it is really time consuming, and we don't see how we could do it and make any money. It limits who we can sell to, so we are really focusing on retail. We used to grow 2 acres of spinach a few years ago; we grow half that much now but make about as much profit on it."

Prices for the hoop-house spinach are as high as $3 per pound. The lowest price Robin gets for spinach anytime during the season is $2 per pound, usually in late spring and early summer. In the fall the price goes back up to $2.50. "This is a decent price for us, and nobody objects; they just get in line at farmers market and buy it up! Wholesale prices are a totally different story: we might get $1 per pound or a little more."

"Wholesale organic produce is getting more competitive, and prices are getting lower. We are

Sidebar 19.14 Enterprise Budget for Spinach (per acre)

Variable Costs

Labor and Machinery Costs

	Labor hrs	Machinery hrs
Rake straw off overwintered beds	3	–
Spread compost plus fertilizer	4	4
Rotavate beds	2	2
Rotavate weeds	2	2
Seeding (14-15 times)	7.5	7.5
Beet-hoe cultivation	1.5	1.5
S-tine cultivation	1.5	1.5
Hand-weeding (early beds)	1	–
Set up and move irrigation pipe	5	–
Harvesting	130	–
Washing and packing	20	–
Apply straw (1 planting)	1	1
Drill cover crops	1	1
Total Hours	179.5	20.5
	@ $10/hr	@ $20/hr
	= $1,795	+ $410

Total Labor and Machinery Costs = $2,205

Materials

Compost (1 ton)	$70
Lime and fertilizer	$50
Seeds	$65
Boxes (recycled)	$100
Cover crop seed	$60
Straw mulch	$50
Total Material Costs =	$395

Marketing Costs

Labor ($10 x 40 hours) at markets	$400
Travel ($10 per hour, .30 per mile)	$60
Display and market fees	$30
Total Marketing Costs =	$490

Total Variable Costs = $3,090

Total Fixed Costs
(buildings, land, insurance, interest, office expenses, utilities, taxes, fees, permits)
= $610

Total Costs = $3,700

Gross Returns = $6,156

Net Returns = $2,456

trying to keep wholesale at a lower percent of our sales, and just go with wholesale as a backup to farmers market sales, which are so weather dependent. You can have great crops and then not sell them because of horrible weather or competing events."

Sweet Corn— A Grower Profile

Steve Mong
Applefield Farm, Stow, Massachusetts

The farm is a partnership between Steve Mong, his brother Ray, and their wives. They grow organic vegetables and flowers but are noncertified (because the greenhouse doesn't qualify), even though they follow NOFA-MA certification standards in the field. Total land in production is 35 acres, with about 9 acres of sweet corn. Sales are 95% through the roadside stand located on the farm.

Corn production is preceded by a winter rye cover crop. Then, in late April or early May, 5 tons of relatively fresh chicken manure is spread and immediately plowed down using a three-bottom plow. There isn't a master plan for crop rotation. In many fields, Steve has been growing sweet corn on the same land for three or four years, usually rotating out for one or two years at a time. If he quickly plows under cornstalks and also has generous additions of cover crops, manure, or compost, he feels there's a net gain of nutrients. That plus the fact that there are no real disease concerns does not make continuous corn a problem. Finding land for rotation of other crops like pumpkins is what's driving his rotation plans. Steve tries to find fields for his corn that are near a good water source for irrigation.

Soil tests are performed in most fields, including the pre-sidedress nitrate test on fields that did not get chicken-manured. Steve has been experimenting with compost instead of chicken manure, and he plans to use more rye-vetch cover crops to supply nitrogen. If he uses vetch, then he doesn't plow it down until late May. When using these non-manure sources, it is tricky to interpret the soil-nitrate test results. However, fields managed as described show that little or no N fertilizer is needed. On fields where the test indicates that nitrate levels were close but not quite sufficient, an organic bagged fertilizer is side-dressed to supply about 15 pounds N per acre. All corn gets 15 pounds of N banded at planting.

"Once fields are plowed, furrows are left in place until the field is needed. I used to rotavate before planting, but now I use an Unverferth Perfecta II field cultivator instead. The rotavator leaves soil too soft, while the Perfecta makes a nice, firm, uniform seedbed. It also lifts the rocks up out onto the soil surface, which doesn't seem to bother the machine. Workers can then go back and pick out the big rocks. This has helped bring some fields back into smaller row crop production. The Perfecta is also about three times faster than rotavating, since it travels twice as fast and it's wider. It leaves a 1-inch "mulch" of fine soil on top, but the ground is firmed underneath. This helps with subsequent Lely tine cultivation to kill weeds and germinated seeds near the soil surface. However, the Perfecta doesn't work so well before using the Powell transplanter, which has trouble opening a furrow deep enough in the firm soil; so rotavation is still used before transplanting other crops."

"A John Deere (Pequa) two-row plateless planter is used to plant corn seed. Previously, we used plate-type planters; now the plateless planter makes it much easier to plant, since plates don't have to be changed and sprockets don't need to be adjusted for different varieties. A much more uniform stand results, as a result of uniform seed depth and spacing. Early uniform emergence really helps with cultivation for weed control because it allows for the earliest possible cultiva-

"Early uniform emergence really helps with cultivation for weed control because it allows for the earliest possible cultivation without burying any corn. It's a lot of money for a plateless planter, but it's worth it. The planter is also used for squash, pumpkin, and beans."

tion without burying any corn. It's a lot of money for a plateless planter, but it's worth it. The planter is also used for squash, pumpkin, and beans."

Steve plants 1.5-acre blocks of four to five varieties approximately every ten days, for six plantings. The first planting is about the last week of April, using only three varieties. Once a planting has sprouted, it's time to do the next planting. The last planting is usually the first week of July. With late plantings, a single variety block may hold up for a longer time than in earlier plantings; but smaller areas are sown since sales tail off and early frost can be a problem.

Planting depth is relatively deep, 1.5 to 1.75 inches down, to avoid damage by Lely weeding and to deter crow pulling. Spacing is 36-inch rows, 8.75 inches in the row. Tighter spacing is used to compensate for some loss from mechanical cultivation.

"I like Seneca Daybreak and Double Gem as varieties for my early plantings. I don't try to be the earliest, and I stay away from lousy early corn that doesn't taste good or yield well. Instead, I buy in very early corn and post a sign that says it's not mine. My main-season varieties include Tuxedo, Delectable, and Lancelot. I use one variety of late white corn, Argent. It has good tip cover but that does make it harder to apply the oil treatments on silk for corn earworm control. Constant experimenting is needed to find varieties that primarily combine flavor and vigor, with some attention also paid to tip-fill and appearance. In general, I prefer sugary enhanced varieties and see no reason to grow super-sweets for roadside sales."

"Lely cultivation has got to be done three days after seeding once soils are fully warm. In the early spring, this can wait five or six days or more because soils are cool. The goal is to get in with this 'blind' cultivation before seeds are up within half inch of the soil surface, otherwise the tines will snap off a bunch of plants. I used to do a second Lely 'over-the-top,' when corn was 2–3 inches high with the flag leaf open, but now I think it may do more harm than good. Perhaps it's not necessary at that time to control the little

weeds, which will be killed with the subsequent Bezzerides cultivation anyway.

"Before using the Bezzerides, I wait as long as possible until the corn is up and moderately sturdy, about 3–4 inches high. The taller the corn, the faster you can go without worrying about burying it. Speed helps give good soil disturbance and soil throwing and improves the resulting weed control. The pairs of Spyder™ wheels and spring-hoes are mounted so they run right along the plant row, spaced about 3 inches apart. Wide sweeps are mounted away from the crop row to work the center strip between the rows that the Bezzerides tools miss. This setup is belly mounted on a high-clearance tractor and cultivates one row at a time. It takes about an hour per acre, depending on conditions. Often, only part of an acre is ready to do at once. Timing cultivation to match the growth of different corn varieties, as well as the weeds, is critical to getting good weed control.

"On average, two passes are made with the Bezzerides, although three passes may be needed for early corn because it grows slower and is smaller, requiring slower tractor speed. Late corn often gets by with one Bezzerides cultivation, because corn gets big so quickly. At the time when the corn is 2–4 feet tall I can go in with a final aggressive cultivation, using hilling disks that throw soil up into the row, making a ridge up to 8 inches high. This digs out and buries large and small weeds. At the same time, fertilizer, if needed, can be dropped down in front of disks. The hilling also helps hold up corn in event of storms. The timing of this final cultivation is important, so that the soil is clean just before the corn is about to 'jump' and the canopy closes quickly.

"In some blocks, usually the early ones, hand-removal of weeds is needed. This is often where cultivation missed some spots, or at beginning and end of rows where tractor speed wasn't fast enough. Only the big weeds, about the same size as corn, are pulled. A couple of kids can do an acre in an hour. This prevents weeds from going to seed, really helps with picking later on, and prevents competition and shading of corn. But they don't pull any small weeds; our goal is not totally weed-free fields."

European corn borer and corn earworm and sometimes fall armyworm are the key insect pests. Steve participates in whatever state or university IPM programs are available, which in some years provides for insect scouting. Spraying for borer takes place based on a 15% damage threshold. The only insecticide used is Bt. A mixture of Bt plus corn oil is used to control corn earworm.

Spraying for corn borer is done with a hydraulic boom sprayer, which can get up as high as 4 feet. Usually the spraying is down into whorl for first-generation borer, which is generally a problem in the earlier corn. With second-generation borer (which is less frequently a serious problem), plants may be quite tall when spraying is needed, and it can be hard to spray directly into the whorl.

Corn earworm arrival is monitored with heliothis-type pheromone traps. When control is needed, the mixture of corn oil and Bt is applied by hand to silks that are four to six days old. The later you wait, the easier it is to see the silk channel (the opening that leads down to the neck of the ear), but waiting too long is risky because you may not get good control. Only one application is needed per plant for the whole silking period. Some growers use an oil squirt can, with a wooden stop that helps them apply a uniform quantity of material with each squirt. Steve has developed a system that does not require as much effort for the hand because it eliminates any handle for squirting. He uses a garden sprayer with the hose cut partway off and a pressure regulator attached. A simple on-off valve is near the end of the line instead of a squeezing device. By using a very low rate of pressure (a pound or two) at a constant flow, it's easy to apply the equivalent of a couple of large drops to the silk. The material oozes out at a fairly constant slow drip, and the end of the tube is placed on the silk long enough for two or three drops to be applied. An elastic band holds the tube to the finger tip.

Recently a commercial applicator has been developed called Zea-Later. It has an ergonomically-designed trigger and handle and comes with a 2-liter plastic oil sack, quick-connect tubing, and shoulder strap. (See appendix C, page 245, for contact information.)

Sidebar 19.15 Enterprise Budget for Sweet Corn (per acre)

Variable Costs
Labor and Machinery Costs

	Labor hrs	Machinery hrs
Plant rye	.5	.25
Spread manure	1	1
Plow and Perfecta cultivate	2	2
Fertilize and seed	2	1.5
Lely cultivations (2 x)	1	1
Bezzerides/disk cultivations (2 x)	1	1
Hand-pull weeds	2	–
Mix, spray, rinse Bt for borer	1.5	1
Apply oil + Bt for earworm*	5	–
Harvesting, sorting, handling	21	–
Total Hours	37	7.75
	@ $10/hr	@ $20/hr
	= $370	+ $155

Total Labor and Machinery Costs		
	=	**$525**

Marketing costs (display, accounts, etc.)		
	=	**$70**

Materials

Seed (corn, rye)	$80
Fertilizer	$30
Compost or manure	$25
Bt and oil	$35
Total Materials	$170

Total Variable Costs	=	**$765**

Fixed Costs
(buildings, land, insurance, interest, office expenses, utilities, taxes, fees, permits)

	=	**$110**

Total Costs	=	**$875**

Gross Returns

83 bushels @ $20	=	**$1,660**

Net Returns	=	**$785**

*Average of all corn acreage; about half is treated

"It takes about twenty minutes to walk down a 500-foot row applying oil mixture. It probably takes eight hours to do an acre, but you can go faster if only doing small blocks. It gets tiring pretty quickly. Control is quite good— around 85% clean ears or more in a very heavy earworm year. Since not all the rows are treated, I try to hold the clean corn for the weekend sales when the presence of worms would have a more negative impact than during the week, when the majority of sales tend to be to loyal customers that understand my organic production."

"Harvest is by hand. I pick half the day's needs in the morning, the other half in early afternoon. I take pride in offering only the freshest corn. Ears are picked into bushel crates that hold five dozen ears, then trucked to the stand. At the stand, ears go into walk-in cooler. If it's hot in the afternoon, the corn will be hosed down to keep it cool as soon as it arrives at the stand. Generally, corn is sold within a few hours of being picked. The sugary enhanced varieties are relatively tender and do not tolerate being thrown into a truck, so I always handle corn with care, and I pick all the corn myself to assure quality. I sort it in the field to save time."

"Average sales are about 12 bushels per day at $4 per dozen ($20 per bushel) throughout the season, from the end of July to the beginning of October. Sales total 750 bushels, plus a few dozen bushels that are wholesaled for about $12 per bushel when retail sales are slow. Marketable yields are relatively low, since only the best ears are picked. In some blocks almost everything is picked, when everything is coming in well. At other times, when blocks all come in on top of each other, perhaps only a third of the ears are harvested. I always select the best corn that I have available on a given day and don't worry about leaving the rest, since I get the full retail dollar. You couldn't operate this way if you were a wholesale grower."

Field Tomatoes— A Grower Profile

David Trumble
Good Earth Farm, Weare, New Hampshire
David Trumble grows 3 acres of certified organic vegetables. A few years ago, he had just about an acre in field tomatoes, mostly for wholesale through an organic farmers cooperative. The other 2 acres are highly diversified and sales are through a CSA. Since the time this profile was written, David has switched completely to the CSA market, and now has nearly a hundred families as members. He says, "the economics and job satisfaction are more favorable with the CSA."

Prior to planting his crops, David applies approximately 20 tons per acre of finished compost each spring. During the first two years on the farm, bagged organic fertilizer was also used every year to supplement crop nutrition, based on soil test results. After three years, use of these fertilizers stopped, and after five years of applying compost, soil tests indicated very high levels of all nutrients. David felt that the soil was finally in really good condition.

During the first couple of years, fields would be plowed in the spring. As their condition improved, plowing no longer seemed necessary. Instead, in early spring the fields are harrowed with a heavy disk to incorporate winter rye while it is still short, before it becomes hard to control. Then the composted manure is spread and disked in immediately, often later the same day. To kill early-season weeds, fields are then disked every two weeks until planting.

Black plastic is laid as late as possible before planting, to avoid having to deal with weeds while the plastic is in the field, which requires additional time. Because irrigation is not available, weather affects when plastic can be laid, since the soil must be moist but not wet. Ideally, this occurs close to the end of May, which is the average last frost date.

Tomato transplants are set by hand, about 6 inches deep in the ground. Relatively deep placement keeps the plants from blowing around in the wind too much, and encourages a strong root system to develop, but any deeper is not useful because the ground is still cold below the surface. Before the plants are set, holes are burned in the plastic, which makes a nice tight seal around plants, or a post hole digger is used, which makes a nice deep planting hole. Transplanters were tried but didn't work too well with 4-inch pots. If there's time, bone meal to provide early season phosphorus is hand-applied to each planting hole.

Individual plants are spaced 4 feet apart in the row, with 6 feet between rows. The wide between-row spacing is convenient for using a cultivating tractor and leaves sufficient room to walk the crop and do the picking later in the season when plants have spread out a lot. The in-row spacing is a compromise density aimed at balancing the desire for high early yields and good air movement among plants to control foliar diseases.

In June, during the month after plastic is laid and plants set, one pass through the field between the rows is made with a cultivating tractor, and the edges of the plastic are hand-hoed. Then clean straw mulch is put down between the plastic.

"Delaying application of straw until the end of June allows the soil to warm up quickly and minimizes problems from sprouting of grain from the straw. It's also a question of time management; things are too busy on the farm to lay straw earlier. Although it's hard to get clean straw, hay causes a lot more problems with weed seeds."

"I think it's worth using straw mulch between the plastic because it prevents soil splashing onto plants and thus helps minimize early blight, as well as suppressing between-row weeds that are hard to cultivate once the plants begin to sprawl. It also provides a clean place for the plants to go and keeps the fruit relatively clean. In addition, it is a source of organic matter for the soil once it decomposes, and it helps conserve soil moisture, which is important on a farm without irrigation. I apply at least 4 tons, and preferably 6 tons of straw per acre. It takes fifty hours to spread straw by hand on one acre. At $8 per hour and $150 per ton, the cost of mulching an acre is $1,300.

"Straw mulching is really an alternative to the basket-weave system of staking and pruning. Both systems work well to control disease by keeping plants and fruit off the ground, which also improves fruit quality. The basket-weave system also encourages early fruit production—in other words, better yields in August. But it takes more time and definitely reduces late-season yield. It may work well in North Carolina with multiple plantings that can pick up the slack, but in southwestern New Hampshire the season is so short that staking didn't seem to pay for itself.

"Staking also makes it difficult to protect the crop from cold temperatures by using a floating row cover, a practice that is profitable in locations prone to early chilling temperatures. It is difficult to put the cover over the plants and take it off, although using upside-down milk jugs on top of the stakes helps the cover slide.

"There's a lot of work involved in staking tomatoes, and once I fell behind and got into big trouble. Plants started to hang over the string, and the stems bend, causing damage. To prevent this, new rows of string have to be added at just the right time; and if your plants aren't growing uniformly in height this can be a challenge. Just letting them run and using straw is easier for me from a management point of view. That choice

"There's a lot of work involved in staking tomatoes, and once I fell behind and got into big trouble. . . . Just letting them run and using straw is easier for me from a management point of view. That choice depends on how serious you are about tomatoes: does the high-management or low-management option fit your needs? But one thing is for sure: you can't just let the plants run on the bare ground or you'll get too much disease."

depends on how serious you are about tomatoes: does the high-management or low-management option fit your needs? But one thing is for sure: you can't just let the plants run on the bare ground or you'll get too much disease."

In the greenhouse, transplants are started to meet the timing of field production and marketing plans. To produce an early crop, about one-fifth of the crop is started April 1 to accommodate the early planting scheduled for the third week in May. Roughly three-fifths of the crop is started around April 15 for setting out on or about June 1 as the main-season crop. To produce the late-season crop, on May 1 another fifth of the total crop is started, to be ready for mid-June field setting.

"Using 4-inch pots to finish transplants in the greenhouse picks up at least ten days earliness over standard six-pack trays that hold thirty-six plants. If you have greenhouse room it's worth it."

David feels it's OK to have a flower cluster open on transplants when they are set, especially for the early crop. Later crops ideally have buds but no flowers open. It's hard to get the crop in exactly at the stage of growth he wants, since he doesn't have irrigation. He tries to plant right before a predicted rainfall, and that determines the stage of development the plants are at when they are set out.

"For early varieties, Early Cascade is good if your markets want anything that is red. It has a small fruit but good disease resistance and long-season productivity. If your markets want or demand larger fruit (as wholesalers do), then Jet Star, Ultra Sweet, or Sunbeam are good choices. Mountain Pride is good for the late crop. All of these put out good-sized fruit and hold up well against early blight. If you choose to use a fungicide and have the equipment to apply it frequently, then your choice of varieties is wider because early blight tolerance is not as critical.

"I try to apply liquid copper fungicide just before a heavy rainstorm arrives, which usually happens three or four times a season. My farm also gets heavy dews late in the season, and I feel it's worth

protecting the crop from that type of moisture, which can also promote foliar disease. One year I did spray eight or nine times and it really made a difference; but with only a backpack sprayer, it's a

Sidebar 19.16 Enterprise Budget for Field Tomatoes (per acre)

Variable Costs
Labor and Machinery

	Labor hrs	Machinery hrs
Disk and harrow field	2	2
Apply compost	4	4
Disk weeds 3 x	3	3
Greenhouse time	35	–
Lay plastic	5	5
Set transplants	16	–
Cultivate row middles	3	3
Apply straw mulch	50	–
Spray copper 4 x	4	4
Apply and remove row cover	7	–
General field and farm upkeep	15	–
Harvest	250	–
Wash, sort, box, deliver	300	–
Total labor/machine hours	694	21
	@ $8/hr	@$20/hr
	= $5,552	+ $420

Total Labor and Machinery Costs
　　　　　　　　　　　　= **$5,972**

Materials	
Seed (½ oz.)	$40
Transplant production costs (2,100 @ .20 each)	$420
Compost (20 tons)	$450
Black plastic mulch	$200
Straw mulch (6 tons @ $150 per ton)	$900
Sprays (0.5 gallons liquid Cu, 5 gallons seaweed)	$80
Tomato boxes (1,000 @ $0.80)	$800
Total Materials =	**$2,890**

Marketing
Sales commission to co-op (20% of gross sales)
　　　　　　　　　　　　= **$2,900**

Fixed Costs (buildings, land, insurance, interest, office expenses, utilities, taxes, fees, permits)
　　　　　　　　　　　　= **$1,500**

Farm Management Time
　　　　　　　　　　　　= **$700**

Total Costs = **$13,962**

Gross Returns
(1,000 boxes @ $14 per box; 50 boxes seconds @ $10 per box) = **$14,500**

Net Returns = **$538**

nasty job that I would rather limit. If you have enough acreage and a tractor sprayer, spraying at least seven or eight times would definitely be worth it." David always mixes seaweed extract in with the copper sprays to foliar-feed the crop at the same time.

Although he gets some septoria leaf spot, early blight is consistently his main pest problem in tomatoes. It wipes out the foliage, reduces fruit quality, and ends the season early. In addition to using copper, he tries to get heavily diseased plants out of the field, and he may pick off lower leaves that are infected. He has tried planting strips of grass or a non-tomato crops like broccoli between early, middle, and late tomato plantings, a practice he feels can slow the spread of disease from early plantings into later plantings. "This can complicate your rotation, but is worth it if you're just focusing on a few crops."

Workers pick fruit by hand into baskets, boxes, or pails. If a variety is not firm, the fruit cannot be stacked too high and pails especially need to be sorted very quickly to keep fruit from getting mushy. A hand-wipe of the fruit with a rag in the field helps with cleaning. Then, in the packing shed, fruit are wiped again if needed, but not washed. They are sorted by four colors, or degrees of ripeness, and three size-grades. Then canners are sorted into a couple of colors, too, so the really ripe ones can be sold quickly.

"In a typical year, we harvest about 1,000 twenty-pound boxes of marketable fruit per acre. Ten tons of fruit is not a great yield compared to published figures for tomatoes, but about half the fruit we produce isn't marketable as number ones. One year, local growers got together to sell their seconds to a juice company, and that helped. The price for boxed tomatoes starts out high but falls off as the season goes on. Yields start slow as the early crop is coming in, then are quite high since fruit quality is good while disease pressure is low. Toward the end of the season there is a lot of disease that sometimes reduces marketable yields to as little as 20% of what's picked."

Greenhouse Tomatoes— A Grower Profile

Mike Collins
Old Athens Farm, Westminster, Vermont
Since 1990 Mike Collins has been growing organic greenhouse tomatoes using compost-amended soil as a growing medium at several rented sites in southeastern Vermont. Two years ago he purchased land and set up two 32- x 100-foot greenhouses primarily for growing tomatoes, plus a small number of greenhouse cucumbers. He maintains a half acre of field vegetables and strawberries "so the workers don't get bored." He markets within a 25-mile radius to three farmers markets plus grocery stores and farm stands. His crop has been certified organic for the past four years. "Certification only matters for big whole-sale accounts; otherwise I wouldn't bother."

In preparation for greenhouse construction, a half-acre of land was leveled, plowed, and disked. Then 20 yards of compost, 200 cubic feet of peat moss, and 500 pounds of rock phosphate were rototilled in. Construction of the first of the two greenhouses was completed by late fall so that growing could begin the following spring. The greenhouses are OvalTech, made by Harnois, a Canadian manufacturer. They feature heavy-gauge steel frames with lots of reinforcing purlins, W-braced cross members, and passive ventilation through roll-up sides and automatic peak vents. These greenhouses are one of the sturdiest brands available, engineered to withstand northern winter snow loads and a heavy crop load.

Each greenhouse is laid out in five beds, about 5.5 feet on center, with two narrow side rows for lettuce and peppers where growing height is limited. The beds are 1 foot high, and 3 feet wide, with 2.5 feet between beds. After allowing for end alleys, each growing bed is 90 feet long and contains 125 plants, spaced 9 inches apart.

The beds are maintained permanently, rather than re-formed each year. Prior to setting plants, a blend of organic residues and fertilizers is added directly onto the beds and incorporated with hand tools. Each house is top-dressed with 8 to 10 yards of high-quality "potting soil grade" compost, plus 125 pounds each of sul-po-mag (or 50 pounds of potassium sulfate, if Mg is already high) greensand, rock phosphate, soybean meal, wheat bran, and precipitated bone meal. About 50 pounds of dried blood is also added per house to assure sufficient available nitrogen. Mike feels that hand-hoeing rather than rototilling to mix in these materials conserves the earthworm populations and protects soil structure.

Each year, four drip irrigation lines are laid down on each bed, two on either side of the plants. Disposable, twin-wall tubing with 9-inch emitter spacing is placed directly on the surface, then covered with white 4-mil plastic mulch. The 2-foot-wide strips of mulch on either side of the plant rows are used to hold in soil moisture, suppress weeds, retain soil heat, and reflect light back up into the canopy. There is a small PVC header pipe for the drip lines in each bed, so that water can be zoned to match various needs of the beds. Zoned irrigation accommodates the limited water pressure supplied from the well, which also supplies household needs.

Heating is done by a wood boiler and an oil furnace backup. This system heats both the greenhouse air and the water that is used for soil "bottom heat." The bottom-heat pipes are ¾-inch flexible plastic buried 4 inches below the base of the bed, or about 16 inches under the soil surface. There is one loop per bed, running off a 1 ¼-inch PVC header for each house. The system is zoned using ball valves; and this allows hot water to be directed where it is needed, based on readings of soil thermometers in various locations. The zoned heat is also useful for heating sections of the house if some of the crop is planted sequentially. Soil temperatures are checked daily, and the target is 80°F.

Air temperature is automatically controlled with timers and thermostats, so that the daytime temperature regime kicks in about an hour before daylight. Mike tries to run the house at about 65°F at night, and 68°F in the daytime. Ventilation is initiated at 72°F. Usually, Mike manually vents the house for two or three minutes to rid it of humid air just prior to loading the wood boiler, and he may do the same thing on high-humidity days where a lot of condensation is evident in the greenhouse. This helps prevent foliar disease.

Plants are started in a small seedling greenhouse around the first of January. Seeds of the cultivar "Buffalo" are sown in a peat-vermiculite-based potting mix with a small amount of organic fertilizers. In about three weeks, the plants are grafted onto plants of the disease-tolerant rootstock cultivar "Kyndia," which has the vigor to provide more continuous and higher yields than ungrafted plants. "Grafting is a delicate and time-consuming operation, and some special equipment is needed to assure success. It took a couple of years to become proficient at it."

"A lot of growers are interested in producing greenhouse tomatoes because of the large cash flow from a small area of production, but if you're a small producer it's not easy to be profitable. For me, even with the high prices I get, a lot of my profit comes from finding ways to save on operating costs. For example, I use waste wood for heating to reduce fuel costs, and I recycle plastic trays instead of buying new tomato boxes."

After grafting, the plants are held in a misting chamber that provides high humidity and carefully controlled temperature. Four days later, the plants are set into 4-inch pots filled with two parts peat, one part compost, one part vermiculite, and one part perlite and a fertilizer mix of dried blood, bone meal, greensand and lime. The pots are spaced so that leaves will not overlap, and the plants are grown for another two to three weeks before being set into the greenhouse soil. The plants may be fertigated with a fish emulsion solution if transplanting is delayed and the plants look a little pale.

Sustainable Vegetable Production from Start-Up to Market

"The plants are set into the ground beds at the same soil line as in the pots, so that the graft remains above the soil. The soil is watered before setting, and then watered again after setting. Ideally, there are no flowers open on the plants, and they are as wide as they are tall. Within days, strings are set from the purlins by hanging twine and bobbins over the plants. As soon as they need it the plants are tied up, using plastic clips that snap onto the twine and clamp around the plant. One-inch-round clips are great, but they are hard to find; now they are being made oval. Clips are added under every cluster of fruit, or truss, to support the plants as they grow, with the clip about halfway between the base of the truss and the leaf. The early clips have to be checked and sometimes moved so they don't damage the plant. Positioning the clips properly is important.

"Between the fourth and sixth truss, depending on the extent of fruit load and stress on the plant, I will fertilize with fish emulsion, using 10 gallons of concentrate per greenhouse, diluted into a 300-gallon stock tank. This is watered on by hand with a hose, and repeated every week to ten days until I get too busy and don't get around to it."

Bumblebees are used to assure good pollination. "I pollinate by hand until the first truss is fully open on most of the plants. Then I bring in the bees. I use one Class B hive per greenhouse. The order has to be called in only a few days before they are needed. These can be shipped U.S. Mail, and contrary to what the suppliers tell you, it is not necessary to go to the airport to get them. The hives are kept in the head house out of the sun on a little platform, or placed on the ground in the crop, well-covered by foliage. The hives have to be replaced once during the course of the growing season, when you stop seeing as much bee activity as you would like and pollination seems to be going down. To determine this, I examine open flowers, looking for a bruised appearance of the pistil, which usually has three or four small brown spots if it has been properly pollinated by bees."

Once a week, all "suckers" are removed when they are as small as possible. Fruit load is managed by hand-thinning to four fruit per cluster, ideally when fruit are the size of a dime or smaller. No deformed fruit are left, regardless of the number of the fruit, and large multilobed fruit are also removed. Bottom leaves are trimmed when the plants reach 4 feet in height, about when the fifth truss is flowering. Leaves are cut off an inch away from the stem, and at the next pruning the stubs are snapped off by hand to minimize Botrytis infection sites.

"I usually increase night temperatures to promote ripening, starting when I see the seventh truss in flower. Then in a couple of weeks the first ripe fruit are harvested. This is normally four months after sowing seed, with real production beginning two weeks later."

"The level of CO_2 in the greenhouse is enhanced to about 1,200 parts per million (ppm) during the early months of growth, when the greenhouse is closed for the most part. Later in the season, on cloudy days when the house is not fully vented, CO_2 is also generated. A propane burner with an adjustable flame size is used, and the CO_2 level is checked with a manual test kit once or twice during the season."

"The major pest problem I have is aphids, and I deal with these by purchasing several predators, before I even see any aphids. I start with these a few weeks after transplanting and get biweekly deliveries until I notice they have established and the aphids are clearly under control. Sometimes just the removal of older bottom leaves helps reduce the pressure. This year I sprayed a botanical insecticide, since I saw aphids in the upper half of the plant and it made me nervous; and then after several applications I noticed the predators had built up again.

"I've never had whiteflies until this year, and since it was late in the season I just let them go. Next year I'll probably introduce Encarsia, an aphid parasitoid, early in the season. I also have some spider mites this year and will introduce predatory mites early to keep them from getting out of hand."

"We harvest into used plastic tomato trays, obtained from supermarkets. These are put on a modified wheelbarrow that has a flat plywood platform and is pulled down the alleys between the plants. The fruit is then graded in the head house and repacked into plastic trays for local accounts or into cardboard tomato boxes for wholesale accounts that will not return containers. Even if you buy the plastic trays new at $3.40 apiece, once you've used them four times they have paid for themselves in saved cardboard box costs. I have some trays I've been using for three years. The fruit is graded by size, using plastic inserts in the trays that also reduce bruising in transit. The fruit is all picked as ripe as possible, so no grading for color is necessary. For some relatively long-distance accounts we specially harvest less-ripe fruit, but part of the market demand is based on the excellent flavor that our customers have come to expect."

Mike has one employee working thirty-five hours per week from March through the end of July. She is full-time in the greenhouse for the first three months, then does some field work as well. Another person is hired for twenty hours a week during the summer to work in the field.

Sidebar 19.17 Enterprise Budget for Organic Tomatoes (32' x 100' greenhouse)

Construction Costs

	Materials Cost	Labor Cost
Site preparation—dozer work	–	$500
Perimeter drain, black plastic	$300	$160
Head house shed	$1,468	$800
Greenhouse construction	–	$2,100
Frame	$9,200	–
Lumber and hinges	$260	–
Rigid poly for end wall	$160	–
Extra purlins and wire for tomato support	$185	–
Jet fan	$450	–
Carbon dioxide generator and control	$534	–
Thermostats	$192	–
Used circulation fans	$80	–
Soil heat, drip irrigation, bed prep	–	$800
Fittings, clamps, and pipe	$620	–
Heating system	–	$2,400
Used wood boiler system	$1,400	–
Used oil heating system	$1,000	–
Used 350-gallon oil tank	$50	–
Gas and oil lines and hookups	$90	–
Well, electric service (portion of shared cost)	$1,041	$600
	$17,030	+ $7,360
Total Construction Costs	=	$24,390

Fixed Costs

Greenhouse construction (÷ 15 years)	$1,626
Interest (construction financed @ 7% for fifteen years)	$1,005
Taxes, land, office expenses, fees	$1,377
Total Fixed Costs	**= $4,008**

Variable Costs

Materials, Machinery

Grafted plants (600 @$2.40)	$1,440
Fertilizer and compost	$650
Drip irrigation tubing, fittings	$50
Plastic mulch	$100
String, hangers, and clips	$230
Firewood and oil heat	$700
Propane for carbon dioxide	$500
Bees for pollination	$300
Beneficial insects and insecticides	$250
Poly covering, roof and side (prorated)	$350
Plastic trays	$300
Transportation @.25 per mile	$560
Subtotal	= $ 5,430

Labor Costs
(production labor @$8/hr)

Bed preparation and fertilization	$800
Transplant, tie up, lay drip and plastic	$800
Prune, tie, irrigate, spray, etc.	$4,880
Harvest, grade, pack	$1,170
Delivery and sales	$1,620
Clean up greenhouse	$320
Subtotal	= $9,590

Total Variable Costs	**= $15,020**
Total Costs	**= $19,028**

Gross Returns
15 pounds per plant x 600
= 9,000 pounds x 2.40 average price

	= $21,600
Net Returns	**= $2,572**

Sustainable Vegetable Production from Start-Up to Market

"The wholesale price this year for organic greenhouse tomatoes was $2.30 per pound, and the average retail price at farmers market was $3.00. Usually the grocery stores retailed for $4.00. Slightly blemished or oversized tomatoes are sold as seconds for $2.50 at the farmers market. Prices have gone up slightly over the past few years, but I don't know how far they'll continue to go up. For the most part, people are willing to pay the high price once they have tasted the tomatoes. The price drops when the local outdoor crop starts to come in around early August, gradually going down to $1.50 wholesale and $1.75 retail. By mid- to late August, the plants in one of the two greenhouses are removed since demand drops so much; and I plant fall lettuce or greens.

"Before the price drops I have usually picked 14 pounds per plant. Total yields can be around 20 pounds. The crop doesn't get a lot of care into the fall, but I leave it and get whatever I can from it without much maintenance. The market price doesn't usually go up again until mid- to late October, and the cost of heating makes it uneconomical to pursue the late market."

"A lot of growers are interested in producing greenhouse tomatoes because of the large cash flow from a small area of production, but if you're a small producer it's not easy to be profitable. For me, even with the high prices I get, a lot of my profit comes from finding ways to save on operating costs. For example, I use waste wood for heating to reduce fuel costs, and I recycle plastic trays instead of buying new tomato boxes."

Appendix A

Additional Information Resources

Obtaining timely information is an ongoing effort that requires tapping into a variety of networks—of individuals, publications, and organizations where knowledge is stored and shared. The explosion of information in recent years is both a blessing and a burden. There is more access than ever to a wide array of relevant facts and experiences, but the challenge is to keep up to date and answer questions without being overwhelmed by unwanted input. The following is an overview of available resources that may help. Addresses for the publishers mentioned in this appendix are listed in appendix B, beginning on page 240.

Organizations
COOPERATIVE EXTENSION

Farmers are blessed with an abundance of formal organizations devoted to supplying them with information and advice. One of these is the *Cooperative Extension System*, the outreach arm of land grant universities in all fifty states. The original mission of extension was to improve agricultural productivity, and thus rural quality of life, by presenting factual information to farmers. Today, the audience of cooperative extension has been expanded beyond farmers and rural citizens, and the mission has been widened to include promoting environmental, community, and personal well-being.

Once a three-way cooperative effort among county, state, and federal governments, extension is now showing a trend away from county involvement and focus in some states. In other words, the county agent with a general understanding of all types of agriculture is disappearing and being replaced by fewer regional, state, or multistate specialists with relatively narrow subject-matter expertise, who are better able to advise farmers as agriculture gets increasingly sophisticated.

In most areas of the country, vegetable extension personnel cooperate across state boundaries to offer region-wide conferences, publications, meetings, tours, and trainings. Your state vegetable specialist or a county or regional agent with vegetable expertise can help you tap into these resources. Vegetable specialists have different subject-matter strengths and when necessary will generally contact a colleague in response to a grower request for information. In some cases, the specialist may refer the grower directly to another specialist.

Extension offers the following types of information, education, and connection to applied research: fact sheets, crop production guides, booklets, videotapes, computer programs, and newsletters; trainings, workshops, and demonstrations on specific topics such as nutrient or pest management; one-day meetings and multi-day conferences on the range of vegetable production issues; on-farm or "twilight" meetings that focus on research projects or innovative farm practices; farm tours to other production areas; and individual consultation through phone calls, written inquiries, or on-site farm visits. Fees to cover costs are requested for some of these services; others are provided at no charge. To contact your extension office, check in your telephone white pages under Cooperative Extension for your county or under the name of your state agricultural college.

Farm visits are a valuable resource that extension offers a farmer. Farm visits require a lot of time from the agent or specialist. Because visits must be spread out over a wide area and many producers, the individual grower won't get a lot of them. Don't waste yours. Get the available written materials ahead of time, and be prepared with questions, issues, and production records to get the most out of this free consultation. Also be aware that farm visits are a two-way street, in which extension specialists also learn. Farm visits expose extension personnel directly to key concerns of farmers, so that outreach and research programs can be adjusted to growers' needs.

ATTRA

Appropriate Technology Transfer for Rural Areas (ATTRA) is a unique national organization that serves as an information clearinghouse, providing written information to farmers and educators on a variety of alternative crops and practices. ATTRA's publications cover topics from sustainable vegetable production to shitake mushrooms, and everything in between.

Although ATTRA is a worthwhile information source on many issues, it is still advisable to consult local extension first. While ATTRA provides a very valuable service to growers that might otherwise feel isolated as they try to find information about innovative ideas, a nationwide service cannot have the local awareness that is necessary to interpret the applicability or appropriateness of information to specific local conditions. Information requests can be made of ATTRA via phone at (800) 346-9140. ATTRA also maintains a web site at <http://askattra@ncatfyv.uark.edu/>.

Grower/Farmer Organizations

Most states have a *vegetable growers association*, often facilitated by extension or the department of agriculture. Other growers associations, state or regional, may be devoted to specific vegetable crops. These associations have annual meetings, often publish newsletters, and sometimes provide marketing, public relations, or research activities. One of the great values of membership in these organizations is the chance to develop a personal network with other growers through regular interaction. In addition, growers have more political and economic clout by banding together. Grower associations can influence land-grant research by providing advice and "seed" funding; they can save money by making bulk purchases of materials; and they can affect public opinion and enhance marketing by developing promotional materials.

Grower organizations usually have officers and a board of directors. To find out what's going on in your state, contact an extension vegetable specialist or ask other growers at farmers markets. Many grower associations hold meetings at their state's annual farm show or other large annual agricultural gathering, where you can easily pick up their membership information.

Besides commodity-specific organizations, there are state- and county-based farmer organizations with a broader orientation, such as the *Farm Bureau*, and organic farming groups such as the Northeast Organic Farming Association (NOFA), which has branches in several Northeast states. The activities of these organizations vary from state to state, as does their mission and political orientation. County farm bureau meetings provide a good means of interacting with the local farming community, as well as an opportunity to shop for services such as insurance. These organizations usually have outreach activities, such as in-school programs, farmers market events, and issue-based pamphlets, press releases, and political lobbying. Try not to stereotype the groups: organic farming organizations may offer a lot of information, such as publications, tours, conferences, and workshops, that would also be of use to nonorganic farmers; and more conventional groups may offer services helpful to farmers outside the mainstream.

Scientific Organizations

Scientific organizations sponsor journals that publish research results, annual conferences with oral presentations and poster sessions, and tours of agricultural research and production facilities. In general these organizations are not grower-oriented, but research-oriented. Thus, they best serve growers through the "trickle-down" of information through extension and industry. However, some effort toward practical orientation has been made by the American Society for Horticultural Science (ASHS), for example, with the recent publication of the journal *HortTechnology,* which emphasizes extension, education, and applied research. Additional organizations of interest to growers are the following:

American Society of Agronomy (ASA)
677 S. Segoe Road
Madison, WI 53711
    Phone: (608) 273-8080

American Society for Plasticulture (ASP)
526 Brittany Drive, State College, PA 16803
    Phone: (814) 238-7045

American Society for Horticultural Science (ASHS)
600 Cameron Street, Alexandria, VA 22314-2562
    Phone: (703) 836-4606

Entomological Society of America (ESA)
9301 Annapolis Road
Lanham, MD 20706-3115
    Phone: (301) 731-4535

Weed Science Society of America (WSSA)
P.O. Box 1897, 810 East 10th St.
Lawrence, KS 66044-8897
    Phone: (800) 627-0629 or (785) 843-1235

Publications

Every grower should have a small library that includes a mix of books, extension production guides, booklets and fact sheets, newsletters, magazines, conference proceedings, and, for the scientifically-inclined, journals. In addition, a collection of product catalogs can be really helpful. The following is a short list of general books on vegetable production that growers may find useful. Additional books covering topics such as soil fertility, marketing, and season extension will also be needed; see the references (beginning on page 257) for the appropriate chapters. Most bookstores can order the books you need, and many vegetable conference trade shows include exhibitors selling books, too.

General Books on Vegetable Production

- Maynard, D. N., and G. J. Hochmuth. 1997. *Knott's Handbook for Vegetable Growers*. New York, NY: John Wiley and Sons.
- Nonecke, I. L. 1989. *Vegetable Production*. New York, NY: Van Nostrand Reinhold.

- Peirce, L. C. 1987. *Vegetables: Characteristics, Production, and Marketing*. New York, NY: John Wiley and Sons.
- Rubatsky, V. E., and M. Yamaguchi. 1997. *World Vegetables*. New York, NY: Chapman and Hall.
- Thompson, H. C, and W. C. Kelly. 1957. *Vegetable Crops*. New York, NY: McGraw-Hill.

Extension Publications

Required reading is your cooperative extension annual or biennial vegetable management guide, which may be state or regional in focus. Getting these from a number of different states can be useful for comparing recommendations. Each state also has its own extension publications catalog, and the topics covered by each state vary. Many publications can be obtained at university web sites, or crop-specific production publications may be ordered from state extension publications offices. For example, the University of Connecticut Cooperative Extension offers the *Northeast Sweet Corn Production and Integrated Pest Management Manual* and the *Integrated Pest Management Manual for Cole Crops*. The University of Massachusetts Cooperative Extension publishes *IPM for Potatoes* and *IPM for Fresh Market Field Tomatoes in Massachusetts* (for publishers' addresses, see appendix B, beginning on page 240.)

NRAES Publications

Natural Resource, Agriculture, and Engineering Service (NRAES) publications include a variety of publications on farm structures, fruit and vegetable production, pesticide management, waste management, livestock production, dairy production, and other topics. NRAES publications are available through extension offices or may be ordered directly from NRAES (see additional information beginning on page 266).

APS Press

APS Press (publications of the American Phytopathological Society) publishes commodity-specific, comprehensive "disease compendia" for beans, cucurbits, corn, onions and garlic, lettuce, peas, tomatoes, and other crops. Although highly technical, these are still very useful for identifying and understanding vegetable diseases.

Sustainable Agriculture Network (SAN)

The Sustainable Agriculture Network (SAN) sells *The Real Dirt: Farmers Tell about Organic and Low-Input Practices in the Northeast,* a book devoted to low-input and organic farming issues and crop production practices from farmers' perspective. Other SAN titles include *Managing Cover Crops Profitably, Steel in the Field: A Farmer's Guide to Weed Management Tools,* and *The Sustainable Agriculture Directory of Expertise.*

Newsletters, Magazines, and Trade Newspapers

Extension newsletters across the nation offer inexpensive, timely, and region-specific information. Be sure to get your state's extension vegetable newsletter if there is one. Many such newsletters are now available electronically via e-mail. This enhances the timeliness of information, since the postal system is avoided, and in many cases also avoids the fee charged for the printed version of the same newsletter.

Examples of useful newsletters and magazines include the following:
- *American Vegetable Grower* and *Greenhouse Grower* (both from Meister Publishing Company) are nationwide magazines aimed at large-scale producers but of use to all commercial growers. Especially useful are the equipment and supply ads and the annual Service Book, which lists product and materials suppliers.
- *Growing for Market* is a newsletter that covers small-scale production and marketing of vegetables, flowers, and herbs.
- *HortIdeas* offers a concise monthly review of lay and academic horticultural publications.
- *The Natural Farmer,* published by NOFA/Mass, is a quarterly tabloid providing in-depth coverage of a specific organic farming topic in each issue.
- *The Packer* is a weekly newspaper covering the wholesale vegetable industry; annual issues also cover trends in the produce industry and pro-

duce merchandising.
- *Pennsylvania Vegetable Growers News* is published by the Pennsylvania Vegetable Growers Association.
- *The Vegetable Growers News* (formerly *The Great Lakes Vegetable Growers News*) is a monthly.

Proceedings

Many major vegetable conferences solicit short papers from their presenters that are compiled into proceedings. The papers published in conference proceedings run the gamut from technical research reports to growers' personal stories and can be a source of valuable, applied information. Some proceedings are organized by topic, others are not. Utilizing information from proceedings often requires some digging, but the papers themselves are usually "user-friendly" and offer practical advice. Proceedings can be purchased if you do not attend the conference, and back issues are often available. Some conferences of interest include the New England Vegetable and Berry Conference, the New York State Vegetable Growers Conference, the New England Greenhouse Conference, the Pennsylvania Vegetable Conference, and the Northeast Direct Marketing Conference.

Meetings

Information on upcoming local and statewide vegetable meetings will be available through your vegetable association and extension specialist and any newsletters they produce. Attending these meetings is highly recommended, and most of the best vegetable growers do. Listings of major meetings can also be found in agriculture newspapers and magazines such as those listed above.

Farm Tours and Twilight Meetings

Visiting farms and hearing other farmers describe their practices, observations, thoughts, and innovations is a wonderful way to learn. The generosity of vegetable farmers with information is remarkable. Rather than seeing other farmers as competitors, most realize that it's a win-win situation to share information, that "a rising tide lifts all boats." Many growers complain that they can't seem to find the time during the growing season to participate in farm tours or twilight meetings. Unfortunately, there's little to see in the off-season locally, so the best tours and twilight meetings are always during the growing season. As I heard one farmer say, "If you come home with just one good idea, it's worth a day away from the farm." Obviously, you need to develop reliable help to oversee the farm in your absence.

Twilight meetings are an extension tradition, usually featuring on-farm demonstrations of research results or innovative production practices and marketing strategies. In many states, the vegetable specialist will develop a schedule of twilight meetings prior to each growing season. Other groups, such as NOFA or commodity associations, may hold similar meetings, sometimes called on-farm workshops.

Farm tours may be essentially extended twilight meetings that are comprised of multiple stops to local farms, or they may be trips to out-of-area production regions. Often, an extension person will arrange for his or her counterpart in the region to be visited to set up the stops and accompany the visiting group, providing background before each farm stop.

Videos

The few extension videos pertaining to the Northeast that are available cover useful topics: *Sweet Corn IPM* (University of Massachusetts) shows how to use traps and scout for corn insect pests. *Vegetable Farmers and Their Weed Control Machines* (University of Vermont Center for Sustainable Agriculture) features farmers in three states describing cultivation and flame weeding tools. *Innovations in Mechanical Weed Control* is available from the Cornell University Department of Fruit and Vegetable Science.

NOFA has available over a hundred videos taped at the annual summer conferences over the past few years. Topics range from soils, cover crops, and greenhouse management to specific crop production talks.

The "Farmer-to-Farmer" video series includes *Vegetables, IPM for Vegetables and Small Fruits,*

and *High-Value Marketing,* all available from Rooy Media.

Internet

If you have e-mail, a useful resource is the commercial vegetable production discussion group. This is a highly focused, applied network designed to ask and answer production questions, announce useful resources, and share extension-oriented electronic publications. It is used primarily by extension personnel, but some farmers use it, too. To subscribe, e-mail the message "subscribe veg-prod" with no other text to the following address: majordomo@reeusda.gov

If you subscribe to this discussion group, do not abuse it with non-farming questions or philosophical inquiries. There are plenty of other electronic discussion groups for people with extra time on their hands.

It is possible to obtain useful farming information on the World Wide Web, but you will have to find it among the clutter. To do so, you need to use search language that narrows the sites returned. Simply typing "vegetable production" will return thousands of hits; typing "maggots" will get you dozens of sites on Shakespearean insults. Advanced search language is needed that searches for specific phrases, such as "cabbage root maggot." Consult the instructions for advanced searching provided by the search engine you are using. Another problem is that some sites offer very simplistic or brief information. However, you will discover that there are more and more useful sites, often provided by universities and government agencies, such as those listed below. (Also see "Publications on Using the Internet" below.)

Selected Web Sites of Interest to Vegetable Growers

This list of web sites is not complete. No endorsement of named sites is intended, nor is criticism implied of similar sites that are not mentioned. Content and address of web sites are subject to change at any time. Addresses were current as of June 1999. (Also see "Publications on Using the Internet" below.)

- Appropriate Technology Transfer for Rural Areas (ATTRA) Horticulture Series <www.attra.org/attra-pub/horticulture.html>

- Crop Enterprise Cost and Return Estimates (University of Kentucky Department of Agricultural Economics) <http://www.uky.edu/Agriculture/AgriculturalEconomics/hort96.html>

- Database of IPM Resources (DIR) <http://ippc.orst.edu/dir/>

- Illinois Fruit and Vegetable News <www.aces.uiuc.edu/ipm/news/fvnews.html>

- Integrated Pest Management in New York State <www.nysaes.cornell.edu/ipmnet/ny/>

- The Ohio State University Extension Vegetable Crops (Veg Net) <www.ag.ohio-state.edu/~vegnet>

- Oregon State University Commercial Vegetable Production Guides <http://osu.orst.edu/Dept/NWREC/vegindex.html>

- Penn State College of Agricultural Sciences Horticulture Resources Page <http://www.cas.psu.edu/docs/CASHOME/agdir/Hort.html>

- Plant Disease Information Notes—Vegetables (North Carolina State University) <http://www.ces.ncsu.edu/depts/pp/notes/Vegetable/vegetable_contents.html>

- Postharvest Technology Research and Education Center (University of California Davis) <http://postharvest.ucdavis.edu/>

- Prices of fruit and vegetables by city (Market Information System, University of Florida) <gnv.ifas.ufl.edu/~marketing/menu/fvcity.html>

- Sustainable Practices for Vegetable Production in the South (North Carolina State University) <http://www.cals.ncsu.edu/sustainable/peet/>

- Texas Aggie horticulture <http://aggie-horticulture.tamu.edu/vegetable/vegetable.html>

- Vegetable IPM Resource for the Midwest (Minnesota Extension Service) <http://www3.extension.umn.edu/vegipm/>

- Vegetable Insect Pest Management Notes (North Carolina State University) <http://www.ces.ncsu.edu/depts/ent/notes/Vegetables/vegetable_contents.html>

- Vegetable Research and Information Center (University of California) <http://vric.ucdavis.edu/>

Publications on Using the Internet

- Campidonica, M. 1997. *How to Find Agricultural Information on the Internet.* Oakland, CA: Division of Agriculture and Natural Resources, University of California.
- James, H. 1996. *The Farmer's Guide to the Internet.* Lexington, KY: TVA Rural Studies, University of Kentucky.
- McGiffen, M. E. Jr., et al. 1996. "Compendium: Horticultural Information on the Internet and other Electronic Media." *HortTechnology* 6: 295-350.

Appendix B

Publishers' Addresses*

Journals

BioCycle, Journal of Waste Recycling
419 State Avenue, Emmaus PA 18049
    Phone: (610) 967-4135

Growing for Market
Fairplain Publications Incorporated
P.O. Box 3747, Lawrence KS 66046
    Phone: (800) 307-8949 or (785) 748-0605

HortIdeas
750 Black Lick Road, Gravel Switch, KY 40328
    Web site: www.users.mis.net/~gwill/
    E-mail: gwill@mis.net (no phone orders)

HortTechnology
American Society for Horticultural Science
600 Cameron Street, Alexandria, VA 22314-2562
    Phone: (703) 836-4606

The Natural Farmer—See NOFA/Mass

The Packer
Vance Publishing Corporation
P.O. Box 2939, Shawnee, KS 66201
    Phone: (800) 255-5113 or (913) 438-8700

Pennsylvania Vegetable Growers News—See
Pennsylvania Vegetable Growers Association

Small Farmer's Journal
P.O. Box 1627, Sisters OR 97759
    Phone: (541) 549-2064

The Vegetable Growers News
Great American Publishing, Inc.
P.O. Box 128, Sparta, MI 49345
    Phone: (616) 887-9008

Videos

Steve Groff, Cedar Meadow Farm
679 Hilldale Road, Holtwood, PA 17532
    Phone: (717) 284-5152

Anne and Eric Nordell
3410 Route 184, Trout Run, PA 17771
    (No phone orders)

Rooy Media
7407 Hilltop Drive, Frederick, MD 21702
    Phone: (877) 226-4276 or (301) 473-8797

Books, Fact Sheets, and Other Publications

AgAccess c/o Fertile Ground Books
P.O. Box 2008, Davis, CA 95617
    Phone: (800) 540-0170 or (530) 297-7879

APS Press
The American Phytopathological Society
3340 Pilot Knob Road, St. Paul, MN 55121
    Phone: (800) 328-7560 or (651) 454-7250

CAB International
10 East 40th St. Suite 3203, New York, NY 10016
    Phone: (800) 528-4841 or (212) 481-7018

California Dept. of Pesticide Regulation
Environmental Monitoring and Pest Management
830 K St., Sacramento, CA 95814
    Phone: (916) 324-4100

Canadian Organic Growers, Inc.
Box 6408, Station J
Ottawa, Ontario K2A 3Y6 Canada
    Phone: (613) 231-9047

*This list of publishers is not complete. No endorsement of named publishers is intended, nor is criticism implied of publishers that are not mentioned. Information is current as of June 1999.

The Center for Rural Pennsylvania
212 Locust Street, Suite 604
Harrisburg, PA 17101
    Phone: (717) 787-9555

Chapman & Hall
101 Philip Drive, Norwell, MA 02061
    Phone: (781) 871-6600

Chelsea Green Publishing Company
P.O. Box 428, Gates-Briggs Building #205
White River Junction, VT 05001
    Phone: (802) 295-6300 or (800) 639-4099

Cornell Cooperative Extension
Distribution Center
7 Cornell Business and Technology Park
Ithaca, NY 14850
    Phone: (607) 255-2080

Cornell University Press
CUP Services, Box 6525, Ithaca, NY 14851-6525
    Phone: (607) 277-2211

CSA Farm Network (c/o Steve Gilman)
130 Ruckytucks Road, Stillwater, NY 12170
    Phone: (518) 583-4613

Doe Hollow Publishing
10 Doe Hollow Lane, Belvidere, NJ 07823
    Phone: (908) 474-3872

Edaphic Press
P.O. Box 107, Newbury, VT 05051
    Phone: (802) 222-4277

Entomological Society of Canada
393 Winston Avenue, Ottawa, Ontario
Canada K2A 1Y8
    Phone: (613) 725-2619

Garden Way/Storey Publishing
Schoolhouse Road, Pownal, VT 05261
    Phone: (800) 359-7436

Good Earth Publications
1702 Mountain View Road
Buena Vista, VA 24416
    Phone: (800) 499-3201 or (540)261-8775

Hot Line Farm Equipment Guide
1003 Central Avenue, P.O. Box 1115
Fort Dodge, IA 50501
    Phone: (800) 673-4763 or (515) 955-1600

IPM Practitioner
P.O. Box 7414, Berkeley, CA 94707
    Phone: (510) 524-2567

Island Press
P.O. Box 7, Covelo, CA 95428
    Phone: (800) 828-1302 or (707) 983-6432

John Deere and Company Service Publications
P.O. Box 186, Moline, IL 61266
    Phone: (800) 522-7448

John Wiley and Sons
605 Third Avenue, New York, NY 10158
    Phone: (800) 225-5945

Kansas State University Cooperative Extension
Production Services, 26 Umberger Hall
Manhattan, KS 66506-3402
    Phone: (785) 532-5830

Macmillan Publishing Company, Inc.
(c/o Simon & Schuster)
200 Old Tappan Road, Old Tappen, NJ 07675
    Phone: (800) 257-5157

McGraw-Hill Companies
P.O. Box 545, Blacklick, OH 43004-0545
    Phone: (800) 262-4729

Meister Publishing Company
37733 Euclid Avenue, Willoughby, OH 44094
    Phone: (800) 572-7740 or (440) 942-2000

Michigan State University Extension
MSU Bulletin Office, 10-B Agriculture Hall
East Lansing, MI 48824-1039
    Phone: (517) 355-0240

MidWest Plan Service
122 Davidson Hall, Iowa State University
Ames, IA 50011-3080
    Phone: (515) 294-4337

The Minnesota Project
1885 University Avenue West, #315
St. Paul, MN 55104
  Phone: (651) 645-6159

NRAES (Natural Resource, Agriculture,
and Engineering Service)
Cooperative Extension, 152 Riley-Robb Hall
Ithaca, NY 14853-5701
  Phone: (607) 255-7654

National Academy Press
2101 Constitution Ave, NW, Lockbox 285
Washington, DC 20055
  Phone: (888) 624-8373 or (202) 334-3313

National Agricultural Library, Room 304
Alternative Farming Systems Information Center
10301 Baltimore Ave.
Beltsville, MD 20705-2351
  Phone: (301) 504-6559

New Alchemy Publications c/o The Green Center
237 Hatchville Road, East Falmouth, MA 02536
  Web site: <www.fuzzylu.com/greencenter/>
  (No phone orders)

New England Small Farm Institute
P.O. Box 937, Belchertown, MA 01007-0937
  Phone: (413) 323-4531

New York State IPM Program
c/o C. H. Petzoldt, IPM Building, NYSAES
Geneva, NY 14456
  Phone: (315) 787-2206

New York State Vegetable Growers Association
P.O. Box 4256, Ithaca, NY 14852
  Phone: (607) 539-7648

New World Publishing
3085 Sheridan Street, Placerville, CA 95667
Placerville, CA 95667
  Phone: (916) 622-2248

NOFA/MASS (Northeast Organic Farming Association of Massachusetts)
411 Sheldon Road, Barre, MA 01005
  Phone: (978) 355-2853

NOFA-NY (Northeast Organic Farming Association of New York)
26 Towpath Rd., Binghamton, NY 13904
  Phone: (607) 724-9851

NOFA-VT (Northeast Organic Farming Associa-
tion of Vermont)
P.O. Box 697, Richmond, VT 05477
  Phone: (802) 434-4122

Northeast Region Sustainable Agriculture Research and Education Program (SARE)—See
Sustainable Agriculture Publications

Northern Plains Sustainable Agriculture Society
9824 79th Street, SE
Fullerton, ND 58441-9725
  Phone: (701) 883-4304

Northwest Area Foundation
332 Minnesota St., Suite E-1201
St. Paul, MN 55101
  Phone: (651) 224-9635

Oklahoma State University
Cooperative Extension
University Mailing Services
Stillwater, OK 74078
  Phone: (405) 744-5385

PC Services
P.O. Box 7294, Bismark, ND 58507-7294
  Phone: (701) 224-9858

The Pennsylvania State University
Publications Distribution Center
112W Agricultural Engineering Building
University Park, PA 16802-2602
  Phone: (814) 865-6713

Pennsylvania Vegetable Growers Association
R.R. 1, P.O. Box 392, Northumberland, PA 17857
  Phone: (570) 473-8468

Rodale Institute Research Center
611 Siegfriedale Road, Kutztown, PA 19530-9749
  Phone: (800) 832-6285

Rodale Press, Inc.
33 E. Minor St., Emmaus, PA 18098
  Phone: (610) 967-5171

Rutgers Cooperative Extension
Publications Distribution Center
57 Dudley Road, New Brunswick, NJ 08901-8520
  Phone: (732) 932-9762

Sustainable Agriculture Network (SAN)—See
Sustainable Agriculture Publications

Sustainable Agriculture Publications
SARE USDA Program, Northeast Region
Hills Building, Room 10, University of Vermont
Burlington, VT 05405-0085
  Phone: (802) 656-0471

TS Books
P.O. Box 1244, Santa Cruz, CA 95061
  Phone: (800) 624-2665 or (831) 427-1620

TVA Rural Studies
400 Agricultural Engineering Building No. 2
University of Kentucky, Lexington, KY 40546
  Phone: (606) 257-1872

United States Department of Agriculture (USDA)
c/o Government Printing Office, Superintendent
of Documents
  Web site: < www.access.gpo.gov/su_docs/
  sale.html >
  Phone: (202) 512-1800

University of California
Communications Services
Division of Agriculture and Natural Resources
6701 San Pablo Avenue, Oakland, CA 94608
  Phone: (800) 994-8849 or (510) 642-2431

University of California
Department of Pomology, One Shields Ave.
Davis, CA 95616-8683
  Phone: (530) 752-6941

University of Connecticut Cooperative Extension
System, Distribution Center
C.I.T. U-35, 1376 Storrs Road
Storrs, CT 06269-4035
  Phone: (860) 486-3336

University of Illinois Extension
Marketing and Distribution
1917 South Wright St., Champaign, IL 61820
  Phone: (217) 333-2007

University of Maryland Cooperative Extension
College of Agriculture and Natural Resources
Production and Distribution, 6200 Sheridan St.
Riverdale, MD 20737
  Phone: (301) 403-4263

University of Massachusetts Extension
UMass Extension Bookstore
Draper Hall, Box 32010
Amherst, MA 01003-2010
  Phone: (413) 545-2717

University of Nebraska Cooperative Extension
IANR/Communications & Information Technol-
ogy
PO Box 830918, University of Nebraska
Lincoln, NE 68583-0918
  Phone: (402) 472-3023

University of New Hampshire Cooperative Exten-
sion, Publications Center, 120 Forest Park
University of New Hampshire
Durham, NH 03824
  Phone: (603) 862-2346

Van Nostrand Reinhold—See John Wiley and
Sons

Vermont Agency of Natural Resources
Compost Center DEC-EAD
103 South Main St., Waterbury, VT 05671-0411
  Phone: (802) 241-3448

Western Society of Weed Science
P.O. Box 963, Newark, CA 94560
  Phone: (510) 790-1252

Woods End Research Laboratory, Inc.
P. O. Box 297, Mount Vernon, ME 04352
  Phone: (207) 293-2457

Yellow Wood Associates, Inc.
95 S. Main Street, St. Albans, VT 05478
  Phone: (802) 524-6141

Appendix C

Supplier Contact Information*

Equipment, Composting

Compost Covers
Champlain Valley Compost Company
245 Ten Stones Circle, Charlotte, VT 05445
Phone: (802) 425-5556
Fax: (802) 425-5557

Compost Test Kits
Woods End Research Laboratory, Inc.
P.O. Box 1850, Mount Vernon, ME 04352
Phone: (207) 293-2457
Fax: (207) 293-2488

Equipment, Irrigation

Charles W. Harris Company, Inc.
451 Old Somerset Avenue, N. Dighton, MA
Phone: (888) 928-3731 or (508) 824-5607
Fax: (508) 884-9939

DripWorks
190 Sanhedrin Circle, Willits, CA 95490
Phone: (800) 616-8321
Fax: (707) 459-9645

Rain-Flo Irrigation
884 Center Church Road, East Earl, PA 17519
Phone: (717) 445-6976
Fax: (717) 445-8304

Roberts Irrigation Products, Inc.
700 Rancheros Drive, San Marcos, CA 92069
Phone: (800) 685-5557 or (760) 744-4511
Fax: (760) 744-0914

Schumacher Irrigation, Inc.
P.O. Box 289, Platte Center, NE 68653
Phone: (800) 246-3685 or (402) 246-3685
Fax: (402) 246-2072

Trickle-Eez Company
4266 Hollywood Road, St. Joseph, MI 49085
Phone: (616) 429-8200
Fax: (616) 429-6669

Zimmerman Irrigation, Inc.
3550 Chambersburg Road, Biglerville, PA 17307
Phone: (717) 337-2727
Fax: (717) 337-1785

Equipment, Weed Control

Basket and finger weeders
Buddingh Weeder Company
7015 Hammond Avenue, Dutton, MI 49316
Phone: (616) 698-8613

Brush weeders
Baertschi FOBRO
1715 Airpark Drive, Grand Haven, MI 49417
Phone: (877) 463-6276 or (616) 847-0300

Field cultivators
Brillion Iron Works
200 Park Avenue, Brillion, WI 54110
Phone: (920) 756-2121
Fax: (920) 756-3355

Kongskilde Ltd.
19551 N. Dixie Hwy., Bowling Green OH 43402
Phone: (419) 354-1495
Fax: (419) 353-5892

*This list of suppliers is not complete. No endorsement of named manufacturers or suppliers is intended, nor is criticism implied of similar companies that are not mentioned. Information is current as of June 1999.

Unverferth Manufacturing
P.O. Box 357, Kalida, OH 45853
    Phone: (800) 322-6301 or (419) 532-3121

Flaming equipment
Flame Engineering
P.O. Box 577 W. Highway 4, LaCrosse, KS 67548
    Phone: (800) 255-2469 or (785) 222-2873
    Fax: (785) 222-3619

Goss Incorporated
1511 Route 8
Glenshaw, PA 15116
    Phone: (800) 367-4677 or (412) 486-6100
    Fax: (412) 486-6844

Thermal Weed Control
N1940 Highway 95, Neilsville, WI 54456
    Phone: (888) 318-9738 or (715) 743-4163
    Fax: (715) 743-2921

Rolling cultivator
Bush Hog Implements
P.O. Box 1039, Selma, AL 36701
    Phone: (800) 363-6096 or (334) 872-6261
    Fax: (334) 872-0168

Spyders™, torsion bars, spring-hoes
Bezzerides Brothers, Inc.
P.O. Box 211, Orosi, CA 93647
    Phone: (209) 528-3011

Sweeps, shovels, shanks
Central Tractor
3915 Delaware Avenue, Des Moines, IA 50313
    Phone: (800) 247-7508 or (515) 266-3101

R & H Machine
Box 1348, Caldwell, ID 83605
    Phone: (800) 321-6568 or (208) 459-1507
    Fax: (208) 457-1508

Wasco Hardfacing Company
P.O. Box 2476, Fresno, CA 93745
    Phone: (209) 485-5860
    Fax: (559) 233-9714

Tine weeders
Lely Corporation
P.O. Box 1060, Wilson, NC 27894
    Phone: (800) 334-2763 or (252) 291-7050

Equipment, Miscellaneous

Soil blocker (made by Visser/Dewa)
Nexus Corporation
10983 Leroy Drive, Northglenn, CO 80233
    Phone: (303) 457-9199

"Zea-Later" applicator for applying oil to sweet corn for control of corn ear worm and other insects
c/o Ruth V. Hazzard
University of Massachusetts Extension
Agricultural Engineering Building/Entomology
University of Massachusetts, Amherst, MA 01003
    Phone: (413) 545-3696

Supplies, General

A.M. Leonard
P.O. Box 816, Piqua, OH 45356
    Phone: (800) 543-8955 or (937) 773-2694
    Fax: (937) 773-9993

Ben Meadows Company
3589 Broad Street, Atlanta, GA 30341
    Phone: (800) 241-6401 or (770) 455-0907

Central Tractor
3915 Delaware Avenue, Des Moines, IA 50313
    Phone: (800) 247-7508 or (515) 266-3101

Gardener's Supply Company
128 Intervale Road, Burlington, VT 05401
    Phone: (800) 863-1700

Gempler's
P.O. Box 328, Belleville, WI 53508
    Phone: (800) 382-8473 or (608) 424-1544
    Fax: (800) 551-1128

General Supply Corp.
P.O. Box 9347, Jackson, MS 39286
    Phone: (800) 647-6450 or (601) 981-3882
    Fax: (800) 553-2457

Market Farm Implement
257 Fawn Hollow Road, Friedens, PA 15541
    Phone: (814) 443-1931
    Fax: (814) 445-2238

NASCO
901 Janesville Avenue, Fort Atkinson, WI 53538
Phone: (800) 558-9595 or (920) 563-2446
Fax: (920) 563-8296

OESCO, Inc.
P.O. Box 540, Conway, MA 01341
Phone: (800) 634-5557 or (413) 369-4335
Fax: (413) 369-4431

Supplies, Greenhouse

CropKing, Inc.
5050 Greenwich Road, Seville, OH 44273
Phone: (330) 769-2002
Fax: (330) 769-2616

E. C. Geiger, Inc.
Route 63 Box 285, Harleysville, PA 19438
Phone: (800) 443-4437 or (215) 256-6511

Greenhouse Supply, Inc.
12 Acme Road, Suite 212, Brewer, ME 04412
Phone: (800) 696-8511 or (207) 989-1585
Fax: (207) 989-1553

Griffin Greenhouse and Nursery Supplies
P.O. Box 36, Tewksbury, MA 01876
Phone: (978) 851-4346

Hydro-Gardens, Inc.
P.O. Box 25845, Colorado Springs, CO 80936
Phone: (800) 634-6362 or (719) 495-2266
Fax: (800) 634-6362

W. H. Milikowski, Inc.
75 Chestnut Hill, Route 190
Stafford Springs, CT 06076
Phone: (800) 368-9464 or (860) 684-5811

Rough Brothers
P.O. Box 16010, Cincinnati, OH 45216
Phone: (800) 543-7351 or (513) 242-0310
Fax: (513) 242-0816

Supplies, IPM

Gempler's
P.O. Box 328, Belleville, WI 53508
Phone: (800) 382-8473 or (608) 424-1544
Fax: (800) 551-1128

Great Lakes IPM
10220 Church Road NE, Vestaburg, MI 48891
Phone: (517) 268-5693
Fax: (517) 268-5311

Green Spot, Ltd.
93 Priest Road, Nottingham, NH 03290-6204
Phone: (603) 942-8925
Fax: (603) 942-8932

IPM Laboratories, Inc.
980 Main Street, Locke, NY 13092
Phone: (315) 497-2063
Fax: (315) 497-3129

Koppert Biological Systems, Inc.
28465 Beverly Road, Romulus, MI 48174
Phone: (734) 641-3763

Supplies, Organic

Fedco Seeds
P.O. Box 520
Waterville, ME 04903
Phone: (207) 873-7333

Harmony Farm Supply
3244 Gravenstein Highway North
Sebastopol, CA 95472
Phone: (707) 823-9125
Fax: (707) 823-1734

North Country Organics
Depot Street, Bradford, VT 05033
Phone: (802) 222-4277
Fax: (802) 222-9661

Peaceful Valley Farm Supply
P.O. Box 2209, Grass Valley, CA 95945
Phone: (530) 272-4769

Vegetable Seeds

Abbot and Cobb
P.O. Box 307, Feasterville, PA 19053
Phone: (215) 245-6666
Fax: (215) 245-9043

Alf Christianson Seed Company
P.O. Box 98, Mount Vernon, WA 98273
Phone: (360) 336-9727
Fax: (360) 419-3035

Asgrow Vegetable Seeds
556 Armour Street, Tifton, GA 31794
    Phone: (800) 234-1056 or (912) 382-1815

Carolina Seeds
P.O. Box 2658, Boone, NC 28607
    Phone: (800) 825-5477 or (828) 297-7333
    Fax: (800) 825-5477

Chesmore Seed Company
P.O. Box 8368, St. Joseph, MO 64508
    Phone: (800) 383-0865 or (816) 279-0865
    Fax: (816) 232-6134

D.V. Burrell Seed Growers Company
P.O. Box 150, Rocky Ford, CO 81067
    Phone: (719) 254-3318
    Fax: (719) 254-3319

DeBruyn Seed, Inc.
101 E. Washington Street, Zeeland, MI 49464
    Phone: (616) 772-2316
    Fax: (616) 772-4242

DeRuiter Seeds, Inc.
P.O. Box 20228, Columbus, OH 43220
    Phone: (614) 459-1498
    Fax: (614) 422-1716

Ferry-Morse Seed Company
P.O. Box 488
Fulton, KY 42041-0488
    Phone: (800) 283-6400
    Fax: (800) 283-2700

Harris Seeds
P.O. Box 22960, Rochester, NY 14692
    Phone: (800) 544-7938 or (716) 442-0100

Holmes Seed Company
2125 46th Street NW, Canton, OH 44709
    Phone: (800) 435-6077 or (330) 492-0123
    Fax: (330) 492-0167

Johnny's Selected Seeds
1 Foss Hill Road, Albion, ME 04910
    Phone: (207) 437-4395

Liberty Seed Company
461 Robinson Drive SE, Box 806
New Philadelphia, OH 44663

Phone: (800) 541-6022 or (330) 364-1611
Fax: (330) 364-6415

Petoseed
P.O. Box 4206
Saticoy, CA 93007-4206
    Phone: (805) 647-1188
    Fax: (805) 647-9042

Rispens Seeds, Inc.
P.O. Box 5, Lansing, IL 60438
    Phone: (708) 474-0241
    Fax: (708) 474-4127

Sakata Seed America, Inc.
18095 Serene Drive, Morgan Hill, CA 95037
    Phone: (408) 778-7758
    Fax: (408) 778-7751

Seedway
1225 Zeager Road, Elizabethtown, PA 17022
    Phone: (800) 952-7333 or (717) 367-1075
    Fax: (800) 645-2574

Seigers Seed Company
8265 Felch Street, Zeeland, MI 49464
    Phone: (800) 962-4999 or (616) 772-4999
    Fax: (616) 772-0333

Sunseeds Company
18640 Sutter Boulevard, Morgan Hill, CA 95037
    Phone: (800) 733-9505 or (408) 776-1111
    Fax: (408) 776-9375

Twilley Seed Company, Inc.
121 Gary Road, Hodges, SC 29653
    Phone: (800) 622-7333 or (864) 227-5150
    Fax: (864) 227-5108

Vesey's Seeds Ltd.
P.O. Box 9000, Calais, ME 04619
    Phone: (902) 368-7333 or (800) 363-7333
    Fax: (902) 566-1620

Vilmorin Inc.
P.O. Box 707, Empire, CA 95319
    Phone: (209) 529-6000
    Fax: (209) 529-5848

Appendix D

Work Sheet for Developing a Vegetable Enterprise Budget

Crop _____   Year ____   Field Name _____   Acreage _____

Variable Production Costs

Field labor and equipment time   Labor hours   Machinery hours

    Prepare land (plow, disk, rotavate, other _____)   _____   _____
    Apply preplant amendments (lime, fertilizer, manure, compost)   _____   _____
    Grow transplants (fill trays, seed, water, other _____)   _____   _____
    Prepare for planting (form beds, lay plastic, lay
        drip tape, other _____)   _____   _____
    Seed or transplant (set out, water, fertilize, other _____)   _____   _____
    Mechanically cultivate weeds ___ times (preplant, post-plant)   _____   _____
    Hand-hoe weeds (___ times)   _____
    Mow alleys, field edges (___ times)   _____   _____
    Scout crop for pests (___ times)   _____
    Spray pesticides ___ times (herbicides, insecticides, fungicides)   _____   _____
    Irrigate ___ times (set up, manage overhead or drip)   _____   _____
    Harvest (pick, deliver to packing house)   _____   _____
    Postharvest handling (wash, sort, pack, store, other _____)   _____   _____
    Field cleanup (remove plastic, incorporate residues)   _____   _____
    Sow cover crop   _____   _____
    Other _____   _____   _____

General management time
    Repairs, training, supervision, other _____   _____

Total production time cost
    _____ labor hours x $ _____ average cost per hour $ _____
    _____ machinery hours x $ _____ average cost per hour $ _____

        Total Labor and Machinery Cost   = $ _____

Materials Cost
    Seeds or plants $ _____
    Trays and potting mix $ _____
    Fertilizers $ _____
    Plastic mulch, row cover, drip tape $ _____
    Pesticides $ _____
    Boxes, bins, bags $ _____
    Cover crop seed $ _____
    General supplies $ _____
    Other _____ $ _____
        Total Materials Cost   = $ _____

(continued on following page)

(continued from previous page)

Marketing cost

    labor _____ hours @ $ _____ per hour $ _____

    transportation $ _____

    display $ _____

    co-op, broker, or market fees $ _____

    advertising $ _____

    other _____ $ _____

             Total Marketing Cost   = $ _____

Total Variable Production Costs (= Labor + Machinery + Materials + Marketing)

                                           = $ _____

Fixed (Overhead) Costs

Prorate each of the following costs to reflect the proportion of total farm land occupied by this crop:

    Land $ _____

    Buildings $ _____

    Insurance $ _____

    Office expenses $ _____

    Property taxes $ _____

    Utilities $ _____

    Fees, permits $ _____

    Other $ _____

           Total Fixed (Overhead) Costs   = $ _____

Total Costs (= Variable Costs + Fixed Costs)

                                         = $ _____

Gross Returns (= Marketable Yield x Average Price per Unit)

retail _____ units x $ _____ per unit   = $ _____

wholesale_____ units x $ _____ per unit = $ _____

        Total Retail plus Wholesale   = $ _____

Net Returns* (= Gross Returns – Total Costs)= $ _____

*Net returns = pre-tax profit if farmer's labor is included above

Appendix E

Vegetable Crop Nutrient Recommendations

Table E.1 Nutrient recommendations in pounds per acre

Region	Total N	Maximum Phosphate	Maximum Potash
Nutrient Recommendations in pounds per acre			
Asparagus			
New beds:			
Mid-Atlantic	50*	200	200
New England	50*	200	200
New York	100–110*	200	200
*Mid-Atlantic suggests sidedress at first cultivation; others suggest broadcast and incorporate.			
Cutting beds:**			
Mid-Atlantic	50	200	150
New England	50	200	150
New York	50	100	100
**New England suggests broadcast after final cutting; New York suggests before spear emergence; Mid-Atlantic suggests before cutting season. Note: Hybrid strains will require about 50% higher rates of all major nutrients.			
Bean (Snap)			
Mid-Atlantic	60–90	120	160
New England	50	100	100
New York	30–40	100	80
Beets and Swiss Chard			
Mid-Atlantic	75–100	150	150
New England	100–130	150	300
New York	150–175	200	400
Carrot			
Mid-Atlantic	50–80	150	150
New England	110–150	150	400
New York	120–150	160	200

continued

Region	Total N	Maximum Phosphate	Maximum Potash
Nutrient Recommendations *(continued)* in pounds per acre			
Celery			
Mid-Atlantic	125–150	250	250
New England	180	200	300
New York	180	200	300
Cole Crops (Broccoli, Brussels Sprouts, Cabbage, Cauliflower, Kale)			
Mid-Atlantic	100–200*	200	200
New England	160	200	175
New York	120–150	160	200
*Up to 150 for most crops; up to 200 for broccoli.			
Cucurbits (Cucumbers, Muskmelons, Pumpkins, Summer Squash, Watermelon, and Winter Squash)			
Mid-Atlantic cucumber	100–125	150	200
muskmelon, summer squash	75–100	150	200
pumpkin/ winter squash	50–75	150	200
non-irrigated watermelon	80–100	150	200
irrigated watermelon	125–150	150	200
New England	130	150	200
New York	120–140	160	160
Eggplant			
Mid-Atlantic	125–150	250	250
New England	110	200	200
New York	130	200	200
Lettuce			
Mid-Atlantic	100–125*	200	200
New England	75–120	190	190
New York	130	160	200
*60–80 for iceberg			

continued

Sustainable Vegetable Production from Start-Up to Market

Table E.1 Nutrient recommendations in pounds per acre
(continued)

Nutrient Recommendations *(continued)* in pounds per acre			
Region	Total N	Maximum Phosphate	Maximum Potash
Onion			
Mid-Atlantic	75–100*	200	200
New England	130	175	175
New York	100–110	200	200
*Double this N rate for green onions			
Parsnip			
Mid-Atlantic	50–75	150	150
New England	110–150	150	400
New York	120–150	160	160
Peas			
Mid-Atlantic	40–60	120	120
New England	75	150	150
New York	40–50	160	120
Pepper			
Mid-Atlantic	100–130	200	200
New England	140	200	200
New York	130	200	240
Potato			
Mid-Atlantic			
(loams/ silt loams	125–150	200	300
(sandy loams/ loamy sands)	150	200	300
New England	120–180	250–300	225–250
New York	120–175	240–300	200–300

Nutrient Recommendations *(continued)* in pounds per acre			
Region	Total N	Maximum Phosphate	Maximum Potash
Radish			
Mid-Atlantic	50	150	150
New England	50	105	120
New York	60	125	200
Rutabaga and Turnip			
Mid-Atlantic	50–75	150	150
New England	50	100	100
New York	130	125	200
Spinach			
Mid-Atlantic	80–125	200	200
New England	90–110	150	200
New York	130	170	200
Sweet Corn			
Mid-Atlantic	125–150	160	160
New England	100–160	110	200
New York	120–140	160	160
Tomato			
Mid-Atlantic (fresh market) sandy loams/ loamy sands	80–90	200	300
loams/ silt loams	50–80	200	250
New England	140–160	200	250
New York	130	200	240

continued

Source: Adapted from Orzolek et al., 1999; Ferro, ed., 1998; and Bartsch, Hoffmann, Bellinder, Ellerbrock, et al., 1994

Appendix F

Useful Conversions and Calculations

Table F.1 Useful conversions and calculations

	To convert:	Into:	Multiply by:
Length	centimeters (cm)	inches (in)	0.394
	feet (ft)	centimeters (cm)	30.48
	feet (ft)	inches (in)	12
	feet (ft)	yards (yd)	0.33
	inches (in)	feet (ft)	0.083
	inches (in)	millimeters (mm)	25.4
	inches (in)	centimeters (cm)	2.54
	meters (m)	inches (in)	39.37
	meters (m)	feet (ft)	3.281
	meters (m)	yards (yd)	1.094
	yards (yd)	feet (ft)	3
	yards (yd)	centimeters (cm)	91.44
	yards (yd)	meters (m)	0.9144
Area	acres	square feet (ft^2)	43,560
	acres	square yards (yd^2)	4,840
	acres	hectares (ha)	0.4047
	hectares (ha)	acres	2.471
	hectares (ha)	square meters (m^2)	10,000
	square inches (in^2)	square centimeters (cm^2)	6.452
	square centimeters (cm^2)	square inches (in^2)	0.155
	square feet (ft^2)	square centimeters (cm^2)	929.09
	square feet (ft^2)	square meters (m^2)	0.0929
	square meters (m^2)	square feet (ft^2)	10.76
	square meters (m^2)	square yards (yd^2)	1.196
Weight	grams (g)	ounces (oz)	0.0353
	kilograms (kg)	pounds (lb)	2.205
	metric tons (megagrams)	short tons	1.1023
	ounces (oz)	pounds (lb)	0.0625
	ounces (oz)	grams (g)	28.35
	pounds (lb)	ounces (oz)	16
	pounds (lb)	grams (g)	453.6
	short tons	metric tons (megagrams)	0.9078
Volume, solids	bushels (bu)	cubic feet (ft^3)	1.24
	bushels (bu)	cubic meters (m^3)	0.352
	bushels (bu)	liters (L)	35.24

(continued on next page)

Sustainable Vegetable Production from Start-Up to Market

	To convert:	Into:	Multiply by:
Volume, solids (continued)	cubic feet (ft³)	liters (L)	28.32
	cubic feet (ft³)	U.S. gallons (gal)	7.48
	cubic feet (ft³)	cubic inches (in³)	1,728
	cubic feet (ft³)	cubic yards (yd³)	0.037
	cubic feet (ft³)	bushels (bu)	0.804
	cubic inches (in³)	milliliters (ml)	16.39
	cubic meters (m³)	cubic yards (yd³)	1.308
	cubic meters (m³)	U.S. gallons (gal)	264.2
	cubic meters (m³)	cubic feet (ft³)	35.3
	cubic yards (yd³)	cubic feet (ft³)	27
	cubic yards (yd³)	liters (L)	764.6
	cubic yards (yd³)	cubic meters (m³)	0.765
	cubic yards (yd³)	bushels (bu)	21.7
	gallons, U.S. dry (gal)	cubic inches (in³)	269
	liters (L)	cubic inches (in³)	61.02
	milliliters (mL)	cubic inches (in³)	0.0610
	quarts, dry (qt)	cubic inches (in³)	67.2
Volume, liquids	cubic centimeters (cm³ or cc)	milliliters (mL)	1
	cups (c)	fluid ounces (fl oz)	8
	gallons, U.S. (gal)	cups (c)	16
	gallons, U.S. (gal)	cubic inches (in³)	231
	gallons, U.S. (gal)	quarts (qt)	4
	gallons, U.S. (gal)	liters (L)	3.785
	gallons, U.S. (gal)	gallons, Imperial (gal)	0.833
	gallons, Imperial (gal)	cubic inches (in³)	277.42
	gallons, Imperial (gal)	liters (L)	4.546
	gallons, Imperial (gal)	gallons, U.S. (gal)	1.20
	liters (L)	pints (pt)	2.113
	liters (L)	quarts (qt)	1.057
	liters (L)	gallons, U.S. (gal)	0.2642
	milliliters (mL)	fluid ounces (fl oz)	0.0338
	pints (pt)	fluid ounces (fl oz)	16
	pints (pt)	cups (c)	2
	pints (pt)	quarts (qt)	0.5
	pints (pt)	cubic inches (in³)	28.87
	pints (pt)	liters (L)	0.4732
	fluid ounces (fl oz)	cubic inches (in³)	1.805
	fluid ounces (fl oz)	tablespoons (Tbsp)	2
	fluid ounces (fl oz)	teaspoons (tsp)	6
	fluid ounces (fl oz)	milliliters (mL)	29.57

(continued on next page)

	To convert:	Into:	Multiply by:
Volume, liquids (continued)	quarts (qt)	fluid ounces (fl oz)	32
	quarts (qt)	cups (c)	4
	quarts (qt)	pints (pt)	2
	quarts (qt)	U.S. gallons, liquid (gal)	0.25
	quarts (qt)	cubic inches (in^3)	57.7
	quarts (qt)	liters (L)	0.9463
	tablespoons (Tbsp)	teaspoons (tsp)	3
	tablespoons (Tbsp)	milliliters (mL)	15
	teaspoons (tsp)	milliliters (mL)	5
Weight per volume	grams/cubic centimeter (g/cm^3)	pounds/cubic foot (lbs/ft^3)	62.3
	tablespoons/bushel (Tbsp/bu)	pounds/cubic yard (lbs/yd^3)	1 (approx.)
	pounds/cubic yard (lbs/yd^3)	ounces/cubic foot (oz/ft^3)	0.6
	ounces/cubic foot (oz/ft^3)	pounds/cubic yard (lbs/yd^3)	1.67
	pounds/cubic yard (lbs/yd^3)	grams/liter (g/L)	0.595
	kilograms/cubic meter (kg/m^3)	pounds/cubic yard (lbs/yd^3)	1.6821
Light	lumens/square foot (lm/ft^2)	lumens/square meter (lm/m^2)	10.764
	lumens/square foot (lm/ft^2)	foot-candles (ft-c)	1
	foot-candles (ft-c)	lux (lx)	10.764
	lux (lx)	foot-candles (ft-c)	0.0929

Parts per Million (ppm) Conversions

- 1 milligram/liter = 1 ppm
- 1 ounce/gallon = 7,490 ppm
- 1 ounce/100 gallons = 75 ppm

percent fertilizer element x 75 = ppm of element in 100 gallons of water per ounce of fertilizer

For example, for a 9-45-15 fertilizer, the ppm nitrogen (N) in 100 gallons of water per ounce of fertilizer would be:

0.09 (percent N) x 75 = 6.75 ppm N in 100 gallons of water per ounce of 9-45-15

If you want 150 ppm N, and each ounce gives 6.75 ppm, then you need:

150 ÷ 6.75 = 22.22 ounces of 9-45-15 fertilizer in 100 gallons of water

Source: *Herbaceous Perennials Production: A Guide from Propagation to Marketing*, NRAES–93

Glossary

Aerate — To improve the supply of air.

Aerobic — Relating to an environment containing oxygen.

Allelopathy — The chemical suppression of germination or growth of a plant by another plant or its residues.

Anaerobic — Relating to an environment without oxygen.

Annual — A plant that completes its life cycle in a single growing season.

Band — To apply fertilizer or pesticide to crop rows and not to areas between the rows.

Bolt — The sudden emergence of a seed stalk.

C/N ratio — An abbreviation for the ratio of carbon to nitrogen that a material contains.

Calendar spray — To apply pesticide on a regular time interval, e.g., weekly, regardless of need.

Canopy — The uppermost and outermost area of a crop's foliage.

Cation — An ion with a positive electrical charge.

Certified seed — Seed that is inspected by officials for purity and freedom from disease.

Clean-cultivated fallow — Maintenance of vegetation-free land by repeated cultivation.

Cover crop — A crop that is grown to protect and improve the soil, rather than to provide income.

Crop rotation — The systematic alternation of crops on the same field or farm over time.

Crumb structure — The aggregation or binding of soil particles into tiny clumps.

Cultivar — A "cultivated variety"; a group of plants that are roughly identical, arising from or maintained in cultivation, and, when reproduced, maintaining their similarities.

Cultivate — To loosen or move soil around growing plants, usually for the purpose of weed control.

Cultural practices — Nonchemical manipulations for enhancing the quality or yield of a crop.

Denitrification — The conversion of nitrates in the soil to a gaseous form of nitrogen.

Emergence — Appearance of a seedling that breaks through the soil surface after germinating.

Fertigate — To apply fertilizer through an irrigation system.

Flame weed — To use a propane or other fossil-fuel-burning device to control weeds.

Germination — Activation of growth in a seed, culminating in the appearance of the primary root.

Green manure — A cover crop that is turned back into the soil to add nutrients and organic matter.

Harden off — To slow seedling growth in order to prepare it for the shock of outdoor planting.

Heave — The partial lifting of plants from ground as a result of freezing and thawing of the soil.

Heavy soil — Soil that drains slowly and usually

contains a lot of clay.

Inoculant — A preparation for introducing (beneficial) microbes to seeds, soil, or crops.

Inoculum — Material, such as spores or virus particles, that can infect plants or animals with a disease.

Integrated Crop Management (ICM) — A program for comprehensive and efficient management of crops, including management of insects, diseases, weeds, and soil fertility.

Ion — An atom with an electrical charge that is formed when a salt dissolves in water.

Larvae — The immature stage of insects that go through a complete metamorphosis.

Lay-by — The last cultivation of the growing season, when fertilizer is commonly side-dressed.

Leaching — The movement (and loss) of dissolved nutrients as water percolates through soil.

Light soil — Soil that drains quickly and usually contains a lot of sand.

Lodge — With respect to a plant, to fall over, usually due to excessive growth.

Organic compounds — Materials that contain carbon.

Organic farming — A method of crop and animal production that relies on natural sources of soil fertility and pest control and strives to avoid the use of synthetic and toxic materials.

Oxidation — The combining of a chemical with oxygen.

Pathogen — A disease-producing organism.

Perennial — A plant with an overwintering structure that lives more than two years.

Pheromone —A substance (such as a mating attractant) given off by one individual that causes a specific response in other individuals of the same species.

Plow layer — The depth of soil ordinarily moved during tillage to prepare for planting.

Plow pan — A compacted layer in the soil caused by repeated plowing to the same depth.

Rogue — To remove individual plants that are diseased or otherwise inferior.

Rotavator — A tillage tool that churns the soil to incorporate residues and prepare for planting.

Row cover — Lightweight, flexible, and transparent plastic sheet applied over single or multiple crop rows; used primarily to enhance growth. May be supported by hoops or unsupported (floating).

Seedbed — An area prepared for planting seeds or transplanting seedlings.

Side-dressing — An application of fertilizer alongside the rows of a growing crop.

Smother crop — A dense and fast-growing cover crop capable of outgrowing weeds.

Soil fertility — The ability of soil to supply nutrients to plants.

Soil pan — A layer in the soil that is strongly compacted or very dense.

Stale seedbed — An area prepared as if for planting, where weeds are allowed to emerge and then are controlled by flaming or herbicide so that new seeds are not brought to the surface.

Sustainable — Ecologically, economically, and socially durable.

Tillage — The movement of soil to incorporate weeds and residues and to prepare for planting.

Tillering — Formation of side shoots from the base of the stem of grass plants.

Tilth — The structure or physical condition of soil.

Topdressing — Application of fertilizer to the soil surface in a field where crops are growing.

References*

Chapter 1: Sustainable, Integrated, and Organic Production Systems

Hollingsworth, C. S., W. M. Coli, and R. V. Hazzard. 1996. *Integrated Pest Management, Massachusetts Guidelines: Commodity Specific Definitions.* Amherst, MA: University of Massachusetts Extension.

National Research Council. 1989. *Alternative Agriculture.* Washington, DC: National Academy Press.

Northeast Organic Farming Association. 1994. *The Real Dirt: Farmers Tell about Organic and Low-Input Practices in the Northeast.* Burlington, VT: Northeast Region Sustainable Agriculture Research and Education Program.

Northeast Organic Farming Association of New York, Inc. 1996. *Organic Farm and Handling/ Processing Certification Standards and Administrative Procedures.* Port Crane, NY: NOFA-NY.

Northwest Area Foundation. 1994. *A Better Row to Hoe: The Economic, Environmental and Social Impact of Sustainable Agriculture.* St. Paul, MN.

Organic Certification Standards and Applicant Information. 1998. Richmond, VT: NOFA-VT.

Public Law 101-624, Sections 2101-2123. 1990. *Organic Foods Production Act.*

Sustainable Agriculture Research and Education Program. 1998. *Ten Years of SARE.* Washington, DC: USDA (available from Sustainable Agriculture Network).

USDA Study Team on Organic Farming. 1980. *Report and Recommendations on Organic Farming.* Washington, DC: USDA.

Chapter 2: Getting Started in Vegetable Farming

Garthe, J. W., D. J. Murphy, and W. K. Waters. 1987. *Used Farm Equipment: Assessing Quality, Safety, and Economics,* NRAES–25. Ithaca, NY: Natural Resource, Agriculture, and Engineering Service (NRAES).

Gates, J. P. 1999. *Educational and Training Opportunities in Sustainable Agriculture.* Beltsville, MD: National Agricultural Library.

Grudens Schuck, N., W. Knoblauch, J. Green, and M. Saylor. 1988. *Farming Alternatives: A Guide to Evaluating the Feasibility of New Farm-Based Enterprises,* NRAES–32. Ithaca, NY: Natural Resource, Agriculture, and Engineering Service (NRAES).

Haakenson, D. 1995. *The Small Commercial Garden.* Bismark, ND: PC Services.

Healthy Harvest Directory. 1992. Davis, CA: AgAccess.

Hot Line Farm Equipment Guide. 1999. Fort Dodge, IA: Hot Line Farm Equipment Guide.

Humphrey, S., E. Mussen, C. Myers, R. E. Voss, and C. Wyman. 1994. *Small Farm Handbook.*

---

*Addresses for many of the publishers referenced are provided in appendix B, beginning on page 240.

Oakland, CA: University of California.

Lee, A. W. 1993. *Backyard Market Gardening.* Burlington, VT: Good Earth Publications.

Lloyd, R. M., et al. *Should I Grow Fruits and Vegetables?* Fact Sheets 180–186, Stillwater, OK: Oklahoma State University Cooperative Extension.

Marr, C. W., and W. J. Lamont Jr. 1991. *Farming a Few Acres of Vegetables.* Manhattan, KS: Kansas State University Cooperative Extension.

Olson, M. 1994. *MetroFarm: The Guide to Growing for Big Profit on a Small Parcel of Land.* Santa Cruz, CA: TS Books.

Ruhf, K. Z. 1999. *Farmland Transfer and Protection in New England: A Guide for Entering and Exiting Farmers.* Belchertown, MA: New England Small Farm Institute.

Savory, A. 1988. *Holistic Resource Management.* Covelo, CA: Island Press.

Schwenke, K. 1979. *Successful Small-Scale Farming.* Charlotte, VT: Garden Way Publishing.

Chapter 3: Farm Business Management

Christensen, R. L., J. Howell, and A. Miller. 1993. *Production Process Budgets for Fresh Vegetables.* Amherst, MA: University of Massachusetts Cooperative Extension.

Kemp, L. 1996. *Successful Whole Farm Planning: Essential Elements Recommended by the Great Lakes Basin Farm Planning Network.* St. Paul, MN: The Minnesota Project.

Lane, D. and J. Wynne (eds.) 1994. *The Beginner's Guide to Developing a Small Business.* Burlington, VG: Champlain Valley Office of Economic Opportunity.

Maloney, T., C. Bratton, K. Embrey, and J. Petzen. 1988. *Human Resource Management on the Farm: A Management Letter Series.* Ithaca, NY: Cornell Cooperative Extension.

Ruhf, K. Z. 1999. *Farmland Transfer and Protection in New England: A Guide for Entering and Exiting Farmers.* Belchertown, MA: New England Small Farm Institute.

Russell, W., and R. Shelby. 1990. *Business Plans and Loan Proposals.* Houston, TX: Small Business Publications, Inc.

Savory, A. 1988. *Holistic Resource Management.* Covelo, CA: Island Press.

Sciabarrasi, M., D. Morris, and G. Frick. 1992. *Farm Management Review: A Workbook on Whole Farm and Enterprise Analysis and Planning.* Durham, NH: University of New Hampshire Cooperative Extension.

Chapter 4: Marketing Your Crops

Bartsch, J. A., and R. Kline. 1992. *Produce Handling for Direct Marketing,* NRAES–51. Ithaca, NY: Natural Resource, Agriculture, and Engineering Service (NRAES).

Beierlein, J. G., and C. M. Connell. 1986. *Managing for Success: A Manual for Roadside Stands.* University Park: Pennsylvania State University Cooperative Extension.

German, C. L., U. C. Toensmeyer, J. L. Cain, and R. J. Rouse. 1994. *Guide to Planning the Farm Retail Market.* Newark, DE: Delaware Cooperative Extension.

Gibson, E. 1994. *Sell What You Sow! The Growers Guide to Successful Produce Marketing.* Carmichael, CA: New World Publishing.

Gilman, S. 1998. *CSA Farm Network,* Vol. II. Stillwater, NY: CSA Farm Network.

Gilman, S. 1996. *CSA Farm Network,* Vol. I. Stillwater, NY: CSA Farm Network.

Ginder, R., and H. Hoecker. 1975. *Management of Pick-Your-Own Marketing Operations.* Newark, DE: Northeast Marketing Committee. Delaware Department of Agriculture.

Henderson, E., and R. Van En. 1999. *Sharing the Harvest: A Guide to Community-Supported Agriculture.* White River Junction, VT: Chelsea Green Publishing.

Henehan, B. M., B. L. Anderson, T. P. Pezzolesi, and R. L. Campbell. 1997. *Putting Cooperation to Work.* Ithaca, NY: Cornell Cooperative Extension.

How, R. B. 1991. *Marketing Fresh Fruits and Vegetables.* New York, NY: Van Nostrand Reinhold.

Matarazzo, R. 1996. *Marketing for Success— Creative Marketing Tools for the Agricultural Industry.* Belvidere, NH: Doe Hollow Publishing.

Patton, J. 1994. *Starting and Strengthening Farmers' Markets in Pennsylvania.* Harrisburg, PA: The Center for Rural Pennsylvania.

Selders, A., et al. 1992. *Facilities for Roadside Markets,* NRAES–52. Ithaca, NY: Natural Resource, Agriculture, and Engineering Service (NRAES).

Yellow Wood Associates. 1992. *New England Wholesale Produce Market Guide.* St. Albans, VT: Yellow Wood Associates, Inc.

Chapter 5: Soil Fertility Management

Bartok, J. W. 1994. *Fertilizer and Manure Application Equipment.* NRAES–57. Ithaca, NY: Natural Resource, Agriculture, and Engineering Service (NRAES).

Bartsch, J. A., Hoffmann, M. P., Bellinder, R. R., Ellerbrock, L. A., et. al. (1994) *Cornell Cooperative Extension Vegetable Production Handbook.* Ithaca, NY: Cornell Cooperative Extension.

Ferro, D. N. (ed.) 1998. *New England Vegetable Management Guide.* Amherst: University of Massachusetts Extension.

Gershuny, G., and J. Smillie. 1986. *The Soul of the Soil, A Guide to Ecological Soil Management.* St. Johnsbury, VT: GAIA Services.

Hochmuth, G. J. 1994. "Efficiency Ranges for Nitrate-Nitrogen and Potassium for Vegetable Petiole Sap Quick Tests" (review). *HortTechnology* 4:218-222.

Hochmuth, G. J., and D. N. Maynard. 1997. *Knott's Handbook for Vegetable Growers,* fourth edition. New York, NY: John Wiley and Sons.

Howell, J. 1996. "Soil Nutrient Information Work Sheet." Amherst, MA: University of Massachusetts Extension.

Magdoff, F. 1992. *Building Soils for Better Crops: Organic Matter Management.* Beltsville, MD: Sustainable Agriculture Network. (Available from SARE USDA, Northeast Region.)

Orzolek, M.D., P.A. Ferretti, A. A. MacNab, J. M. Halbrendt, S. J. Fleischer, Z. Smilowitz, and W. K. Hock. 1998. *1998 Commercial Vegetable Production Recommendations,* Mid-Atlantic. University Park: Penn State Cooperative Extension.

Parnes, R. 1990. *Fertile Soil, A Grower's Guide to Organic and Inorganic Fertilizers,* Davis, CA: AgAcess.

Sachs, P. D. 1993. *Edaphos—Dynamics of a Natural Soil System.* Newbury, VT: Edaphic Press.

Sarrantonio, M. 1994. *Northeast Cover Crop Handbook.* Kutztown, PA: Rodale Institute Research Center.

Chapter 6: On-Farm Composting

Beierlein, J., J. Harper, and C. Oshins. 1996. *Marketing On-Farm Compost,* Extension Circular 423. University Park: Penn State Cooperative Extension.

Bunt, A. C. 1976. *Modern Potting Composts.* University Park: The Pennsylvania State University.

Dougherty, M. 1999. *Field Guide to On-Farm Composting,* NRAES–114. Ithaca, NY: Natural Resource, Agriculture, and Engineering Service (NRAES).

Mangan, F. X., A. Barker, and P. Borten. 1996. *Compost Use and Soil Fertility.* Fact sheet VEGICM 96-7. Amherst: University of Massachusetts Extension.

Rynk, R. (ed.) 1992. *On-Farm Composting Handbook,* NRAES–54. Ithaca, NY: Natural Resource, Agriculture, and Engineering Service (NRAES).

Zabriskie, P. (ed.) 1991. *Composting Organic Wastes on the Farm: A Look at Agricultural Opportunities in the Solid Waste Dilemma.* Waterbury: Vermont Agency of Natural Resources Compost Center.

Chapter 7: Crop Rotation

Coleman, E. 1995. *The New Organic Grower.* White River Junction, VT: Chelsea Green Publishing Company.

Hazzard, R. 1995. *Crop Rotation for Insect and Disease Control.* Fact Sheet VEGICM 95-2. Amherst: University of Massachusetts Extension.

Kirschenmann, F. 1988. *Switching to a Sustainable System.* Windsor, ND: Northern Plains Sustainable Agriculture Society.

Macey, A. (ed.) 1992. *Organic Field Crop Handbook.* Ottawa: Canadian Organic Growers, Inc.

Nordell, A., and Nordell, E. 1998. "Cultivating Questions Concerning the BioExtensive Market Garden." *Small Farmer's Journal,* Vol. 22, No. 1.

Nordell, A., and Nordell, E. 1996a. *Controlled Rotational Cover Cropping in the BioExtensive Market Garden.* (Video). Self-published.

Nordell, A., and Nordell, E. 1996b. "Weed-Free Onions." *Growing for Market,* May.

Nordell, A., and Nordell, E. 1991. "The Summer Fallow." *Small Farmer's Journal,* Vol. 15, No. 3.

Nordell, E. 1994. "Trashed Out Onions." *Small Farmer's Journal,* Vol. 18, No. 3.

Nordell, E. 1993. "A Few Long Furrows on Horse-Drawn Tillage." *Small Farmer's Journal,* Vol. 17, No. 2.

Nordell, E. 1992. "Crop Rotations Today." *Small Farmer's Journal,* Vol. 16, No. 1.

Chapter 8: Cover Crops and Green Manures

Abdul-Baki, A. A., and J. R. Teasdale. 1994. *Sustainable Production of Fresh Market Tomatoes with Organic Mulches.* Farmers Bulletin 2279. Washington, DC: USDA-ARS.

Coleman, E. 1995. *The New Organic Grower.* White River Junction, VT: Chelsea Green Publishing Company.

Cornell Field Crops and Soils Handbook. 1987. Ithaca, NY: Cornell Cooperative Extension.

Green Manures—A Mini-Manual. 1983. Albion, ME: Johnny's Selected Seeds.

Managing Cover Crops Profitably. 1998. Second Edition. Sustainable Agriculture Network, Handbook #3. Beltsville, MD: USDA.

Sarrantonio, M. 1994. *Northeast Cover Crop Handbook.* Kutztown, PA: Rodale Institute

Research Center.

Schmid, O., and R. Klay. 1984. *Green Manuring, Principles and Practice* (translated by Will Brinton). Mt. Vernon, ME: Woods End Research Lab.

Schonbeck, M. W. 1988. *Cover Cropping and Green Manuring on Small Farms in New England and New York: An Informal Survey.* E. Falmouth, MA: New Alchemy Institute.

Chapter 9: Tillage Equipment and Field Preparation

Buckingham, F., and A. Pauli. 1993. *Tillage.* Moline, IL: John Deere and Company Service Publications.

Curran, W. 1996. "Managing Cover Crops for Conservation Tillage." In *Proceedings, 1996 Pennsylvania Vegetable Conference.* Northumberland: Pennsylvania Vegetable Growers Association.

Garthe, J. W., D. J. Murphy, and W. K. Waters. 1987. *Used Farm Equipment: Assessing Quality, Safety, and Economics.* NRAES–25. Ithaca, NY: Natural Resource, Agriculture, and Engineering Service (NRAES).

Intermediate Technology Publications, Ltd. 1985. *Tools for Agriculture, A Buyers Guide to Appropriate Equipment.* Nottingham, UK: Russell Press.

Kepner, R., R. Bainer, and E. Barger. 1978. *Principles of Farm Machinery.* New York, NY: AVI Publishing Company, Inc.

Chapter 10: Seeds and Transplants

Adams, R., and J. Clark (eds.). 1995. *Northeast Sweet Corn Production and Integrated Pest Management Manual* (Bulletin 95–19). Storrs: University of Connecticut Cooperative Extension System.

Boodley, J. W., and R. Sheldrake Jr. 1982 (revised). *Cornell Peat-Lite Mixes for Commercial Plant Growing.* Cornell Cooperative Extension Bulletin 43. Ithaca: NY.

Dufault, R. J., et al. 1993. *Proceedings of the Colloquium: Status of Transplant Technology in the U.S., Orient, and Australia: New Ideas from Research for Commercial Adaptation. HortTechnology* 3:406-420.

Garton, R. "Post-Greenhouse Management of Vegetable Transplants." 1991. In: *Proceedings, 1991 NY State Vegetable Conference,* pp. 112-114. Ithaca, NY: Vegetable Growers Association.

Heiden, R. W., W. H. Carlson, R. D. Heins, J. A. Biernbaum, and L. Ewart. 1989. *Producing Vegetable Transplants as Bedding Plants.* Bulletin E-2148. East Lansing: Michigan State University Cooperative Extension.

Maynard, D. N., and G. J. Hochmuth. 1997. *Knott's Handbook for Vegetable Growers,* fourth edition. New York, NY: John Wiley and Sons.

Ross, D. S., and K. M. Teffeau. 1996. *Greenhouse Float Systems for Transplant Production.* Extension fact sheet 690. College Park: University of Maryland Cooperative Extension.

Welbaum, G. E., et al. 1994. *Proceedings of the Workshop: New Chemical and Biological Treatments for Horticultural Seeds. HortTechnology* 4:104-110.

Wien, H. C. (ed.). 1997. *The Physiology of Vegetable Crops.* New York, NY: CAB International.

Chapter 11: Irrigation and Spraying Systems

Geohring, L. 1996. "Trickle Systems: Basic Components, Design and Installation Considerations." In: *Proceedings, 1996 New York State Vegetable Conference.* Ithaca: New York State Vegetable Growers Association.

Lamont, W. J. Jr., et al. 1992. *Proceedings of the Short Course: Drip Irrigation of Vegetable Crops. HortTechnology* 2:24-41.

Ross, D. S. 1990. *Pesticide Sprayers for Small Farms.* Bulletin 317, College Park: University of Maryland Cooperative Extension.

Ross, D., R. Parsons, and H. Carpenter. 1985. *Trickle Irrigation in the Eastern United States,* NRAES–4. Ithaca, NY: Natural Resource, Agriculture, and Engineering Service (NRAES).

Scherer, T. F., W. Kranz, D. Pfost, H. Werner, J. A. Wright, and C. D. Yonts. 1999. *Sprinkler Irrigation Systems,* MWPS–30. Ames, IA: MidWest Plan Service.

Chapter 12: Harvest and Postharvest Handling

Bartsch, J., and R. Kline. 1992. *Produce Handling for Direct Marketing.* NRAES–51. Ithaca, NY: Natural Resource, Agriculture, and Engineering Service (NRAES).

Bramlage, W. 1994. "Post-Harvest Handling of Fruit and Vegetables: Minimizing Your Losses." pp. 24-26 in: *Proceedings, 1994 New England Direct Marketing Conference.* University of Massachusetts Extension.

CSA Works Harvest Video. 1997. Hadley, MA: CSA Works.

Docter, M., and L. Hildebrand. 1996. "Harvest Containers." In: *Growing for Market.* Lawrence, KS. January.

Ferro, D. N. (ed.) 1998. *New England Vegetable Management Guide.* Amherst: University of Massachusetts Extension.

Garrison, S. "Postharvest Handling and Chlorination." 1995. In: *Proceedings, 1995 New England Vegetable and Berry Conference.* Storrs: University of Connecticut Cooperative Extension System.

Guyer, D., G. Brown, E. Timm, R. Brook, and D. Marshall. 1994. *Lighting Systems for Fruit and Vegetable Sorting.* E. Lansing: Michigan State University Cooperative Extension.

Hardenburg, R. E., A. E. Watada, and C.Y. Wang. 1986. *The Commercial Storage of Fruits, Vegetables, and Florist and Nursery Stocks.* USDA Agriculture Handbook No. 66. Washington, DC: Government Printing Office.

Hicks, J. 1995. "Vegetable Quality and Grading." In *Capital Vegetable News.* Albany, NY: Cornell Cooperative Extension. August.

Kitinoja, L., and A. Kader. 1995. *Small-Scale Post-Harvest Handling Practices: A Manual for Horticultural Crops.* Davis: University of California Department of Pomology.

Maynard, D. N., and G. J. Hochmuth. 1997. *Knott's Handbook for Vegetable Growers,* fourth edition. New York, NY: John Wiley and Sons.

Postharvest Technology of Horticultural Crops. Publication 3311. 1992. Adel A. Kader, tech ed. Oakland, CA: University of California, Division of Agriculture and Natural Resources.

Zandstra, B. H., and H. C. Price. 1988. *Yields of Michigan Vegetable Crops.* Bulletin E-1565. East Lansing: Michigan State University Cooperative Extension.

Chapter 13: Season Extension

Aldrich, R. A., and J. W. Bartok, Jr. 1994. *Greenhouse Engineering,* NRAES–33. Ithaca, NY: Natural Resource, Agriculture, and Engineering Service (NRAES).

Bartok, J. W., Jr. 1995. *Selecting and Building a Greenhouse.* Fact sheet SEG-117. Storrs: University of Connecticut Cooperative Extension System.

Coleman, E. 1995. *Four-Season Gardening.* White River Junction, VT: Chelsea Green

Publishing Company.

Greenhouse Systems: Automation, Culture, and Environment, NRAES–72. 1994. (Proceedings from the Greenhouse Systems International Conference, New Brunswick, New Jersey, July 20–22, 1994). Ithaca, NY: Natural Resource, Agriculture, and Engineering Service (NRAES).

McCullagh, J. C. 1978. *The Solar Greenhouse Book.* Emmaus, PA: Rodale Press.

Roberts, W. J., J. W. Bartok Jr., E. E. Fabian, and J. Simpkins. 1989. *Energy Conservation for Commercial Greenhouses,* NRAES–3. Ithaca, NY: Natural Resource, Agriculture, and Engineering Service (NRAES).

Ross, D. S. 1991. *Greenhouse Heating, Circulation, and Ventilation Systems.* Bulletin 351. College Park: University of Maryland Cooperative Extension.

Sheldrake, R., Jr., and R. M. Sayles. 1992. *Plastic Greenhouse Manual: Planning, Construction, and Operation.* Report #22. Ithaca, NY: Department of Fruit and Vegetable Science, Cornell University.

Stone, A. (ed.) 1994. *Proceedings of the Northeast Farmer to Farmer Information Exchange: Greenhouse Meeting.* Barre: MA: NOFA/Mass.

Walls, I. G. 1991. *The Complete Book of the Greenhouse.* London, UK: Ward Lock Ltd.

Weiler, T. C., and M. Sailus (eds.). 1996. *Water and Nutrient Management for Greenhouses,* NRAES–56. Ithaca, NY: Natural Resource, Agriculture, and Engineering Service (NRAES).

Wells, O. S. 1996. "Row Cover and High Tunnel Growing Systems in the U.S." *HortTechnology* 6:172-176.

Wells, O. S. 1991. *High Tunnels for Tomato Production.* Durham: University of New Hampshire Cooperative Extension.

Wells, O. S., and J. B. Loy. 1985. *Row Covers for Intensive Vegetable Production.* Durham, NH: University of New Hampshire Cooperative Extension.

Wulster, G., R. Brumfield, B. Roberts, and C. Costaris. 1992. *Starting in the Greenhouse Business.* New Brunswick, NJ: Rutgers Cooperative Extension.

Chapter 14: Integrated Pest Management

Adams, R., and J. Clark (eds.). 1995. *Northeast Sweet Corn Production and Integrated Pest Management Manual* (Bulletin 95–19). Storrs: University of Connecticut Cooperative Extension System.

Benbrook, C. 1995. *Healthy Food, Healthy Farms: Pest Management in the Public Interest.* Washington, DC: The National Campaign for Pesticide Policy Reform.

Boucher, J., and R. Adams. 1993. *Integrated Pest Management Guide for Connecticut Cole Crops.* Storrs: University of Connecticut Cooperative Extension System.

Daar, S., H. Olkowski, and W. Olkowski. 1997. *1998 Directory of Least-Toxic Pest Control Products.* Berkeley, CA: IPM Practitioner Vol. 19 (Nov/Dec).

Green, T. A. (ed.) 1998. *IPM Almanac.* Belleville, WI: Gemplers, Inc.

Hazzard, R. 1996. *IPM for Fresh Market Field Tomatoes in Massachusetts.* Amherst: University of Massachusetts Extension.

Hoffmann, M., C. Petzoldt, and A. Frodsham. 1996. *Integrated Pest Management for Onions.* IPM Publication 119. Ithaca, NY: Cornell Cooperative Extension.

Hollingsworth, C. S. 1996. *Implementing Pheromone Technology in the Northeast,* NRAES–83. Ithaca: Natural Resource, Agriculture, and Engineering Service (NRAES).

Hollingsworth, C. S., W. M. Coli, and R. V. Hazzard. 1995. *Integrated Pest Management, Massachusetts Guidelines: Commodity Specific Definitions.* Amherst: University of Massachusetts Extension.

Hollingsworth, C., D. Ferro, and W. Coli. 1986. *Potato Production in the Northeast: A Guide to Integrated Pest Management.* Amherst: University of Massachusetts Extension.

Meister, R. T. (ed.) *Farm Chemicals Handbook '99.* 1999. Willoughby, OH: Meister Publishing Company.

Orzolek, M.D., P.A. Ferretti, A. A. MacNab, J. M. Halbrendt, S. J. Fleischer, Z. Smilowitz, and W. K. Hock. 1998. *1998 Commercial Vegetable Production Recommendations,* Mid-Atlantic. University Park: Penn State Cooperative Extension.

Pesticide Compendia: Fungicides, Herbicides, Insecticides, Rodenticides: Useful Information Relating to Pesticides Recommended in New York State. 1984. Ithaca, NY: Cornell Cooperative Extension Chemicals-Pesticides Program.

Petzoldt, C., and M. Hoffmann. 1996. *Fresh Market Sweet Corn IPM Scouting Procedures.* New York State IPM Program, Bulletin 111FM. Ithaca, NY: Cornell Cooperative Extension.

Stebbins, T., and J. Ingerson-Mahar. 1987. *Vegetable Pest Scouting.* Bulletin E-2067. East Lansing: Michigan State University Cooperative Extension.

Weinzierl, R., T. Henn, R. Randell, P. Nixon, and M. Gray. 1990. *Alternatives in Insect Pest Management: Beneficial Insects and Mites* (circular 1298); *Botanical Insecticides and Insecticidal Soaps* (circular 1296); *Insect Attractants and Traps* (circular 1297); *Microbial Insecticides* (circular 1295). Urbana: University of Illinois Extension.

Zitter, T., M. Hoffmann, M. McGrath, C. Petzoldt, A. Seaman, and L. Pedersen. 1996. *Cucurbit Scouting Procedures.* IPM Bulletin No. 113.

Ithaca, NY: Cornell Cooperative Extension.

Chapter 15: Insect Management

Davidson, R. H., and W. F. Lyon. 1987. *Insect Pests of Farm, Garden, and Orchard.* New York, NY: John Wiley and Sons.

Flint, M. L. 1990. *Pests of the Garden and Small Farm: A Grower's Guide to Using Less Pesticide.* Publication 3332, Division of Agriculture and Natural Resources. Oakland: University of California.

Foster, R., and B. Flood. 1995. *Vegetable Insect Management with Emphasis on the Midwest.* Willoughby, OH: Meister Publishing Company.

Hazzard, R. (ed.) 1994. *Proceedings of the Northeast Farmer to Farmer Information Exchange: Sweet Corn Meeting.* Barre, MA: NOFA/Mass.

Hoffmann, M. P., and A. C. Frodsham. 1993. *Natural Enemies of Vegetable Insect Pests.* Ithaca, NY: Cornell Cooperative Extension.

Howard, R. J., J. A. Garland, and W. L. Seaman. 1994. *Diseases and Pests of Vegetable Crops in Canada.* Ottawa, Ontario: Entomological Society of Canada.

Hunter, C. D. 1997. *Suppliers of Beneficial Organisms in North America.* Sacramento: California Department of Pesticide Regulation.

McKinlay, R. G. 1992. *Vegetable Crop Pests.* Boca Raton, FL: Macmillan Press/CRC Press.

Moyer, D. D. 1992. *Fabrication and Operation of a Propane Flamer for Colorado Potato Beetle Control.* Ithaca, NY: Cornell Cooperative Extension.

Chapter 16: Disease Management

Cornell Cooperative Extension. *Vegetable Crops Fact Sheets* (with color plates, for a variety of diseases and insects). Ithaca, NY.

Hagedorn, D. J. 1984. *Compendium of Pea Diseases.* St. Paul, MN: APS Press.

Hall, R. 1991. *Compendium of Bean Diseases.* St. Paul, MN: APS Press.

Hooker, W. J. 1981. *Compendium of Potato Diseases.* St. Paul, MN: APS Press.

Howland, R. J., J. A. Garland, and W. L. Seaman. 1994. *Diseases and Pests of Vegetable Crops in Canada.* Ottawa, Ontario: Entomological Society of Canada.

Jones, J. B., J. P. Jones, R. E. Stall, and T. A. Zitter. 1993. *Compendium of Tomato Diseases.* St. Paul, MN: APS Press.

MacNab, A. A., A. F. Sherf, and J. K. Springer. 1983. *Identifying Diseases of Vegetables.* University Park: The Pennsylvania State University.

Schwartz, H. F., and S. K. Mohan. 1995. *Compendium of Onion and Garlic Diseases.* St. Paul, MN: APS Press.

Sherf, A. F., and A. A. MacNab. 1986. *Vegetable Diseases and Their Control.* New York, NY: John Wiley and Sons.

Shurtleff, M. C. 1980. *Compendium of Corn Diseases.* St. Paul, MN: APS Press.

Snowdon, A. 1991. *A Colour Atlas of Post-Harvest Diseases and Disorders of Fruits and Vegetables,* Vol. 2: Vegetables. London: Wolfe Publishing.

Zitter, T. A., D. L. Hopkins, and C. E. Thomas. 1995. *Compendium of Cucurbit Diseases.* St. Paul, MN: APS Press.

Chapter 17: Weed Management

Altieri, M., and M. Leibman. 1988. *Weed-Crop Ecology: Principles in Weed Management.*
Boca Raton, FL: Breton Publishers.

Bowman, G. (ed.) 1997. *Steel in the Field: A Farmer's Guide to Weed Management Tools.* Beltsville, MD: Sustainable Agriculture Network.

Buchholtz, K. P., et al. 1977. *Weeds of the North Central States.* Circular 718. Urbana, IL: University of Illinois.

Colquhoun, J., and R. Bellinder. 1997. *New Cultivation Tools for Mechanical Weed Control in Vegetables.* IPM Fact Sheet 102FSNCT. Ithaca, NY: Cornell Cooperative Extension.

Grubinger, V. P., and M. J. Else. 1994. *Vegetable Farmers and Their Weed-Control Machines.* (video). Burlington: University of Vermont Center for Sustainable Agriculture (available from SARE USDA Northeast Region).

Uva, R. H., J. C. Neal, and J. M. DiTomaso. 1997. *Weeds of the Northeast.* Ithaca, NY: Cornell University Press.

Whitson, T. D. (ed.) 1992. *Weeds of the West.* Newark, CA: Western Society of Weed Science.

Chapter 18: Wildlife Management

Curtis, P., M. Fargione, and M. Richmond. 1994. *Wildlife Damage in Fruit Orchards.* Information Bulletin 236, Ithaca, NY: Cornell Cooperative Extension.

Hygnstrom, S. E., R. M. Timm, and G. E. Larson. (eds.) 1994. *Prevention and Control of Wildlife Damage.* Lincoln, NE: University of Nebraska Cooperative Extension.

Selders, A. W., and J. B. McAninch. 1987. *High-Tensile Wire Fencing,* NRAES–11. Ithaca, NY: Northeast Regional Agricultural Engineering Service.

Other Publications from NRAES

Note: The publications below are just a few of the over 160 publications available from the Natural Resource, Agriculture, and Engineering Service (NRAES). To request a free catalog or for additional information, see the inside back cover.

Composting

Field Guide to On-Farm Composting, NRAES–114

To assist in day-to-day compost system management, this book covers operations and equipment; raw materials and recipe making; process control and evaluation; site considerations, environmental management, and safety; composting livestock and poultry mortalities; and compost use on the farm. It includes an equipment identification table, examples and equations for recipe making and compost use estimation, a troubleshooting guide, and 24 full-color photos. 1999. *128 pages*

On-Farm Composting Handbook, NRAES–54

This handbook presents a thorough overview of farm-scale composting and explains how to produce, use, and market compost. Topics include benefits and drawbacks, the process, raw materials, methods, operations, management, site and environmental considerations, using compost, marketing, economics, and other options for waste management. 1992. *186 pages*

Equipment

Fertilizer and Manure Application Equipment, NRAES–57

This publication discusses types of fertilizer and manure nutrient values and provides guidance on equipment selection. Procedures for calibrating fertilizer and manure application equipment are reviewed. 1994. *22 pages*

Used Farm Equipment: Assessing Quality, Safety, and Economics, NRAES–25

This handbook shows how to inspect machinery for reliability of components and quality of safety features. The economics of owning and operating used machinery and methods of acquiring equipment are discussed. 1987. *34 pages*

Vegetable Farmers and Their Weed-Control Machines, SARE V–1

This color video introduces trade-name and custom-built equipment designed to remove weeds through cultivation and flame-weeding. It features interviews with nine New England vegetable growers, who explain their weed-management strategies and demonstrate effective weed-control equipment. 1994. *75 minutes*

Farm Management

Farming Alternatives: A Guide to Evaluating the Feasibility of New Farm-Based Enterprises, NRAES–32

This book assists rural and farm residents who are considering alternative enterprises. The case study and workbook format helps in evaluating personal and family considerations, resources, market potential, production feasibility, profitability, cash flow, and all factors combined. The guidebook also offers research sources for enterprise ideas. Each chapter includes exercises, self-tests, checklists, and work sheets. 1988. *88 pages*

Workforce Management for Farms and Horticultural Businesses: Finding, Training, and Keeping Good Employees, NRAES–117

This conference proceedings includes papers presenting concepts and practices related to creating a work environment that motivates employees and is productive, profitable, safe, and worker-friendly. 1999. *140 pages*

Greenhouse

Greenhouse Engineering, NRAES–33

This manual contains current information needed to plan, construct, and control the commercial greenhouse. Major sections describe various structures, methods of materials handling, the greenhouse environment, and energy conservation. Other topics include plans for noncommercial greenhouses, access for the handicapped, and remodeling existing greenhouses. 1994. *212 pages*

Greenhouse Systems: Automation, Culture, and Environment, NRAES-72

This conference proceedings provides in-depth information on the engineering principles of greenhouse system design and management. The papers are grouped into four sections concerning automation, culture, environment, and systems integration. 1994. *306 pages*

Herbaceous Perennials Production: A Guide from Propagation to Marketing, NRAES-93

This publication is a comprehensive information source for perennial growers in businesses of all sizes. Key chapters discuss production systems and schedules; propagation; plug production; transplant and seedling care; nursery and field production; pest control; and forcing out-of-season bloom. Discussions of starting a business, marketing and customer service, setting prices for plants, and designing a production facility are included. 1998. *208 pages*

Water and Nutrient Management for Greenhouses, NRAES-56

Preparing stock solutions for proportioners; selecting substrate; interpreting leaf, substrate, and water test results; and estimating crop nutrient needs are necessary skills for managing a greenhouse for zero runoff. This publication will help managers learn these skills. 1996. *110 pages*

Irrigation Systems

Sprinkler Irrigation Systems, MWPS-30

This publication provides a systematic approach to the whys and hows of developing sprinkler irrigation systems. It was developed to provide a planning tool, reference guide, and design manual for a broad audience—including agricultural producers and consultants, engineers, equipment dealers, government agency employees, educators, students, and others interested in the technology of irrigation. Ten chapters cover the following topics: planning a system; system design; water

sources; sprinkler systems; sprinkler characteristics; sprinkler selection and management; pumps, piping, and power units; chemigation; sprinkler application of effluent; and design examples. Included are more than 110 photographs and illustrations and 70 tables. 1999. *250 pages*

Trickle Irrigation in the Eastern United States, NRAES-4

This handbook is a planning and installation guide for growers considering a trickle irrigation system. Information is provided on plant-soil-water relationships, system components, crop recommendations, and system planning. 1985. *24 pages*

Postharvest Handling

Apple Harvesting, Handling, and Storage, NRAES-112

This conference proceedings addresses management for quality; use of Retain™; use of penetrometers, refractometers, gas monitoring equipment, and thermometers; rapid CA storage; research on postharvest decay; spreadsheet analysis of selling for fresh or processing markets; calcium and DPA research; fresh and minimally processed produce and food safety, and other topics. 1997. *84 pages*

The Commercial Storage of Fruits, Vegetables, and Florist and Nursery Stocks, USDA-66

General topics such as quality, precooling, relative humidity, respiration rates, and supplements to refrigeration are covered. Also addressed are optimum storage conditions for specific fruits, vegetables, cut flowers, and nursery stock. 1986. *130 pages*

Facilities for Roadside Markets, NRAES-52

This publication covers site considerations (visibility and accessibility, utilities, drainage, zoning, and building ordinances); market layout (areas for sales, preparation, and shipping and receiving); and market structure and facilities (parking, lighting, fire protection, security, and more). 1992. *32 pages*

Home Storage of Fruits and Vegetables, NRAES–7

This guide covers when to harvest and how to store preserved foods. Specific storage conditions for thirty-two different fruits and vegetables are included. It also provides plans for simple facilities to store homegrown produce. 1979. *28 pages*

Produce Handling for Direct Marketing, NRAES–51

This publication describes postharvest physiology, food safety, produce handling from harvest to storage, refrigerated storage, produce displays, and specific handling and display recommendations for over forty types of fruits and vegetables. 1992. *26 pages*

Refrigeration and Controlled Atmosphere Storage for Horticultural Crops, NRAES–22

General construction procedures for storage facilities are discussed, such as site selection, structural considerations, thermal insulation, vapor barriers, and attic ventilation. Different refrigeration systems are explained, including descriptions of equipment and operating procedures. Controlled atmosphere storage construction, testing, and operation are discussed, especially in relation to apple storage. 1990. *44 pages*

Fruit Production

Bramble Production Guide, NRAES–35

This guide provides detailed information about all aspects of raspberry and blackberry production for both potential and established growers. Topics discussed include site selection and preparation, plant selection, pruning and trellising, pest and disease management, spray technology, harvesting and handling, and marketing. 1989. *189 pages*

Highbush Blueberry Production Guide, NRAES–55

This book covers all aspects of blueberry production including site selection and preparation, blueberry growth and development, maintenance, pest management, harvesting, marketing, nuisance wildlife management, water management, spray technology, and budgeting. 1992. *200 pages*

Strawberry Production Guide for the Northeast, Midwest, and Eastern Canada, NRAES–88

This is the most comprehensive production guide produced for strawberry growers and advisors. It provides in-depth, up-to-date coverage of every aspect of strawberry culture—from site preparation to harvesting and marketing. Budget spreadsheets are provided on a diskette. 1998. *162 pages*

Agrichemical Handling

On-Farm Agrichemical Handling Facilities, NRAES–78

This publication discusses considerations a farmer should make regarding agrichemical storage, principal parts of the facility, storage environmental requirements, safety requirements, and storage alternatives. 1995. *22 pages*